Bible Brain Builders Book 1

Other Bible Brain Builders

Bible Brain Builders Book 2

Bible Brain Builders
Book 1

THOMAS NELSON
Since 1798

NASHVILLE   DALLAS   MEXICO CITY   RIO DE JANEIRO

Published in Nashville, Tennessee, by Thomas Nelson. Thomas Nelson is a registered trademark of Thomas Nelson, Inc.

Book design and composition by Graphic World, Inc.

Original puzzles and mazes created by W. B. Freeman.

Thomas Nelson, Inc., titles may be purchased in bulk for educational, business, fund-raising, or sales promotional use. For information, please e-mail SpecialMarkets@ThomasNelson.com.

The material in this book originally was published in other forms in *Nelson's Super Book of Bible Word Games, Book 1*, © 1992, *Nelson's Super Book of Bible Word Games, Book 2*, © 1993, *Nelson's Super Book of Bible Word Games, Book 3*, © 1993, *Incredible Mazes, Book 1*, © 1993, *Incredible Mazes, Book 2*, © 1994, *Nelson's Amazing Bible Trivia Book 2* © 2000, 2011 by Thomas Nelson Publishers, Inc., all rights reserved.

ISBN: 978-1-4041-8349-0

Printed in the United States of America

14 13 12 11 QG 1 2 3 4 5 6

THE LATIN CROSS

*T*he Latin Cross is the most famous of all cross designs. Perhaps surprisingly, this symbol was not seen publicly until the reign of Constantine the Great, although Christians no doubt had used it privately prior to that time.

The cross speaks of two great truths. First, Jesus died on a simple wooden cross as the sacrifice for our sins. Second, the cross reminds us that Jesus taught us, as His followers, to take up the cross and follow Him. The cross not only represents who Jesus is to us and what He did for us but who we are to be for Him and to others.

Galatians 6:14 tells us, "God forbid that I should boast except in the cross of our Lord Jesus Christ."

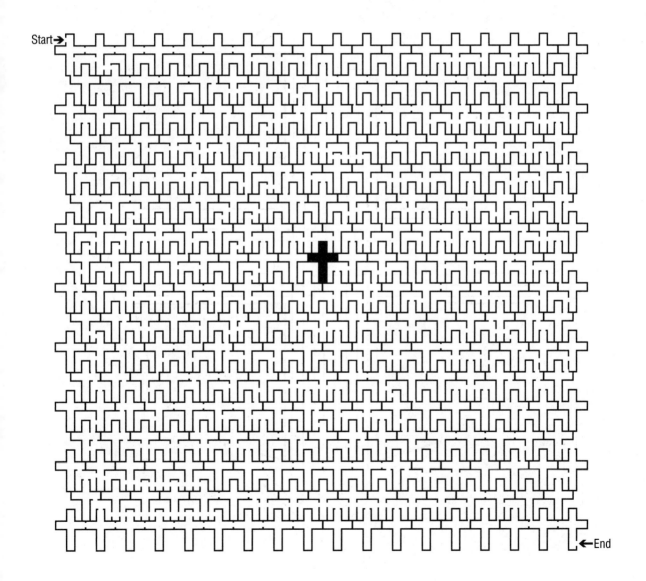

THE BARBÉE CROSS

*T*he Barbée Cross has ends that are like fish hooks or barbs, hence the name of this cross design. This cross reminds us that Jesus once said to Peter and Andrew, "Follow Me, and I will make you fishers of men" (Matthew 4:19).

The cross seems to push outward in all directions—north, south, east, and west—and for this reason this cross is a symbol frequently associated with worldwide or international outreaches and missionary endeavors.

Start

End

*F*alse witnesses came foward to quote Jesus saying these words.

Clue: MESSIAH *is* HKFFXMJ

X PXRR BKFZCVG

ZJXF ZKHYRK ZJMZ

XF HMBK PXZJ JMQBF.

MQB PXZJXQ ZJCKK

BMGF X PXRR LOXRB

MQVZJKC HMBK

PXZJVOZ JMQBF.

QUEEN'S CARAVAN

*F*or the Queen of Sheba, seeing was believing, and until she saw for herself, she couldn't quite believe the rumors of the wealth and wisdom of King Solomon. So she and her retinue made a great journey of over 1,000 miles from southwest Arabia (what is now Yemen) to Jerusalem to "test him with hard questions."

First Kings 10:4-5 says, "when the queen of Sheba had seen all the wisdom of Solomon, the house that he had built, the food on his table, the seating of his servants, the service of his waiters and their apparel, his cupbearers, and his entryway by which he went up to the house of the LORD, there was no more spirit in her." She was overwhelmed. The stories she had heard about Solomon were no exaggeration, for she said, "Indeed, the half was not told me."

← Start

↑ End

Can you find the message from the Lord in the letter box below?
(Hints: Think King James language! And, play leapfrog with the letters.)

Y Y E M S E H N A E L R L U S O E M E O K

R F S K C A T T A E H T D N A H S E L F E

M H E T A F N O D S F T I S N U D L M E E

H T D N A S S E N I Z A L D N A S E I T L

W A H Y E O N L Y D E E S D H I A V L I L

D D N A E D I R P D N A T R A E H F O S S

S E E N A D R R C A H H F A O D R N M A E

E G D E L W O N K E T A R U C C A N I D N

W A I G T N H I A H L C L A Y E O T U T R

C E R R O C N I D N A S W O R R O S R U O

H D E N A A R S T E C N A T S M U C R I C

Now. can you also find 10 things in this letter box that
keep us from doing the Lord's command?
(Hint: Read backwards and don't use any letters you've
already used in deciphering the first message.)

Across

4 Solomon's successor; ten tribes revolted against him
5 Son of Eve, father of Enosh
6 "Brother of the Lord" who led early Jerusalem church
8 Canaanite king he reigned In Hazor, oppressed Israel
11 One of Isaac's sons
12 #2 Down preached, "You are the ____ of the earth."
13 Skilled in driving tent pegs, she defeated Sisera
15 #2 Down said, "Assuredly, I say to you, inasmuch as you did it to one of the ____ of these My brethren, you did it to Me" (NKJ)
18 Gospel writer (3 words)
20 Shechem tried to enter into ____ with #11 Across (Genesis 34:8-10)
21 Earthly father of Jesus
24 Son of Saul, friend to David
27 Mother of all
28 He led tribes in rebellion, followers into idolatry
29 #2 Down taught, "Whatever you want men to ____ to you, ____ also to them, for this is the Law and the Prophets" (NKJ)
30 Wise men came from the ____ to worship #2 Down
31 "God ____ love"
32 City at the southern limits of tribe of #45 Across
35 In list of "sons of Solomon's servants"
36 Mother of Miriam, Aaron, and Moses
37 Descendants of Abraham, later known as #25 Down
41 Son of Pethuel, author of a minor prophetic book
43 Thessalonican believer hospitable to Paul and Silas
45 Fourth son of #11 Across
46 Persons who lived near Jebus

48 As #3 Down cried in the wilderness, his words may have been heard as an ____ in the hills
49 One of the sons of Tola
51 King at eight years old, he ruled for thirty-one years with great integrity
52 #2 Down said, "Where your treasure is, there your heart will ____ also" (NKJ)
53 One of the twelve precious stones in the priest's breastplate
55 Region settled by descendants of Japheth
56 #2 Down said, "If you ____ faith as a mustard seed" (NKJ)
58 Ahab's wicked wife
60 Contraction for Jehovah (Psalm 68:4)
61 One of seven men in 1 Chronicles 5:13
64 One of daughters of #28 Down
65 Disciples of #2 Down asked, "Who then can be ____?"
66 Husband of #58 Across
67 Book that opens with a prophecy by #51 Down
68 Son of Jeshua

Down

1 Gideon's father
2 King of kings
3 Preacher in Judean wilderness (3 words)
6 #2 Down wept over this city
7 Title of #2 Down (3 words)
9 Another word for friend
10 Fish food, temporarily
11 Father-in-law of Moses, priest of Midian
14 Wife of officer in Herod's housebold
16 Short for editor
17 In one of his letters, #18 Across said we must always " ____ the spirits"

19 #2 Down said, "____ their fruits you will know them" (NKJ)
21 One of Hezron's sons
22 Youngest son of Noah
23 One of the sons of Tola
24 A city and plain, battlefield where Gideon won
25 Literally, descendants of Judah
26 Brother of Joel, one of King David's valiant men
28 He suffered, temporarily
32 Mother of #51 Across
33 #2 Down's final command in Matthew 28:19 begins with this word
34 Israelite leader after Moses
38 Helped spies escape from her home city, Jericho
39 Father of eight sons, of whom David was youngest
40 River connecting Sea of Galilee and Dead Sea
41 Gideon's firstborn son
42 One of Esau's wives, daughter of Beeri the Hittite
44 Name used for God, literally means "self-subsisting"
47 Many thought #3 Down was this Old Testament prophet
50 #2 Down is called the ____ by #18 Across
51 Considered one of four great Old Testament prophets
52 City where #2 Down was born
54 #34 Down was part of a group sent by Moses to ____ out the land
57 Firstborn son of #11 Across
59 The nature of #60 Across is ____
60 One of Asher's sons
62 #2 Down is called the "last ____"
63 One of Onam's sons

Bonus "J"

Write down the letters that are circled in the crossword grid. Unscramble them to form yet another "J" word.

— — — — — — —

TREASURED

*J*ewels and precious stones in ancient times, as today, were valued for their beauty and rarity. They were given as gifts, confiscated as spoils of war, and used as a means of exchange.

The ephod worn by the high priest was adorned with twelve jewels listed in Exodus 28:17-20: sardius, topaz, emerald, turquoise, sapphire, diamond, jacinth, agate, amethyst, beryl, onyx, and jasper. Each jewel represented one of the tribes of Israel. And in the New Jerusalem, there will be twelve jewels in the foundations of the walls: jasper, sapphire, chalcedony, emerald, sardonyx, sardius, chrysolite, beryl, topaz, chrysoprase, jacinth, and amethyst (Revelation 21:19-20).

More important, however, is the way in which God ascribes the great value of jewels to the people who obey Him: "If you will indeed obey My voice and keep My covenant, then you shall be a special treasure to Me above all people; for all the earth is Mine. And you shall be to Me a kingdom of priests and a holy nation" (Exodus 19:5).

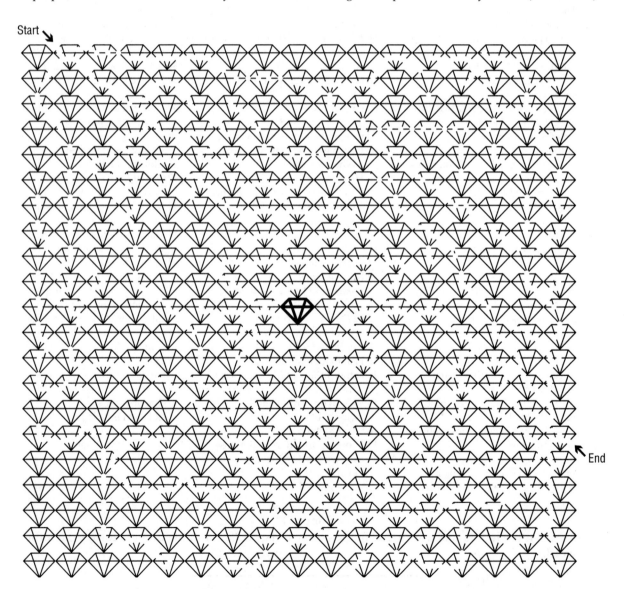

If you think of the Holy Land as desert, you may change your mind after this puzzle.

DRAEC   __ Ⓞ __ __ __

TAHTIHS   __ __ __ Ⓞ __ __ __

LTIROEE   __ __ __   __ __ Ⓞ __   (2 words)

MLETYR   __ __ Ⓞ __ __ __

RFI   Ⓞ __ __

NEPI   __ Ⓞ __ __

TEXOREB   __ __ __   __ __ __ Ⓞ   (2 words)

EVIOL   Ⓞ __ __ __ __

LPMA   __ __ Ⓞ __

FGI   Ⓞ __ __

Unscramble the circled letters to reveal one of the items at the Garden's center:

__ __ __ __   __ __   __ __ __ __

EPIPHANY VISIT

*M*atthew alone tells the story of the visit of the wise men to bring gifts to the newborn baby Jesus in Bethlehem. From their observation of the brightness of the star in the East, the Magi concluded that a king had been born, and they traveled to honor Him with gifts of gold, frankincensce and myrrh.

To the Magi, the birth of Jesus signified the coming of the Christ to the Gentiles. The wise men, who were Gentiles, came to worhsip the child who had been born "King of the Jews." The Jewish King Herod's response to the birth of Jesus, however, was that "he was troubled, and all Jerusalem with him." The visit of the Magi is observed thoughout the Western church on Epiphany, January 6, the twelfth day of Christmas.

End

Start

*T*he many different names for Jesus in the Bible reveal to us who He is. Fill in the blanks, and then fill in the crossword grid.

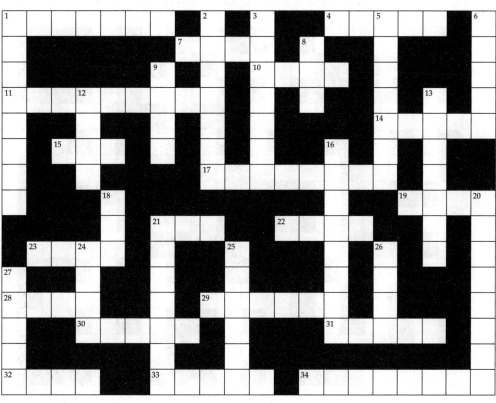

Across

1 Man of ____, acquainted with grief
4 Thou shalt call His name ____
7 I am the #18 Down, the #33 Across, and the ____
10 ____ of the Valley
11 The Great ____
14 #6 Down and ___
15 God's name to Moses
17 I know that my ____ lives
19 ____ of Judah
21 ____ of God
22 ____ of the Church
23 ____ One

28 The last ____
29 ____ of Peace
30 ____ of Life
31 ____ of the world
32 I am the ____
33 I am the #18 Down, the ____, and the #7 Across
34 The ____ of God's glory

Down

1 The Good ____
2 The ____ of our faith *(RSV)*
3 ____ of God
5 Born in the city of David, a ____ (British spelling)

6 ____ and #14 Across
8 Everything: ____ in ____
9 I am the true ____
12 The bright morning ____
13 We have found the ____
16 God with us
18 I am the ____, the #33 Across, and the #7 Across
20 He will be called a ____
21 The suffering ____
24 The sacrifice for our sins
25 Anointed one
26 ____ of ____s and Lord of lords
27 Root of ____

*F*ind the answers to this crossword puzzle in the Christmas story. (See Matthew 2; Luke 2:1-20.) Be sure to use King James spelling.

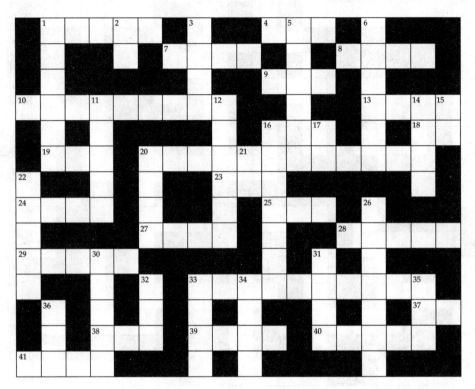

Across

1 His name
4 One word question
7 Star's location
8 Star's purpose
9 Reason for Joseph's trip
10 Birth town
13 Offering
16 Drink made from leaves
18 ____ and behold
19 Feminine pronoun; objective
20 One of the gifts
23 The Father
24 Another gift
25 Hotel
27 Not front
28 Homes of the birds

29 Tranquility
33 Wise men's and shepherds' response
37 A Kennedy's initials
38 Where the babe ____
39 The sign
40 Color of leaves
41 Lifeless

Down

1 Mary' husband
2 Not down
3 Very young child
5 Ultimate home
6 Mary, before the birth
11 King's name
12 His cradle

14 Run away
15 Short preposition
16 News (good ____)
17 Alternating current (abbr.)
20 Apprehension
21 Knock out (slang. abbr.)
22 Baby Jesus' country of refuge
26 Foretold His coming
30 Young person
31 Ruler
32 Happiness
33 Discerning, sage
34 To view written words
35 Lair
36 Opposite the heel

CHARIOT RACES

*B*oxing, wrestling, gymnastics, foot races, and chariot races were among the sports of Bible times. Chariot racing was well known in the Greek and Roman cultures and was a favorite spectator competition.

The apostle Paul's analogy of a race in Philippians 3:13–14 is thought to refer either to a chariot race or to a foot race. In a chariot race, the driver leaned out over the chariot rail and over the back of the horse, with the reins around his body. Stretching ahead and putting his weight on the reins, he drove his horse on to the finish line. In the intensity of this competition, a look behind him could have proven disastrous.

Only one of these three chariots crosses the finish line. Find the way through the maze to see which one is the winner.

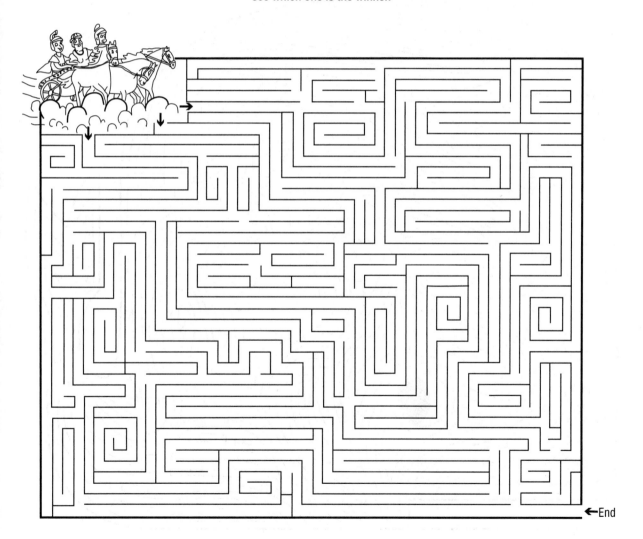

←End

JONAH'S JOURNEY

Although the book of Jonah, particulary Jonah's encounter with the great fish, has been viewed with skepticism by unbelievers, Jesus vouched for its truth in Matthew 12:39-41.

Jonah, a native of Galilee, was one of the earlier prophets. He is sometimes called the "reluctant missionary" since he was largely unwilling to answer God's call to go to Nineveh and warn the enemies of his country of God's coming judgment.

Johah was a mixture of strength and weakness. Obviously a convincing orator, he was something of a whiner who was more concerned with his own reputation than with what God commanded. One of the curious facts of this story is that Jonah was disappointed that the Ninevites repented! (See Johah 3:4–4:1.)

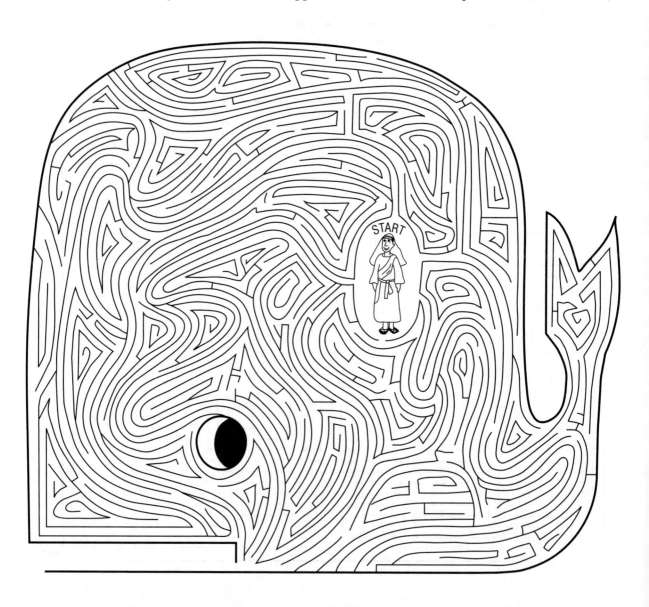

Safari time! Find the names of 38 different animals mentioned in the Bible in the square below.

```
O  Z  D  R  A  Z  I  L  E  L  I  Z  A  M  E
X  D  R  A  G  O  N  T  L  E  L  H  B  E  L
E  E  N  I  W  S  L  Y  E  M  I  C  E  T  G
N  E  L  U  A  E  I  M  P  A  U  O  H  S  A
Y  R  M  G  O  D  O  Z  H  C  B  L  E  G  E
X  T  E  P  L  H  N  C  A  A  A  U  M  R  E
L  L  A  M  B  O  Y  A  N  P  T  T  O  A  H
U  R  U  R  E  R  M  E  T  E  N  Z  T  F  A
D  L  C  S  A  S  S  E  R  Z  E  K  H  L  R
E  C  M  A  R  E  T  A  O  G  P  C  R  E  E
D  H  U  S  L  B  F  X  M  A  R  O  L  S  F
E  A  R  A  O  F  A  L  F  O  E  L  L  A  I
R  C  H  A  M  E  L  E  O  N  S  L  A  E  E
S  W  R  N  V  M  L  I  X  W  T  U  C  W  H
H  P  S  P  E  E  H  S  O  L  I  B  U  L  C
E  N  R  O  C  I  N  U  N  O  N  L  L  O  L
```

WORD POOL

APE ASS BEAR BEHEMOTH BOAR BULLOCK CALF CAMEL CATTLE CHAMELEON DEER DRAGON EAGLE ELEPHANT FOX GOAT GREYHOUND HARE HEIFER HORSE LAMB LEOPARD LION LIZARD MICE MULE OXEN RAM RAVEN ROE SERPENT SHEEP SWINE UNICORN WEASEL WHALE WOLF

*H*ow we can find true strength.

Clue: MESSIAH *is* WXBBMVT

$$\overline{\text{H V P Q T}} \quad \overline{\text{R X}} \quad \overline{\text{V D Z}}$$

$$\overline{\text{F K V R}}. \quad \overline{\text{N X B P}} \quad \overline{\text{R X}}$$

$$\overline{\text{X D P X K}} \quad \overline{\text{M D P G}}$$

$$\overline{\text{P X W F P V P M G D}}. \quad \overline{\text{P T X}}$$

$$\overline{\text{B F M K M P}} \quad \overline{\text{P K C N R}}$$

$$\overline{\text{M B}} \quad \overline{\text{K X V Z R}}. \quad \overline{\text{J C P}} \quad \overline{\text{P T X}}$$

$$\overline{\text{S N X B T}} \quad \overline{\text{M B}} \quad \overline{\text{H X V Y}}$$

*F*ind 20 hidden words about an event that changed B.C. to A.D.

```
L  O  T  E  S  V  C  H  P  E  S  O  J  E
U  O  P  B  A  B  E  R  I  D  O  U  S  M
R  N  R  E  T  N  N  I  R  E  G  N  A  M
O  I  S  T  A  B  L  E  S  L  E  G  N  A
I  G  J  H  I  G  H  U  X  C  L  O  E  N
V  R  E  L  O  P  W  I  N  H  E  L  R  U
A  I  S  E  E  A  C  I  M  I  R  D  O  E
S  V  U  H  O  O  K  A  S  O  S  R  P  L
H  I  S  E  O  N  R  A  M  E  S  U  Y  E
O  K  R  M  A  R  Y  T  X  E  M  R  E  M
S  T  A  R  N  E  W  A  R  T  O  E  G  H
T  G  F  I  S  H  T  E  R  A  Z  A  N  O
```

Word Pool

ANGELS BABE BETHLEHEM EMMANUEL FRANKINCENSE GOLD
HOST INN JESUS JOSEPH MARY MYRRH NAZARETH SAVIOR
STABLE STAR SHEPHERDS TAXES VIRGIN WISE MEN

HOLY HEARTS

"May the Lord make you increase and abound in love to one another and to all, just as we do to you, so that He may establish your hearts blameless in holiness before our God and Father at the coming of our Lord Jesus Christ with all His saints" (1 Thessalonians 3:12–13).

The heart is at the center of our being, where our will, attitudes, and feelings are formed. The first and second great commandments have to do with our hearts: "You shall love the Lord your God with all our heart, with all your soul, and with all your mind." And, "You shall love your neighbor as yourself" (Matthew 22:37, 39).

*T*he beatitudes from Jesus' Sermon on the Mount (see Matthew 5:1-2) are the *good news* of the kingdom of heaven.

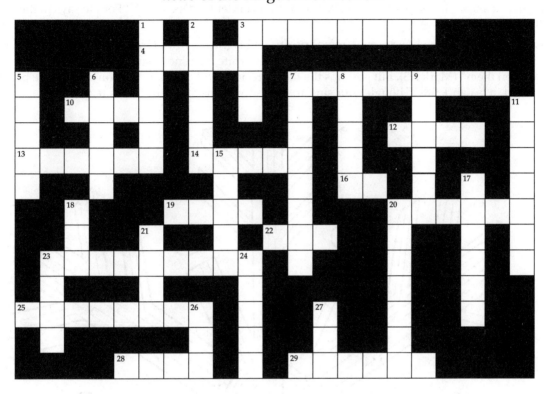

Across

3 Compassionate, lenient
4 Tranquility
7 Soothed
10 Penniless
12 Wicked
13 Crave, long for
14 Will
16 Biblical you
19 Happy
20 Payment
22 Male people
23 Harness
25 Predictors
28 Those people
29 Starve

Down

1 Soul
2 Creators; peace ____
3 Gentle
5 Speaking part
6 Grieve
7 Offspring
8 Clemency
9 Denounce; vilify
11 Empire
15 Core
17 Instructed
18 Witness
20 Be joyful
21 To be, past tense, plural
23 Untainted
24 Terra firma
26 Declare
27 Not me

As White As Snow

*A*lthough snow in the Middle East lands of the Bible is rare, it is mentioned in Scripture. It is called the "treasury of snow" in the book of Job (38:22), and it is under God's control, "For He says to the snow, 'Fall on the earth'" (37:6).

Most often, snow is used to describe moral purity and righteousness. On the Mt. of Transfiguration, Jesus' clothes were described as "shining, exceedingly white, like snow, such as no launderer on earth can whiten them" (Mark 9:3). But perhaps the most precious and familiar verse on snow is the promise contained in Isaiah 1 :18: "Though your sins are like scarlet, they shall be as white as snow."

Start →

↖End

*T*hroughout the Scriptures we find dramatic instances where God has rescued one or more individuals from peril or death. Sometimes He used supernatural means; at other times, seemingly ordinary people and things were used in extraordinary ways. Use the clues to help you unscramble the names of people God rescued.

Clue	Word	Answer
1. He was rescued along with two friends	DGEBAEON	
2. Rehab aided their escape	IPESS	
3. The greatest escape, number-wise!	AREITILESS	
4. Fled to Egypt with his wife and baby	POJHES	
5. Fled from Egypt	SMESO	
6. An angel opened the door for them	PLOTASES	
7. A fish was involved	NOAHJ	
8. His would-be hangman became the victim	DIMAROCE	
9. He "reappeared" in another city	HIPLIP	
10. He dropped his mantle as he went	JEHALI	
11. A basket was his escape hatch	LAPU	

*J*esus doesn't ask us to do anything He wouldn't do Himself.

Clue: MESSIAH *is* XIZZQNE

K E Q Z   Q Z   X O

H B X X N W G X I W K'   K E N K

O I   A B T I   B W I

N W B K E I J

N Z   Q   E N T I

A B T I G   O B S

The Maltese Cross

*T*he Maltese Cross which is formed of four spearheads with points touching at the center, is also called the Cross of Regeneration because of its eight outer points. The number eight is associated with regeneration, in part because of the eight beatitudes (Matthew 5:3–10).

This cross is the emblem of the Knights of St. John (also called Knighths Hospitallers). The order was dedicated to St. John the Baptist in the eleventh century for the protection of European pilgrims on their way to the Holy Sepulchre in Jerusalem. The Turks later drove the order to the island of Malta, which was given to them by Charles V. The cross design takes its name from the name of the island. (Malta was the site of Paul's shipwreck in Acts 27:14–44.)

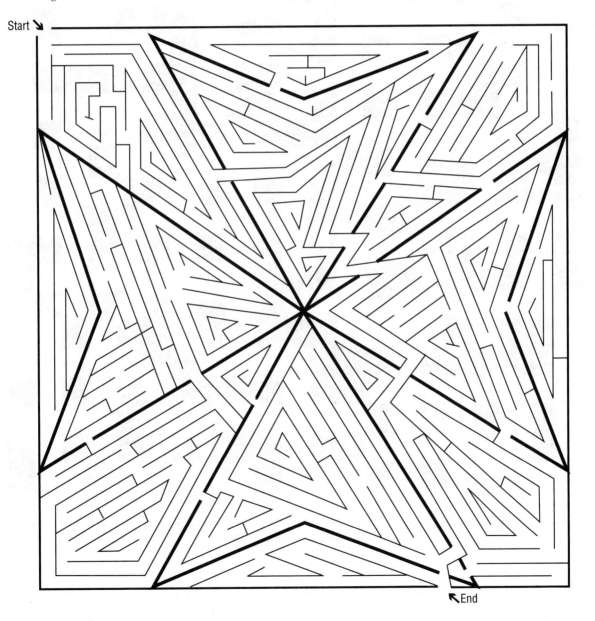

Start

End

*F*or theirs are the kingdoms, His the Kingdom!

Unscramble the circled letters in the crossword grid to reveal something we ascribe to kings and ultimately to King Jesus:

__ __ __ __ __ __ __ __ __

Across

1 King of Kings
4 Last ruler of the Northern kingdom
7 Jesus came from ___ of Jesse
10 Capable
11 You (biblical)
12 Wicked son of Jeroboam II, ruled only six months
14 King's residence
17 Not (prefix)
18 Lure
19 Founder of Samaria, Ahab's father
20 Opposite of kings
22 ___, say can you see
23 King Joash's successor son, ruled 29 years
24 Official halt
26 California mountain range
28 Nebuchadnezzar's name for replacement king Mattaniah
31 Son and successor of King Hezeklah
34 Laughter
36 His Royal Highness (abbr.)
38 Opposite of from
39 Son and successor of King Amon
40 Opposite of exhale
41 By bit
42 Work
45 His son slew Pekahiah and reigned instead
46 The fourth son of Josiah
49 Metal in the raw
51 Type of light
53 Therefore
54 Anointed king by Elisha to replace the house of Ahab
55 Glow brightly
56 Son and successor of King Menahem
60 Founding king of the Northern kingdom after rebellion against Rehoboam
62 From little acorns
63 Goes with hammered
65 Royal
66 Short for Samuel, prophet who anointed the first king of Israel
67 Daughter of a king

Down

1 Son of Jehoram, father of Joash
2 " ___ with his fathers"; buried
3 First king of Israel
4 Godly king of Judah, son of Ahaz
5 Opposite of she
6 Ahab's idolatrous successor
7 Joyous cheer
8 Yours (biblical, KJV)
9 Asa's prosperous son, king of Judah
13 Regret
15 Hebrew name of Abednego
16 Outspoken critic of King Herod
18 ___ for apples
21 A priest who witnessed Isalah's scroll
25 Northeast (abbr.)
27 Son and successor of King Solomon
29 A king after God's own heart
30 Grandfather of Hezekiah
32 Closely related
33 King noted for wisdom
35 Ahab's son, king of Israel
37 King David's royal city for 7 1/2 years
43 Every
44 Word joke
46 King's royal rod
47 Biblical greeting word
48 Killed Shallum and reigned 10 years
50 Foot appendage
52 King's chair
53 Reptiles, Chinese throne ornamentation
54 Jehoshaphat's son and successor
57 Opposite of queen
58 "All ___ the king!"
59 So be it
61 Rowing mechanism
64 Alcoholics Anonymous (abbr.)

*T*he following "game" roster has been posted in Jacob's tent.
Which of Jacob's wives or concubines put it there?

Game Roster			Date
REUBEN	VS	BENJAMIN	4 Tammuz
ISSACHAR	VS	DAN	6 Tammuz
NAPHTALI	VS	JOSEPH	9 Tammuz
GAD	VS	ZEBULUN	12 Tammuz
SIMEON	VS	JUDAH	16 Tammuz
LEVI	VS	ASHER	19 Tammuz
DAN	VS	BENJAMIN	20 Tammuz
ASHER	VS	JOSEPH	22 Tammuz
NAPHTALI	VS	LEVI	25 Tammuz
JUDAH	VS	GAD	28 Tammuz
SIMEON	VS	ISSACHAR	1 Ab
REUBEN	VS	ZEBULUN	4 Ab
JOSEPH	VS	SIMEON	7 Ab
LEVI	VS	ISSACHAR	8 Ab
REUBEN	VS	GAD	11 Ab
DAN	VS	JUDAH	14 Ab
ZEBULUN	VS	ASHER	17 Ab
BENJAMIN	VS	NAPHTALI	18 Ab

*U*nscramble the names of the 12 jewels that will form the foundations of the wall of the New Jerusalem. Refer to the New King James Bible for the answers.

1 PRASJE __ __ __ Ⓞ __ __

2 ARIPHSPE __ __ __ __ __ __ __ __

3 LOYCHEACND __ __ __ __ __ __ __ __ __ __

4 MAREDEL __ __ __ __ __ Ⓞ __

5 YADNORXS __ __ __ __ __ __ __ __

6 DASURIS __ Ⓞ __ __ __ __ __

7 ETHOCLSYIR __ __ __ __ __ __ __ __ __

8 REBLY __ Ⓞ __ __ __

9 POZAT __ __ __ __ __

10 SHASROYCPER __ __ Ⓞ __ __ __ __ __ __ __ __

11 CAITHNJ __ __ __ __ __ __ __

12 EATYSMHT __ __ __ __ __ __ __ __

What jewel will the 12 gates of the wall be made of? Unscramble the circled letters and see!

__ __ __ __ __

For whom will the 12 gates be named? Unscramble these names.

13 UNEBER __ __ __ __ __ __

14 INESOM __ __ __ __ __ __

15 EIVL __ __ __ __

16 DAJHU __ __ __ __ __

17 SACRAHIS __ __ __ __ __ __ __ __

18 ENUZUBL __ __ __ __ __ __ __

19 SJPHOE __ __ __ __ __ __

20 JMBANIEN __ __ __ __ __ __ __ __

21 AND __ __ __

22 HANTPILA __ __ __ __ __ __ __ __

23 AGD __ __ __

24 SERAH __ __ __ __ __

Concealed in this puzzle are the names of seven places mentioned in the New Testament. Can you find all seven, and identify what they have in common?

Y	H	O	U	S	P	A	M	E	H	S	F	T	L	U	A
E	K	L	E	A	E	C	I	D	O	A	L	N	I	P	M
J	U	T	P	R	U	F	A	T	C	A	N	O	R	E	Q
W	A	I	H	P	L	E	D	A	L	I	H	P	C	R	J
F	R	D	E	E	K	G	N	A	W	B	K	F	O	G	O
P	C	M	S	B	S	R	G	C	O	R	I	N	L	A	X
M	O	G	U	N	Y	S	I	N	T	E	Z	M	O	M	D
Z	D	E	S	M	O	B	A	S	A	R	D	I	S	O	T
L	V	A	S	I	P	P	I	L	I	H	P	E	S	S	Y
Q	O	W	I	T	H	Y	A	T	I	R	A	O	C	V	N

A DIFFERENT ROUTE

*I*n following a star, wise men from the East came to Jerusalem in search of a new king born to the Jews. There, the religious advisors to Herod informed them that *should* such a king be born, he would be born in Bethlehem. Herod asked the wise men to return to him if they found a newly born king, so that he might also go and worship him.

Matthew 2:12 tells us that after the wise men had visited the young child Jesus in Bethlehem, "being divinely warned in a dream that they should not return to Herod, they departed for their own country another way. "Herod later sent soldiers to Bethlehem to kill all boys under the age of two in an attempt to get rid of the rival king.

Help the wise men return to their homeland without going by Herod's soldiers. Note: A soldier is able to guard a road in four directions.

Start ↘

↖End

*T*he following puzzle is based on Daniel 1; 3.

Across

1 People, nations and ____ heard command

6 Shadrach, before Babylon

9 Required by God

11 Biblical socks

14 "We ____ not careful to answer thee"

15 Between governors and judges

18 Stringed instrument

20 Shadrach, Meshach, and ____

22 What king does

23 Threescore; cubit height of image

25 "He will deliver us out of ____ hand"

26 Alternative to bow

28 The signal to fall

30 Opposite of in

31 Shadrach, ____, and Abednego

33 Tale

34 A biblical bagpipe

35 ____, Meshach, and Abednego

38 Those gathered together to hear decree

41 Heats many of today's furnaces

43 Province where image was erected

44 They "yielded their bodies, that they might not ____ nor worship any god, except their own God"

45 Tied up

47 Name of plain

48 "Our God whom we serve is ____ to deliver us"

49 Helping friend

51 Fate of mighty men who threw Jews into furnace

53 Deadly fireplace

55 "Burning ____ furnace

56 PM opposite

57 Biblical unit of measure

58 "O king, live for ____"

59 "____ kinds of music"

61 Opposite of women

62 Chaldean activity

63 "Nor the smell of fire had passed on ____"

65 Statue

68 The Almighty

70 Empty

74 "The form of the ____ is like the Son of God"

75 ____ of fire

76 What Nebuchadnezzar was, plural

78 Small cities

80 Give adoration

81 "We will not serve ____ gods"

82 "At what time ye bear the ____"

Down

2 Abednego, before Babylon

3 A long time ____

4 ____ of God

5 Furnace product

6 Opposite of she

7 "We will ____ serve thy gods"

8 Opposite of yes

10 Also made of king's gold

11 Another name for Jews

12 Opposite of happy

13 All ____ down

15 Ancestor of today's trumpets

16 Buddies

17 Image breadth of cubits

19 Instrument similar to harp

21 King

24 Opposite of no

25 Number thrown In furnace

27 King was "full of ____"

29 Between treasurers and sheriffs

31 Meshach, before Babylon

32 Sizzled hair

36 Rescue

37 Comet Is one type

39 Not to be worshiped

40 Last seen (abbr.)

42 "We will not ____ thy gods"

46 Prophet friend of Shadrach, Meshach, Abednego

48 Opposite of courageous

50 Times furnace heated hotter

51 Reason for gathering before image

52 Official proclamation

53 Wind instrument

54 Between counselors and rulers

60 Long, detailed account

61 Power

64 Furnace opening

66 Wait for

67 All

69 Direction of fall

71 "____ it was in the beginning"

72 No kill (abbr.)

73 To fall in worship

74 Homonym of four

77 "He ____ it up in the plain Dura"

79 "There ____ no other God that can deliver after this sort"

The following puzzle is based on 2 Chronicles 20.

Across

1 Region In which fast was proclaimed
4 City under siege
9 Gain
11 "0 ____ God of our fathers"
12 Direction; show me the ____
13 Habitat
14 Either ____
15 Founder of Ammonites
17 Priests and ____
19 Mealtime furniture
21 Ancient name for God
22 "a Levite of the sons of ____"
24 Fiction
25 Morning
27 Son of Zechariah
28 They "stood up to ____ the Lord God of Israel with a loud voice on high"
31 Jahaziel
32 Son of Benalah
35 "Fear not, nor ____ dismayed"
36 Cliff name

37 Verbal abuser
38 Individual portion, area, or mark
39 Name of wilderness
40 To place, set
41 Son of Mattaniah
42 Equipped with weapons
44 ____ of the Lord came upon the prophet
46 Needed to see salvation of Lord
48 "Our __ are upon thee"
49 Fast and ____
50 What singers render

Down

1 Precious part of spoil (singular)
2 "On the fourth ____ they assembled themselves in . . . Berachah"
3 Take ____; have courage
4 King
5 Rousing defeat
6 To say
7 Ancient name for God

8 The children of Ammon and Moab and ____"
9 Good (abbr.)
10 Number of days it took to gather the spoil
16 "The children of Ammon and ____ and Mount Seir"
18 Those who seek one's destructlon
20 Son of Jeiel
23 Enemy campground
24 Mean and strong
26 Goes before others
27 The Spirit of the Lord came on him
28 According to
29 Reward of battle
30 Member of Levite family that led praise
33 Abraham's, before name change
34 Enemy goal
35 "Praise the ____ of holiness"
40 Dessert (plural)
41 Atmosphere upon return to Jerusalem
43 Opposite of night
45 "None ____ able to withstand thee"
47 ____ - Gedi

30

*U*sing the completed crossword grid in puzzle #29, decipher the following words of the prophet to Jehoshaphat and his people.

Across rows are numbered 1-18
Down rows are lettered A-S

3-J 11-G 1-D 18-O 16-K   17-R 2-E   15-O 5-O 17-F 16-E 5-A

7-E 7-Q 2-Q   16-M 5-B 11-F   11-G 11-E 15-E

10-A 2-C 2-N 5-C 11-M 15-S 13-P 14-B 4-O   12-I 7-K

16-R 11-E 16-B   9-L 4-G 10-K 1-C

HEAVEN'S BELLS

Bells have been associated for centuries with religious use. In the Old Testament, bells were attached to the hem of the priest's robe so he could be heard as he came before God in the Holy Place in the temple. The bells were made of pure gold and alternated with pomegranates around the edge of the robe. (See Exodus 28:33-35.)

Traditionally the peal of bells is a signal to call the faithful to worship and prayer. The earliest use of bells for Christian worship dates as far back as the fifth century. Today some of the largest and most famous bells in the world are in cathedrals and church towers.

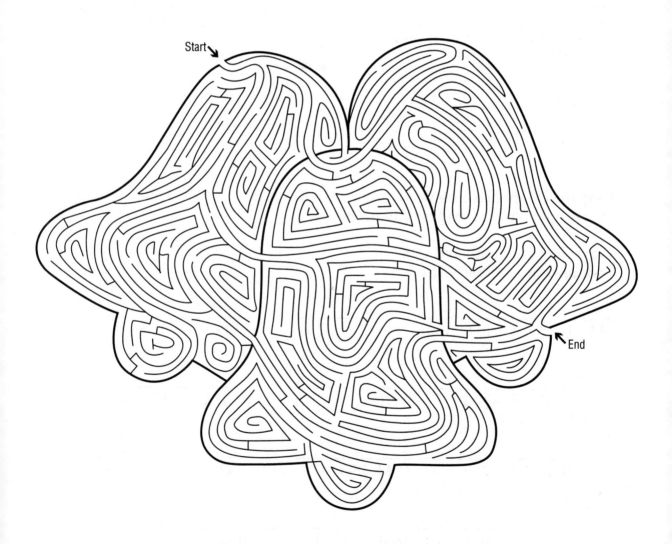

*T*he writer of First Timothy says if we have this and clothing, we can be content.

STUN __ __ __ __

MALDNOS __ __ __ __ __ __ __

BRUTET __ __ __ __ __ __

KMIL __ __ __ __

NOHEY __ __ __ __ __

SECEHE __ __ __ __ __ __

LAVE __ __ __ __

TOMTUN __ __ __ __ __ __

DAREB __ __ __ __ __

THEWA __ __ __ __ __

LAREBY __ __ __ __ __ __

ROLUF __ __ __ __ __

NORC __ __ __ __

SENAB __ __ __ __ __

TINSELL __ __ __ __ __ __ __

BUMSCERCU __ __ __ __ __ __ __ __ __

SLOMEN __ __ __ __ __ __

SHIF __ __ __ __

SINONO __ __ __ __ __ __

CRAGIL __ __ __ __ __ __

SELEK __ __ __ __ __

NANAM __ __ __ __ __

VOILES __ __ __ __ __ __

THCIF __ __ __ __ __

SHASPOPSERGR

__ __ __ __ __ __ __ __ __ __ __ __

NIWE __ __ __ __

IRISNAS __ __ __ __ __ __ __

GFIS __ __ __ __

REIGNAV __ __ __ __ __ __ __

NMIT __ __ __ __

SAINE __ __ __ __ __

LIDL __ __ __ __

MUNIC __ __ __ __ __

LAST __ __ __ __

COSLUST __ __ __ __ __ __ __

GREATMOAPEN

__ __ __ __ __ __ __ __ __ __

PAGERS __ __ __ __ __ __

VOILELOI __ __ __ __ __   __ __ __ (2 words)

TAGO __ __ __ __

XO __ __

SNIVENO __ __ __ __ __ __ __

LIQUA __ __ __ __ __

FLIGHT TO EGYPT

*M*atthew 2:13-18 tells us that an angel came to Joseph in a dream to warn him that Herod sought to kill the newborn king. The angel gave Joseph specific instructions to take the child and His mother to Egypt. Joseph's obedience saved Jesus from the massive slaughter of male infants in Bethlehem and surrounding districts. Herod had ordered the slaughter after his discovery that the wise men (whom he had relied on to tell him of Jesus' whereabouts) had deceived him and returned to their land by another route instead of through Jerusalem.

Travel from Bethlehem to the Egyptian pyramids without entering the center section where Herod's soldier awaits.

*F*ind the names of 18 of God's creations hidden in the square by going across (both left and right), up, down, and diagonally.

```
S  T  A  N  O  X  N  F  A  O  L
H  E  M  A  N  T  G  O  L  D  D
E  L  T  T  A  C  A  W  D  O  S
R  B  T  R  W  H  A  L  E  S  M
B  U  T  E  A  O  E  F  I  S  H
T  C  H  E  T  E  M  C  E  T  L
I  A  G  A  E  W  H  A  A  A  A
U  T  I  R  R  A  A  S  N  R  N
R  R  N  T  A  T  B  D  R  S  C
F  E  E  H  M  S  L  A  T  R  A
S  X  Y  N  O  T  S  Y  A  L  T
```

Word Pool

CATTLE   DAY   EARTH   FISH   FOWL   FRUIT   GOLD   GRASS
HERB   LAND   MAN   NIGHT   ONYX   SEA   STARS
WATER   WHALES   WOMAN

35

Prepare to enter the throne room of her royal highness.

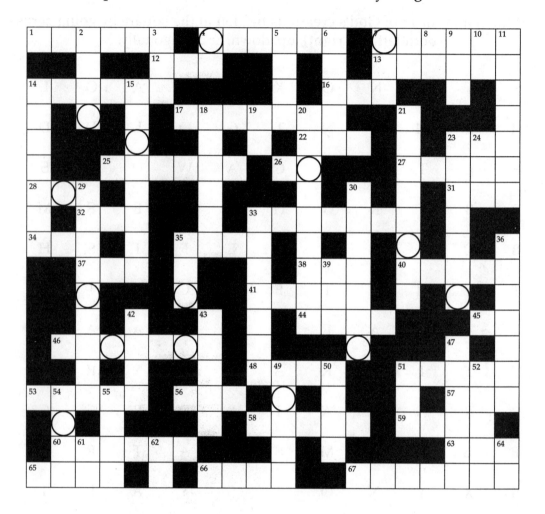

Bonus

Unscramble the circled letters in the crossword grid to reveal what God says we are as believers.

_ _ _ _ _ _ _ _ _ _ _ _ _ _ _ _

Across

1 Queen's home
4 Ruling authority
7 Queen's chair
12 For hearing royal whispers
13 David's royal city for 7 1/2 years
14 Saul's daughter, David's wife
16 Happy-go-lucky
17 Uzziah's wife, Jotham's mother
22 Extrasensory perception (abbr.)
23 Go from ____ (sing.) to riches
25 Esther's predecessor
26 Opposite of down
27 Regent's headpiece
28 Weep with a catching of breath
31 Opposite of no
32 Mother of Hezekiah
33 Ahab's wicked wife
34 Even still
35 Opposite of enslaved
37 Her Royal Highness (abbr.)
38 Sack
40 Place of sacrifice
41 Jeweled headpiece
44 Inheritor
45 Opposite of off
46 Wife of Ammon, mother of Josiah
48 Trick
51 To buy off
53 Parcel of land
56 And flow
57 Natural or furnace
58 Opposite of king
59 Magic stick
60 Herodias's dancing daughter
63 Hen's produce
65 A dark greenish-blue
66 Castle protection
67 Royal rod

Down

2 Gown trimming
3 Snakelike fish
4 Royal Regiment (abbr.)
5 One of three divisions of the psyche (pl.)
6 Roman garments
7 Your (biblical)
8 Royal Baby (abbr.)
9 A celestial sphere
10 Opposite of yes
11 Heraldic bearings
14 Her royal ____
15 Wicked daughter of Jezebel
18 Xerxes' Jewish queen
19 We (objective case)
20 Manasseh's mother
21 Azariah's mother
23 Peerage
24 High esteem
29 David's wife, Solomon's mother
30 Wife of David, Chileab's mother
33 Court amusers
35 Opposite of near
36 Queen's sons
39 Is (pl.)
42 Parliament in some countries
43 Solomon's visitor from afar; Queen of ____
47 Royal ring
49 Royalty meeting place
50 Come together
51 Bend low
52 Garment sign
54 Royal flower
55 Summon
61 After All (abbr.)
62 Myself and I
64 Great Ruler (abbr.)

*F*ind the names of all twelve of the apostles by going left, right, up, down, or diagonally. Remember there are two apostles with the same name.

P	A	L	A	J	A	M	E	S	T	W
T	H	O	M	O	E	S	I	I	E	A
H	T	W	E	H	T	T	A	M	R	E
O	A	H	N	N	M	E	O	O	T	C
M	W	T	A	S	R	L	E	N	L	A
A	E	R	P	D	O	I	S	J	M	E
S	R	A	E	H	D	J	A	M	E	S
T	D	D	T	A	I	A	R	R	O	U
E	N	R	E	J	U	L	E	M	L	S
A	A	S	R	W	E	M	I	U	T	S
B	A	P	J	U	D	A	S	P	S	E

*P*salm 150 gives us good reasons and ways to praise God. Use the New King James version.

Across

2 Violins and cellos are members of this "family" of instruments

4 A lofty term for the heavens

6 A brass instrument similar to a bugle or horn

7 "____ God from whom all blessings flow"

8 A New Testament book: The ____ of the Apostles

11 One of the instruments Paul refers to in 1 Corinthians 13:1 (plural)

12 A stringed instrument with a pear-shaped body

Down

1 David frequently played this instrument for King Saul

2 The part of the church where the worship service is held

3 Move your feet in time to the music

5 Another word for excellence

9 A small hand drum or tambourine (British spelling)

10 An instrument made of reeds (plural)

When you finish deciphering this puzzle, you will have a Bible prayer for your spiritual well-being. (Hint: This is *not* a cryptogram.)

DOGF OS SENLL UFEHT LLA HTIWDELLI FE BYA MUOYTA HT EGD ELWON KS

ES SAPHCIHWTSIR HCFO EVOLE HTWONKO TTH GIEHDN AH TPE

DDNAH TGN ELDN AHTDIW EHT SITAH WS TNIA SEHTLL AHTIWDN EHERP

MOCO TEL BAEBY AMEVOL NID EDNUORGD NA DETO ORG NI EBUO YT

AHTHTIAFHG UORH TST RAE HRUOYN ILLE WD YAM TSIRH CTA HTNAMR

ENN IEHTN ITI RIPSSI-HH GUOR HTT HGIM HT IWDENE HTGNE RTSEBO

TYROLGSIH FOSE HCI REH TO TGNIDR OCCA UOY TNA RGDLUOWE HT AHT

T H A T __ __ __ __ __ __ __ __ __ __ __

__ __ __ __ __ __ __ __ __ __ __ __ __ __ __

__ __ __ __ __ __ __ __ __ __ __ __ __ __

__ __ __ __ __ __ __ __ __ __ __ __ __

__ __ __ __ __ __ __ __ __ __ __ __

__ __ __ __ __ __ __ __ __ __ __ __ __ __ __ __

__ __ __ __ __ __ __ __ __ __ __ __ __ __ __

__ __ __ __ __ __ __ __ __ __ __ __ __ __ __

__ __ __ __ __ __ __ __ __ __ __ __ __ __ __

__ __ __ __ __ __ __ __ __ __ __ __ __

__ __ __ __ __ __ __ __ __ __ __ __ __ __

__ __ __ __ __ __ __ __ __ __ __ __ __

__ __ __ __ __ __ __ __ __ __ ;

__ __ __ __ __ __ __ __ __ __

__ __ __ __ __ __ __ __ __ __ __

__ __ __ __ __ __ __ __

LOTS OF CIRCLES

*E*very school child knows that there was a time before Columbus when people thought the earth was flat. But had those people had access to the Scripture and read Isaiah 40:22, all doubt about the earth's shape would have been erased. "It is He who sits above the *circle* of the earth," it says (emphasis added). Did you ever wonder what wide knowledge of the Scripture might have meant to world history?

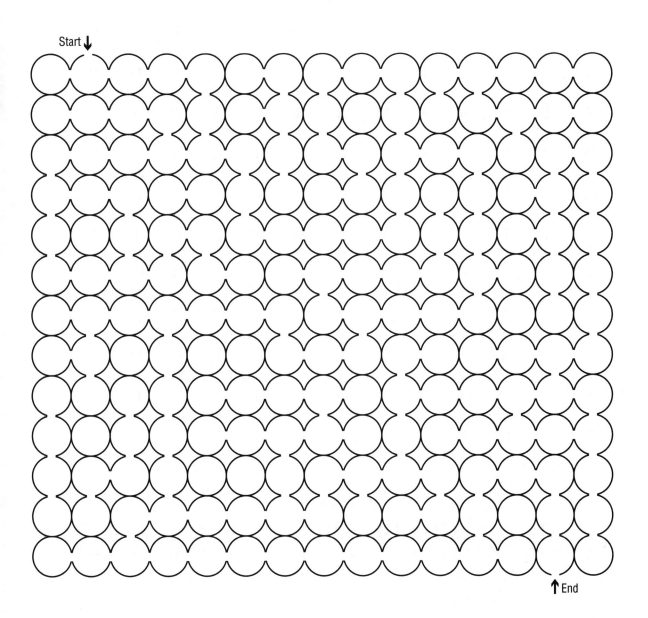

Start

End

*F*ind 16 cities mentioned in the Bible.

P S U S R A T A R L D C M

A T M S I H P M E M I Y A

R U E M Y O U E E J E J E

M X H U I N D L S A L M N

C L E S A M A R I A O J O

A B L L E S E H R R R E L

T E H E U A R T T C A R Y

R T T R C E Y M A E R I B

A H E J H S T L D N B B A

P J B O Y U R U O O R O B

S Y A P P O J E R I C H O

E R E H O B O T H Z Z L B

H O L I H S T B A B E L Y

Word Pool

BABEL   BABYLON   BETHANY   BETHLEHEM   JERICHO
JERUSALEM   JOPPA   MEMPHIS   REHOBOTH   ROME   SAMARIA
SHILOH   SPARTA   TARSUS   TYRE   ZION

*T*ry to to solve this equation without consulting the story of Noah and the great Flood (Genesis 5:32-9:29).

The number of every clean animal that God told Noah to take into the ark

_____

The number of every unclean animal that God told Noah to take into the ark

$\times$ _____

The number of the month in which the rain began to fall

$\times$ _____

The day of the month that the rain began to fall

$\times$ _____

The number of days that "the waters prevailed upon the earth"

$+$ _____

The number of days and nights that the rain fell on the earth

$-$ _____

The number of the month when the tops of the mountains could be seen

$+$ _____

The number of Noah's sons

$+$ _____

The number of times Noah sent out birds to see how dry the earth had become

$+$ _____

The number of decks in the ark

$-$ _____

Noah's age when he entered the ark

$=$ _____

Warfare—both military and spiritual—is found throughout the Bible. The battles and the enemy are real, but we are confident of a glorious and triumphant victory!

Across

1 Arrow propulsion device
3 Conflicts
5 Heavy sword with curved blade
8 Hand-to-hand
11 Title when knighted
12 Good ____; reconnaissance necessity
13 Clutch tightly
14 Frequently concealed knife
15 Top gun
16 And fire
18 Fiery, to Paul
20 Rock propulsion device
21 Protects skull
23 Final weapon to Paul: "praying always . . . in the ____"
26 Tiffs
28 Most effective with sharp point
29 Goliath's was like a weaver's beam
31 Goes with chain
32 ____ fight; clenched hand
33 Of faith, to Paul
35 For lions and slaves
37 Nature of enemy darts, to Paul
40 Wound aftermath
41 War professional
42 Attached by iron links
44 Cousin to frog
45 Metal stocks
46 Gash
47 Distress signal

Down

1 A forceful blow; also a party
2 Sword of the Spirit
3 Practice fights (2 words)
4 Word of God
5 What Saul pitched at David
6 Righteousness, to Paul
7 Expressing uncontrolled anger
8 Pharaoh's were lost to Red Sea
9 Accompaniment to compass
10 Tumult
17 For giving lashes
19 Quiver contents
22 Rap on shoulder
24 Make a comeback
25 Long spears
26 Away from harm
27 Full collection of arms
30 For holding arrows
33 Protective covering for feet
34 Taunting temptations
36 Secret Service (abbr.)
37 Opposite of skinny
38 Durable, strong metal of ancient war
39 Sticks for beatings
43 Not Intentional (abbr.)

God's plans have a lot to do with your plans.

Clue: MESSIAH *is* NVHHRZS

X L N N R G   G S B   D L I P H

F M G L   G S V   O L I W.

Z M W   G S B   G S L F T S G H

H S Z O O   Y V

V H G Z Y O R H S V W.

*T*he names of these people are found throughout the Bible—unscramble the names, then unscramble the circled letters to find out what they have in common.

AASHII _ _ _ _ _ _

AHOBIDA _ _ _ _ _ _ _

ALUP _ _ _ _

ARMK _ _ _ _

ASHOE _ Ⓞ _ _ _

CHAIM _ _ _ _ _

CLAIMHA _ _ _ _ _ Ⓞ _

EUJD _ _ _ _

GAGAHI _ _ _ _ _ _

HIAPHAZEN _ _ _ _ _ _ _ _ _

HIRAJMEE _ _ Ⓞ _ _ _ _ _

HUMAN _ _ _ _ _

KAKAKHUB _ _ _ _ _ Ⓞ _

KLEU _ _ _ _

LIKEEZE _ _ _ _ _ _ _

LOSMOON _ _ _ _ _ _ _

MASEJ _ _ _ _ _

MULESA _ Ⓞ _ _ _ _

NALDIE _ _ _ _ _ _

NOAHJ _ _ _ _ _

NOJH _ _ _ _

RAZE _ _ _ _

REACHHIZA _ _ _ _ _ _ _ _ _

SHOAJU _ _ _ _ _ _

SOMA _ _ _ Ⓞ

SOMES _ _ _ _ _

TREPE _ _ _ _ _

VADID _ _ _ _ _

WHATEMT _ _ _ Ⓞ _ _ _

Circled letters:

_ _ _ _ _ _ _

*E*arth, sky and sea ... what more is there?

Clue: MESSIAH *is* SKYYOGN

GTJ   MUJ   HRKYYKJ

ZNKS   GTJ   MUJ   YGOJ

ATZU   ZNKS   HK   LXAOZLAR

GTJ   SARZOVRE   GTJ

XKVRKTOYN   ZNK   KGXZN

GTJ   YAHJAK   OZ   GTJ

NGBK   JUSOTOUT   UBKX

ZNK   LOYN   UL   ZNK   YKG

GTJ   UBKX   ZNK   LUCR   UL

ZNK   GOX   GTJ   UBKX

KBKXE   ROBOTM   ZNOTM

ZNGZ   SUBKZN   AVUT

ZNK   KGXZN

*E*lijah, whose story is told primarily in 1 Kings 17-19, was a prophet after our own hearts. Despite numerous displays of God's miracle-working power, he still had doubts and fears. But in the end, he was "the prophet who did not die." Refer to the New King James Bible.

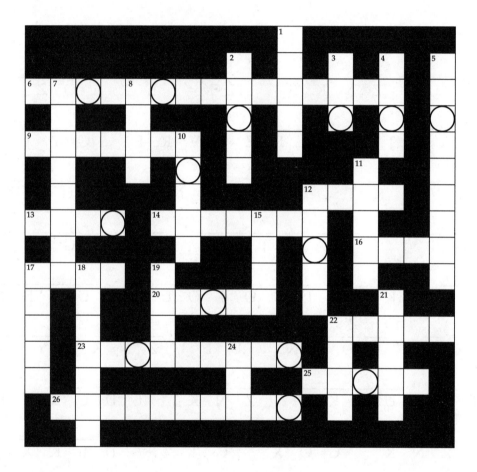

Uscramble the circled letters to find out how the people responded when fire ignited the wet wood.

___ ___ ___   ___ ___ ___ ___.   ___ ___ ___   ___ ___ ___   ___ ___ ___!

Across

6 God revealed Himself to Elijah as a (3 words)

9 This Canaanite goddess was worshiped by the king's wife

12 God was not in these "flames"

13 God was not in this "breeze"

14 This wife of Israel's king was known for her massacre of God's prophets

16 The king who reigned in Israel during Elijah's time

17 One of the foods brought to Elijah by a bird during the drought

20 This heavenly being brought Elijah food in the wilderness

22 How many days and nights Elijah survived in the wilderness, after eating just two meals

23 A town in Sidon where Elijah met an elderly woman on the verge of starvation

25 A woman whose husband has died (she's the one in #23 Across)

26 God was not in this "trembling of the ground"

Down

1 This bird fed Elijah during Israel's drought

2 The structure on which sacrifices were placed

3 One of two ingredients left in the larder of #25 Across

4 Elijah didn't anoint this man king of Israel as God commanded; Instead, Elisha did

5 The town Elijah first ran to when his life was threatened by the queen

7 Someone from Elijah's hometown would be known as a ____

8 Elijah frequently called on the name of the

____

10 Location of the "mountain of God"

11 The other food brought to Elijah by a bird during the drought

12 The other ingredient left in #25 Across's larder

15 False god worshiped by the king during Elijah's time

17 On ____ Carmel. Elijah's sacrifice caught fire, miraculously

18 Son of the king who became king when his father died

19 Where Elijah stayed while on the "mountain of God"

21 Type of tree under which Elijah sat in the wilderness

22 If you don't succeed, you ____, as the false prophets did

24 Before Elijah's time, this king of Judah is credited with tearing down images made for false goddess, worshiped during the prophet's time

*F*ind 16 words that relate to Jesus' healing ministry. Not all the words to be found are proper names. Some words may be people who were friends and relatives of those Jesus healed.

P	S	U	E	A	M	I	T	R	A	B	G	L	A
D	N	B	A	R	T	D	M	A	E	U	S	I	C
A	E	I	A	I	E	M	N	I	S	E	R	E	C
U	T	S	M	Z	B	D	A	I	R	C	E	L	E
G	A	U	S	M	E	I	N	R	L	T	P	P	N
H	D	S	U	E	M	E	T	I	T	B	E	E	T
T	E	D	S	N	S	E	N	T	L	H	L	N	U
E	T	A	E	D	C	S	C	O	T	B	A	J	R
R	E	D	L	A	Z	M	O	S	J	V	A	A	I
L	A	A	U	E	D	D	E	P	R	U	I	R	O
K	C	I	S	L	D	A	Z	E	W	O	M	A	N
S	L	A	Z	A	R	U	S	U	R	I	A	J	S

Word Pool

BARTIMAEUS   BLIND   BLOOD   CENTURION   DAUGHTER   DEAD
DUMB   HEALED   JAIRUS   LAZARUS   LEPERS   MARTHA
POSSESSED   SERVANT   SICK   WOMAN

*A*ll but a few of the words in this puzzle are found in Peter's sermon in Acts 2.

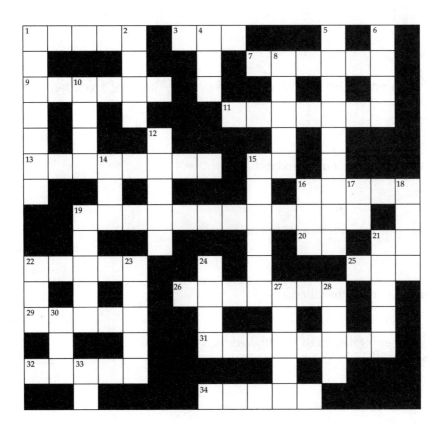

Across

1 Instrument of death
3 Male people
7 Royal seat
9 Ask forgiveness
11 Lifted up
13 Foretell
15 Preposition
16 Hip region
19 Act of being raised to new life
20 Spanish "the"
21 Explorer Livingston's initials
22 Goes with wonders
25 Not good
26 Miracles, rarities

29 The preacher
31 Sprinkled, poured, or
   dipped
32 Wed
34 Core, center

Down

1 Evil, impure
2 Transgressions
4 Finale
5 Place for feet
6 Not living
8 Same as #34 Across
10 Ball game played on
   horseback
12 Savior's name

14 Prefix meaning before
15 Rise, climb
16 Untruth
17 Not out
18 Traded in merchandise
19 Correct
21 King after Saul
22 Tree's "blood"
23 Repentant
24 Burial place
27 Go in
28 Magnitude
30 Estimated time of arrival
   (abbr.)
33 Second note of scale

*T*he equation below is based on the Book of Exodus.

The number of tablets of commandments God
gave to Moses   _____

The number of years the Israelites ate manna in
the wilderness   ✕   _____

The number of curtains in the tabernacle   ✕   _____

The number of omers of manna to be gathered the
day before the sabbath   ÷   _____

The number of shekels of cinnamon to be used in
making the holy oil   +   _____

The number of chariots Pharaoh used in pursuing
Moses and the children of Israel   −   _____

The number of gerahs in a shekel   +   _____

The number of elders of Israel (which is the same
number of disciples sent out by Jesus in Luke
10:1-17)   =   _____

*W*arnings, revelations, and divine messages were all proclaimed by these men who had a holy calling to declare the word of the Lord. Unscramble the names to find out who they are.

JILHAE Ⓞ __ __ __ __ __

HAMCIAI __ __ __ __ __ Ⓞ __

HJNOA __ __ Ⓞ __ __

HASILE __ __ __ __ __ __

SAMO __ __ __ __

SHEAO Ⓞ __ __ __ __

SAAIIH __ __ __ __ __ __

HAMIC __ __ __ __ __

RUHIA __ __ __ __ __

HEERMAJI __ __ Ⓞ __ __ __ __ __

MUANH __ __ __ __ __

ZHPHNAAIE __ Ⓞ __ __ __ __ __ __ __

KAKAKHUB __ __ __ __ __ Ⓞ __ __

DABOHIA __ __ __ __ __ __ __

Unscramble the circled letters to reveal an appropriate reaction to the words of a true prophet:

__ __ __ __ __ __ __

*A*ll four Gospel writers recorded the most glorious event in history: the resurrection of God's only Son, Jesus Christ.

Across

2 Killed, as on a cross
5 Uncertainty made Jesus' followers ____
7 The "other side" of Christmas
8 The women experienced this feeling when they saw the angels in Jesus' tomb
11 Cloth for Jesus' burial clothes
12 ____-inspiring
14 And then there were eleven . . .
16 It was probably one of those carved into a limestone hill
17 "He is ____ indeed!"
18 This object was no obstacle
22 One of three women who paid an early call on Jesus' burial place
23 This form of extreme happiness was appropriate to the occasion
24 Perform a deed
25 Mary mistook Jesus for this man

Down

1 One of the two who "became like dead men"
3 Jesus' ____ truly were shod with the preparation of the gospel of peace
4 "My ____ and my God!"
6 "They have taken Him ____ !"
9 It was customary in Jesus' day to use these fragrant materials on a corpse
10 They were movers and shakers
11 Jesus healed one of these during His earthly ministry
13 The tears flowed
14 Mary Magdalene used to have seven of these
15 To do this, apply oil or other appropriate materials
18 White as ____
19 His mother also visited the tomb
20 This piece of apparel was long and white
21 There's one in Galilee, where Jesus met several of His disciples for breakfast

*U*nscramble the words below that are associated with the greatest act any of us can ever experience, and place the unscrambled answers on the grid. Use the Scripture pool if you need clues.

FIEGEFRT	OUGTRONINTGD	NRADPO
OOSRRW	NIEVEIBLG	ACLEINSNG
MEPDTEORIN	CYREM	TBPAIMS
SNSEINFOOC	RORTEISATON	TNAEPNERCE
NRSIUGOHETSES	JOODOFDLESBHSESU	MORESISINFOISSN
TIPIPARTONIO	ICFAIITTSOUNJ	

— — — — G — — — (2 words)

— O — — — —

— — D — — — — — —

— — — F — — — — —

— — — — — — O — — — —

— — R — — — — — — — — — —

— — — — — G — — — — — (3 words)

— — — I — — — —

WE FORGIVE OTHERS

— E — — —

— — S — — — — — — —

— — — — — O — — — — — — — — (4 words)

— U — — — — — — — —

— — R — — —

— — — — S — — —

— — — I — —

— — — N — — — —

— — — — S — — — — — — — (3 words)

Scripture Pool

Matthew 6:14   Acts 2:38   2 Corinthians 7:10   Ephesians 2:8   Isaiah 55:7
Joel 2:13   Matthew 26:28   John 3:16   1 John 1:7-9   1 Peter 1:3   Psalms 23:3
Romans 3:24,25   Romans 5:1   Ruth 4:15

*M*ost of the answers to this crossword are about a Bible character who was in the right place at the right time.

"Yet who knows whether you have come to the
kingdom for such a time as this?"
(Esther 4:14, NKJ)

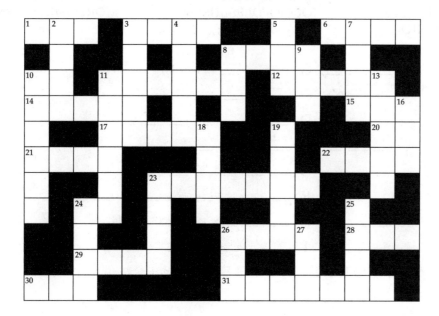

Across
1 Declare
3 Refrain from eating
6 Years and years
8 Mordecai's father
10 Veterans Administration (abbr.)
11 King's house
12 Part of year
14 Part of Mordecai's "mourning wear"
15 What Esther invited the king to do
17 A second, separate one
20 Personal pronoun
21 Assistance

22 What a little child shall do for them
23 Big meal
24 Maine (abbr.)
26 String up
28 Decree
29 Kind of cloth that goes with ashes
30 Trench
31 Hanging place

Down
2 Biblical "O, Dear!"
3 Celebration with food
4 Expanse
5 Poorly lit

7 Entrance
8 Esther was one
9 Fish eggs
10 Queen's name
11 Folk
13 Mordecai's enemy
16 Theodore's nickname
18 Circular adornment
19 Esther's title
23 King's midnight entertainment
24 Where the sail is attached
25 Soared
26 Embrace
27 Liquid measure (abbr.)

*S*tring the letters together (horizontally, vertically, or diagonally) to reveal one of the greatest promises in the Bible.

START

O R D C E T O T O O A

C I L A T H H D G L H

N C L E E D O R L T I

G A D R O T O S O G N

P T O A T G E F S W O

O R H H O E H W R R T

S U I H O V O E T O K

E P S W E S O L H E G

*A*t the end of his letters to the churches, the Apostle Paul frequently named names. He sent personal greetings to people he cared about, and relayed greetings from his fellow workers. Many of the names are not familiar to us, but Paul considered them worth remembering. (Use the New King James Bible if you're stumped!).

Across

1 A Jewish Christian tentmaker; husband of Priscilla

4 The writer relayed her greetings to Timothy

7 A man whose name is a slight "misspelling" of the mount where the chief gods of ancient Greece resided

10 Paul's host and host of "the whole church" sent his greetings to the Romans

11 "The beloved physician"

14 This Christian shared the name of the "divine messenger of the Greek gods"

15 He is greeted in Romans, along with his sister; possibly the son of Philologus

19 She and Andronicus, who may have been her husband, were Paul's "kinsmen and fellow-prisoners"

21 She shares the name of Lazarus' sister

22 Paul left his cloak and books with this man of Troas; Timothy was sent to fetch them

Down

1 A native of Thessalonica, he was with Paul on the final trip to Jerusalem

2 A "fellow worker in Christ," from Romans (NKJ)

3 Paul told Titus to send this man and Zenas the lawyer on their journey "with haste, that they may lack nothing" (NKJ)

5 This friend was "approved in Christ" (change the second and third vowels in #3 Down, and you'll have #5 Down)

6 A house church met in his home. His name is a form of the Greek word for "a minor divinity of nature represented as beautiful maidens dwelling in mountains, woods, and waters."

8 Was perhaps a member of a house church; Paul sent greetings at the end of Romans

9 Paul's original name

12 His name is a "longer" version of the name of the king who tried to track down the baby Jesus

13 A woman called "beloved" by Paul, her name is four letters short of a word that means "tenacious"

16 The "treasurer of the city" (probably Corinth), his name in Greek means "beloved"

17 Another "beloved" friend, greeted by Paul in Romans

18 A woman who perhaps was married to Philologus

20 The "cousin of Barnabas," he could be the man who penned one of the gospels

*F*ind 14 birds mentioned in the Bible.

O	P	M	A	S	W	O	L	L	A	W	S
P	E	C	R	P	I	G	E	O	N	S	T
G	A	M	O	N	A	C	I	L	E	P	C
O	C	K	E	M	A	R	N	V	R	A	L
L	O	O	H	P	M	E	O	U	R	R	R
I	C	W	C	S	V	D	W	L	O	R	A
A	K	A	I	A	E	L	L	T	W	O	P
U	U	L	R	L	Q	U	T	U	S	W	S
Q	L	S	T	O	R	K	A	R	T	K	T
U	M	R	S	K	Q	C	E	E	W	H	W
A	U	C	O	R	M	O	R	A	N	T	A
T	H	A	W	L	O	A	H	C	A	W	H

Word Pool

CORMORANT HAWK OSTRICH OWL PEACOCK
PELICAN PIGEONS QUAIL RAVEN SPARROW STORK
SWALLOW TURTLEDOVE VULTURE

57

Scrambled below are the names of some whom Jesus "transformed":

LAPU __ __ __ O

RAYENMAEMDAGL __ __ __ __   __ __ __ O __ __ __ __ __ (2 words)

PREEL __ O __ __ __

EPORSNETIM __ __ __ __ __   __ O __ __ __ (2 words)

HJNO __ __ O __

STDUALERSE __ __ __ __ __ O __ __ __ __

TAMIARSBUE O __ __ __ __ __ __ __ __ __

TROUNNCIE __ __ __ __ __ __ __ O __

OEMNDICA __ __ O __ __ __ __ __

OWANMTALLEW __ __ __ O __   __ __ O __ __ __ (3 words)

Unscramble the circled letters to reveal the consummate healing prayer:

__ __   __ __ __ __   __ __ __ __ __ __
(3 words)

*W*hat it all comes down to.

Clue: MESSIAH *is* YLCCQWZ

$$\overline{D}\ \overline{Z}\ \overline{X}\ \overline{B} \qquad \overline{C}\ \overline{Z}\ \overline{W}\ \overline{V}\ \overline{D}$$

$$\overline{S}\ \overline{L}\ \overline{W}\ \overline{J} \qquad \overline{D}\ \overline{Z}\ \overline{L} \qquad \overline{V}\ \overline{X}\ \overline{J}\ \overline{H}$$

$$\overline{D}\ \overline{Z}\ \overline{R} \qquad \overline{K}\ \overline{X}\ \overline{H} \qquad \overline{W}\ \overline{T}\ \overline{H}.$$

$$\overline{C}\ \overline{L}\ \overline{J}\ \overline{N}\ \overline{L} \qquad \overline{Z}\ \overline{Q}\ \overline{Y} \qquad \overline{W}\ \overline{T}\ \overline{H}.$$

$$\overline{C}\ \overline{Z}\ \overline{W}\ \overline{V}\ \overline{D} \qquad \overline{C}\ \overline{P}\ \overline{L}\ \overline{W}\ \overline{J}$$

$$\overline{F}\ \overline{R} \qquad \overline{Z}\ \overline{Q}\ \overline{C} \qquad \overline{T}\ \overline{W}\ \overline{Y}\ \overline{L}.$$

*B*ehold what manner of love the Father has bestowed on us, that we should be called children of God! (1 John 3:1. NKJ)

Across

1 Answer to Manoah's prayer

5 Progeny

9 Although his stepfather was a carpenter, this is one place where a Bible 12-year-old did business for his Father

12 Timothy's grandmother

13 Despise

14 Victim of sibling rivalry

16 This boy's grandfather gave his dad some good advice so he could get some quality time

18 Child's toy

21 This child had the first water bed

22 Manuscript (abbr.)

24 Fermented grapes, haircuts and corpses were off-limits to these people (sing.)

26 One of the ways in which children grow

28 First of two fraternal twins

29 Out of sight

31 This child didn't have anything to laugh about when his half-brother was born

34 This youth's blue blood was bad, but that didn't make him bad

36 This child had a cradle, but not a grave

40 Train children in the ____ they should go

41 The oldest of "my three sons," he respected his father's dignity

42 Kinsman of the Redeemer

43 His father was at a loss for words when he found out he was going to be a dad
46 This child followed close on his brother's #50 Across
47 Part of early growing-up process
50 Achilles' weak spot
53 An orphan child with heroic courage
54 A "significant other" to a boy who grew up in the temple
55 A young boy's offering to Jesus
56 Female child

Down

1 This king knew how to get to the heart of the mother
2 Female sibling (shortened form)
3 New Testament (abbr.)
4 Children grow ____
5 God's only Son has ____ come the world
6 A child's unselfishness, two of these, and miraculous multiplication made a lot of hungry people happy
7 Child's transport (English)
8 A fateful day for this newborn when the Philistines captured the ark of the covenant
10 First mom
11 Youth renewed like an ____
15 This son could call his father his "old man" with all due respect
17 Father of Bezaleel, the tabernacle craftsman
19 Son in the faith to the apostle Paul
20 Stood lookout on her little brother's behalf

22 The offspring of incest, this man became the leader of a nation that included Jesus' maternal lineage
23 Child (slang)
25 A devastating prophecy from Ahijah came true with the death of this young prince and the demise of the royal house
27 "Kid brother" handpicked for a royal destiny
28 A godly man who loved his wife, he became the father of a son because of his wife's prayers
30 Perform
32 Hush
33 Promise
35 This child had a ready response
37 First child
38 When he died, his father uttered words that have become a classic expression of the grief of a parent's loss of a child
39 This man lost his children, but he did not lose his trust in God
41 Born after the death of his older brother, his genealogy continued on through Noah
43 For a while, his life was the "pits" because of his favorite son status
44 Antediluvian patriarch
45 Rebekah and Tamar had this in common
48 Jesus ____ in wisdom and stature
49 Child's bed
51 Epoch
52 Young boy

*P*eople like these have what it takes.

Clue: MESSIAH *is* QRDDOSJ

D I G G R T   W O R R W Y

V J O L F T R M'   S M F

G P T N O F   Y J R Q   M P Y'

Y P   V P Q R   I M Y P   Q R :

G P T   P G   D I V J   O D

Y J R   L O M H F P Q

P G   J R S B R M .

*F*alse accusations against the Apostle Paul led to his eloquent defense before officials. Most of the clues and answers of this crossword relate to this trial.

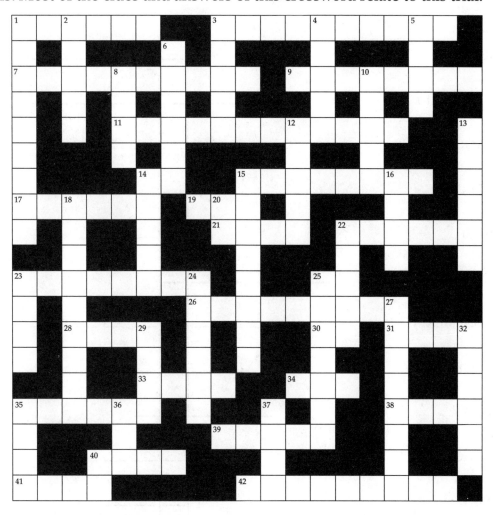

Across

1 Place of worship
3 Moral sensitivity
7 Instigator
9 Divine reckoning
11 Act of being raised to new life
14 Senior (abbr.)
15 Not Jews
17 Unrighteous
19 More than one
21 Sinister
22 Procurator of Judea
23 Official's wife
25 Place (abbr.)
26 Julius, for example
28 Contributions
30 Large bovine
31 Eastern continent
33 Legal defense
34 Early Christian movement
35 Disturbance
38 Capital city
39 Demonstrate truth
40 Persuade, influence
41 Gain illegal money
42 Grievance against Paul

Down

1 Paul's accuser
2 Medium of exchange
3 Without offense
4 Tribunal council
5 Band
6 Roman ruler
8 Sneak
10 Rumble
12 Artificial waterway
13 Female Israelite
14 Delay
15 Ruling official
16 Not difficult
18 Holy City
20 You and I
22 Official open to bribe
23 Lifeless
24 Present charges
25 Defile
27 Religious group
29 Faction
32 Take into custody
35 Wrongful act
36 Word of Moses
37 Expectation of good
40 Southeast (abbr.)

*U*nscramble the words to the left to reveal things we hope to do *without* and things we hope to be *without* one day.

ERGTYAD
— — — — — — —

ALELHILTH
— — — — — — — —
(2 words)

SEATR
— — — — —

OTMRNET
— — — — — —

TADEH
— — — — —

ROSROW
— — — — — —

GDSUIJMENMT
— — — — — — — — — —

ENSEIEM
— — — — — —

RORWY
— — — — —

UREHGN
— — — — — —

NSI
— — —

ANPI
— — — —

RFLAUIE
— — — — — — —

ROEPTVY
— — — — — — —

ISNUMPHNET
— — — — — — — — — —

*A*ll the scrambled words have to do with Jesus' triumphal entry.

RULEJAMES __ __ __ __ __ Ⓞ __ __ __

STRANGEM __ __ __ __ __ Ⓞ __ __

LAMP __ __ __ __

ACHESBRN __ __ __ __ __ Ⓞ __ __

CLOT __ Ⓞ __ __

SUJES __ __ Ⓞ __ __

VASEPORS __ __ __ __ __ __ __ __

SAFET __ __ __ __ __

LESBEDS __ __ __ __ __ __ __

UNTOMILESFOOV __ __ __ __ __ __ __ __ __ __ __ __ __ (3 words)

ERICJOE __ __ __ __ __ __ __

SPEARI __ __ Ⓞ __ __ __

CAPEE __ __ __ __ __

YGROL __ __ __ __ __

TESSON __ __ __ Ⓞ __ __

Unscramble the circled letters to find out what the people said:

*T*he following equation relates to Bible kings.

The number of years that it took Solomon to build his palace

_____

The age of Josiah when he became king

−   _____

The number of years that Solomon had reigned as king before he began to build the Temple

$\times$ _____

The number of years that Asa ruled in Jerusalem

$+$ _____

The number of years that Ahaziah reigned over Israel

$+$ _____

The number of months it took for Joab and his men to conduct a census for King David

$\div$ _____

The number of years that it took Solomon to build the Temple

$=$ _____

*F*ind the hidden command from the Apostle Paul in the letter box below:

B	X	E	L	S	I	T	V	R	E	O	D	N	E	G	H	I	T	N
F	O	S	E	L	I	W	E	H	T	D	N	A	S	E	C	A	L	P
T	H	H	G	E	I	L	H	O	N	R	I	D	S	A	S	N	E	D
N	D	E	K	C	I	W	L	A	U	T	I	R	I	P	S	D	N	A
I	D	N	L	T	R	H	O	E	W	P	S	O	I	W	H	E	T	R
F	O	S	S	E	N	K	R	A	D	E	H	T	F	O	S	R	E	L
O	U	F	R	H	D	I	N	S	A	M	S	I	R	G	E	H	W	T
O	P	D	N	A	S	E	I	T	I	L	A	P	I	C	N	I	R	P

This letter box also contains 5 things that come
against all of us. Can you find them, too?

1. _____

2. _____

3. _____

4. _____

5. _____

Most of the answers to these clues are found in the Book of Revelation although the clue may not refer to its usage there.

Across

1 Remains when light is gone
7 Drink made from leaves
9 Sugary
11 Splendor
13 Sufficiently skilled
14 Frog relative
15 Each (abbr.)
16 Affirmative
17 Man's name
19 Lord's prayer—first word
20 Limited (abbr.)
22 Female deer
23 The New City
26 Astonishing, spectacular
29 Flexible, resilient
32 Memo or jotting
33 Mother or father
35 Suffix meaning more
36 Two words to wed

37 Beelzebub
38 Annoy, nettle
39 Satan's garden persona
41 Resting place
44 Jewish homeland
45 Have debt
46 Fifth note of the scale
47 Feeble
48 Island of revelation

Down

1 Mythical reptile; Satan
2 Sovereign
3 Property, land
4 Weapon; Bible
5 Stamp, imprint
6 Era
7 Endeavor
8 Window of the soul
10 Edward's nickname

12 John saw seven; candleholders
17 Vapor, haze
18 One who swears
21 Blemish, stain
23 Precious stone, first foundation of New Jerusalem
24 Ample, great
25 Abraham's nephew
26 Exalt, revere
27 Bird's homemaking
28 God's promissory note
30 Flower necklace
31 Rock
34 First boat of note
38 Notion
40 Betrayal signal
42 Female sheep
43 Sitting place for child

YHWH is what this Bible character calls himself. Solve the cryptogram to find out who it is.

Clue: MESSIAH *is* UKPPWJF

J V Z   X T Z   P J W Z   R T

U T P K P   "W   J U   M F T   W

J U."   J V Z   F K   P J W Z

"R F O P   E T O   P F J B B   P J E

R T   R F K   G F W B Z Q K V   T S

W P Q J K B   'W   J U   F J P

P K V R   U K   R T   E T O.'"

These clues and answers, for the most part, have to do with the letter "H."

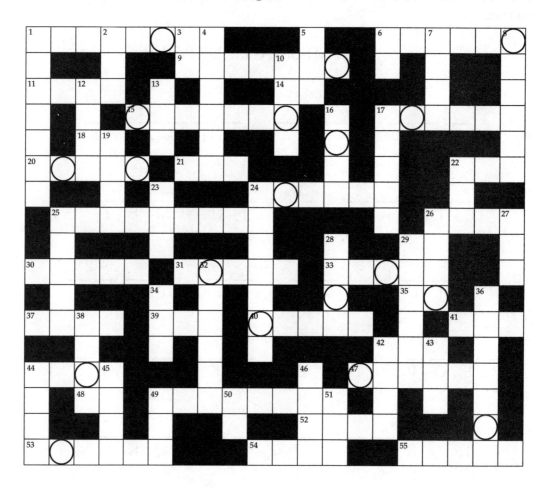

Across

1 Devout king of Judah

6 She was insulted and scorned, she wept and refused food, but God answered her prayer with an heir

9 Pagan

11 David single-handedly determined this creature's fate

14 Hand implement

15 White fields are ready for this

17 Concealing

18 Former president's initials

20 Cereal grass

21 Lord, faith, baptism

22 Fire-tested and found lacking

24 Offered as a burnt sacrifice

25 Whitewashed wall

26 First-born son, most often

29 Hectare (abbr.)

30 Esau's hands

31 OT song

33 Heavenly harbinger

35 Behold

37 Paean

39 Second son of Noah

40 The Syrians probably heard a lot of this and broke camp

41 Lent Moses a hand

42 To chisel, as in stone tablets

44 Eucharistic bread

47 To announce

48 Hither-____

49 Mary, mother of Jesus

52 Flowing with milk and honey

53 Hosea's wife

54 Set apart

55 Useful for manual labor

Down

1 Chosen people

2 To give ____ is to hearken

3 Sigh of contentment, relief

4 Home for Christians

5 Curse

6 Masculine pronoun

7 Have not

8 Jesus, after forty days

10 God's attitude toward idolatry, injustice, insincere worship, evil

12 Hurt

13 Fedora, bowler, panama

16 Manasseh and Ephraim had this in common

17 Center of things

19 Lyre

22 Color

23 Hall, for example

24 Jesus' ministry: teaching, preaching, and ____

25 Gray with age

26 Angel headgear

27 To hearken is better than a part of this

28 Haman's fate

29 Holy Spirit

32 He-man

34 American Heart Association (abbr.)

36 Thirty, sixty

38 Superlative

42 Salome's request

43 To strengthen, become (bibl.)

44 Hilkiah's position

45 Hacksaw, hammer

46 Zion, the holy ____

49 Not cold

50 Treat others as you want to be treated

51 Twenty-four hours

Uscramble the circled letters to reveal a hidden message to the King of Kings.

___ ___ ___ ___ ___ ___ ___   ___ ___

___ ___ ___ ___ ___ ___ ___ ___ ___ ___!

In the box below find the names of 25 items that the Bible speaks of having been broken.

A	H	T	I	A	F	U	M	E	A	T	S	P	L	T
E	T	M	L	S	T	A	F	R	I	R	P	N	A	B
T	N	A	I	S	E	I	D	I	A	T	O	I	M	R
W	A	L	L	R	L	N	Y	L	S	I	S	P	E	E
S	N	T	E	W	A	R	O	D	L	R	R	W	A	A
L	E	A	U	M	T	F	K	B	B	I	O	Y	I	D
M	V	R	M	W	S	R	E	D	R	P	E	T	R	H
T	O	O	D	H	L	I	A	A	E	S	T	A	O	I
E	C	S	I	E	A	K	C	E	N	S	S	E	P	F
G	A	P	W	H	E	E	L	I	H	L	T	R	E	S
T	S	G	G	E	I	D	A	E	A	O	L	T	S	T
S	T	E	R	L	O	H	B	R	P	D	A	O	A	R
M	A	T	I	D	C	A	E	D	F	I	S	H	M	E

Word Pool

ALTAR ARM BONES BREAD CHAIN COMMAND COVENANT
EGGS FAITH FISH HEART IDOLS LION NECK POWER ROD
ROPES SHIP SPIRIT TOP TREATY TREE WALL WHEEL YOKE

*U*nscramble these names, and then determine what these Bible characters have in common. The first letter of each name is given for you.

(Refer to NKJ Bible)

BAHMARA   A __ __ __ __ __ __

MABANAIMD   A __ __ __ __ __ __ __ __

JAHIAB   A __ __ __ __ __

ZHAA   A __ __ __

BUDIA   A __ __ __ __

ZOAR   A __ __ __

CHIAM   A __ __ __ __

LIAEMKI   E __ __ __ __ __ __

IDEUL   E __ __ __ __

AREALEZ   E __ __ __ __ __ __

HATOSJAPHEH   J __ __ __ __ __ __ __ __ __ __

TMOAJH   J __ __ __ __ __

SHAJIO   J __ __ __ __ __

NEACHIOJ   J __ __ __ __ __ __ __

ABOCJ   J __ __ __ __

OSNAML   S __ __ __ __ __

LOONMOS   S __ __ __ __ __ __

ELHASLEIT   S __ __ __ __ __ __ __

Use the clues in this puzzle to find names of people and places, adjectives, objects, and other words related to the many uses of "hands" in the Bible (NKJ).

Across

2 God's prophets suffered at this Queen's hand

3 David didn't want the hand of this type of person to drive him from God

7 Left-handed son of Gera; killed King Eglon to deliver the children of Israel

11 Nehemiah's servants rebuilt the wall of Jerusalem with one hand; they held one of these in the other hand

13 Stood at Heman's right hand; sang at the dedication of the Temple

15 Ezra said, "the silver and the gold and the articles" (NKJ) were weighed by the hand of Meremoth, son of _____ the priest

17 In Daniel's vision, the ram had two of these but no one could deliver him from the goat's hand

18 Through Jeremiah, God said He would give Jerusalem into the hand of the king of _____

19 He put his hand in his bag and took out a stone

20 Jeremiah prophesied King Zedekiah would not escape the hand of the _____

25 Peter credited God with delivering him from the hand of this king

26 Job asked his wife if they should accept, _____ from the hand of God, instead of adversity (KJV)

27 "Deliver me, I pray, from the hand of my brother, from the hand of ____," (NKJ)

31 Saul told Ahijah to do this with his hand, and then he battled the Philistines

33 If you put your hand to the ____ (KJV) and then look back, you aren't fit for the Kingdom of God

35 This man made a promise to the king of Sodom by lifting his hand to the Lord

36 He asked his friends for pity because the hand of God had struck him

37 When he stretched out his hand, there was a dry aisle in the place

38 The Assyrian enemy will do this with their fist on the day the remnant returns

39 The returning son received the best robe and a ____ for his hand

Down

1 This prophet had hard words for Baasha who had angered God with the works of his hands

4 In days to come an angel will bring this in his hand to bind the devil

5 The king of Assyria said, "Don't listen to King Hezekiah. Have the gods delivered ____ from my hand?"

6 Life for life, eye for eye, tooth for tooth, hand for hand, ____ for ____

8 Jesus touched the man's withered hand, and ____ it

9 Like a thorn in the hand of a ____ is a proverb in the mouth of fools

10 Blessed is the man who keeps his hand from doing ____.

12 A wicked man's ____ would be required at the hand of a prophet who failed to warn the wicked man with a word from the Lord

14 God drove out with His hand nations that were ____

16 A wise man's ____ is at his right hand, but a fool's is at his left

21 These animals will be on His right hand; goats will be on the left

22 Nathan reminded King David of his deliverance by God from the hand of ____

23 God told Isaiah He would hold his hand and keep him to be a light to these people

24 These people used both hands to throw stones and shoot arrows to save David's life at Ziklag

28 Manual communication used to ask Zacharias what name was to be given his son

29 God pleaded the cause of David's reproach from this man's hand because David forgave the man's insults

30 After leaving Egypt and forgetting God, the Israelites were sold into the hand of the king of ____

32 Saul was staying under a tamarisk tree in this town with a spear in his hand when he learned David had been discovered

34 John saw a mighty angel come down from Heaven with a little ____ open in his hand

DESCENDING DOVE

*T*he descent of the Holy Spirit like a dove at Jesus' baptism and the voice from heaven saying, "You are My beloved Son; in You I am well pleased" (Luke 3:22) inaugurated Jesus' public ministry. Though Jesus did not need to be made righteous by baptism, He so identified with man's sin that He was baptized as an example to His followers and to equip and empower Him in ministry.

John the Baptist said he baptized with water, but Jesus is the one who would baptize with the Holy Spirit. Through the death of the sinful man symbolized by baptism and the coming of Jesus into a person's life, one is equipped and empowered by the Holy Spirit to live the Christian life.

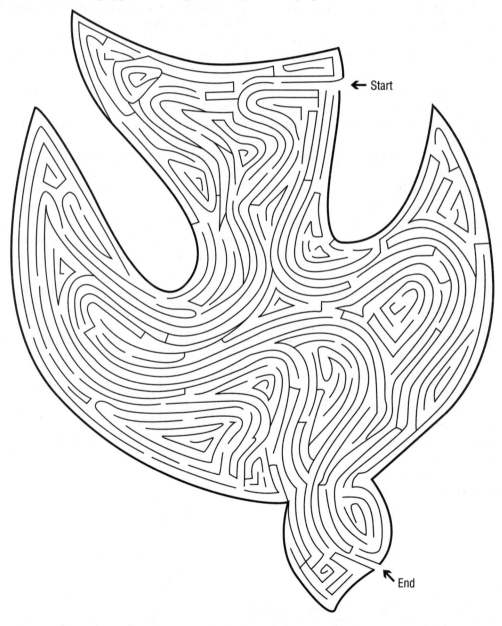

In the box of letters below, find eleven objects that the Bible describes as being "white."

```
A  F  G  H  J  O  H  L  K  P  O  I  L  U  W  I
I  W  Q  F  X  T  A  K  S  I  Q  O  P  X  R  K
R  S  K  M  E  Y  I  N  B  E  O  X  C  V  O  I
S  N  L  E  F  M  R  E  O  W  B  K  W  S  D  F
T  I  T  Q  I  A  S  D  F  J  K  O  T  Y  M  L
N  S  T  N  E  M  R  A  G  I  B  H  R  E  P  O
L  O  P  S  L  X  U  Y  O  L  R  I  W  K  I  R
E  A  W  E  D  N  V  D  U  O  L  C  R  N  E  V
Y  O  Y  T  S  X  F  J  N  W  O  I  R  O  H  D
P  N  B  O  W  G  G  E  A  S  D  F  J  D  S  A
```

Word Pool

CLOUD   DONKEYS   EGG   FIELDS   GARMENTS   HAIR
ROBES   SINS   TEETH   THRONE   WOOL

*W*e all know the story of the Old Testament heavyweight and the woman who belied the term "weaker sex." Samson's love for Delilah turned out to be misplaced, but his love for God brought him victory against all odds. Before you refer to Judges 13-16 in the New King James Bible, see how many details of this story you can recall.

Across

2 Lacking license plates, this was Samson's jailhouse occupation

5 Samson could have written a book entitled "The Secret of My ____"

6 In the end, Samson had to do it. (But he had company.)

8 How many bowstrings did Delilah tie on Samson?

9 These "windows" were closed

13 This wedding vow verb led to Samson's downfall

14 With the batten of this, Delilah wove Samson's tresses

18 Samson's father placed his offering on this

19 Samson was one of these from the womb

20 Samson's was tangled before he came clean

22 The "edge" of Samson's night

24 Samson's father made this type of offering
27 Hometown of Samson's father
28 Samson mocked Delilah with one of these—three times
29 How many years Samson determined right and wrong in Israel
31 Delilah's reward would be ____ hundred pieces of silver from each Philistine ruler
32 Samson could spin one, but it had no power to hold him
34 These fetters would come in third at the Games
36 Samson brought this house down
37 A less-than-gilded cage

Down

1 This potable never touched Samson's lips
3 The Philistines' god
4 Samson brought in the verdict
7 Samson carried the gateposts of this city to a hilltop facing Hebron. (This happened before he met Delilah.)

8 Delilah chose not to go for the gold
10 Down in this valley, Samson met Delilah
11 Samson's mother had to avoid food that wasn't spotless, lust as any sacrifice offered to God could not be this
12 Seven locks were Samson's key
15 As long as he avoided barbers, Samson's power switch was in this position
16 Samson's father
17 Samson tore one apart as if it were a young goat
21 Samson's mother shared this condition with Abraham's wife, Sarah
23 Column A and Column B
25 New or used, these weren't the ties that bound Samson
26 How many thousand men and women died after Samson's last performance
30 Interlace
33 It wasn't safe for Samson to take one of these with Delilah around
35 This one told no tails after the fire

In the circled letters you will find God's promised provision for you to overcome temptation—*if you look for it!*

___ ___ ___   ___ ___   ___ ___ ___ ___ ___ ___

THE SPIES RETURN

*J*oshua sent two men to spy out the promised land, especially Jericho. While in Jericho, the spies lodged with Rahab, a harlot. When the king of Jericho ordered Rahab to turn the men over to his custody, she hid them and later helped them escape at night over the city wall. Once outside the city, the two spies went into the mountains and stayed there three days.

The Bible says, "The pursuers sought them all along the way, but did not find them" (Joshua 2:22). When the pursuers returned to Jericho, the spies came out of the mountains and crossed back over the valley to where Joshua and the Israelites were encamped at a place called Acacia Grove.

Help these two spies escape to the mountains without being seen by the men of Jericho.
Note: A Jericho man can guard a pathway in all four directions.

*S*ome things aren't what they appear to be.

Clue: MESSIAH *is* CPEEYIO

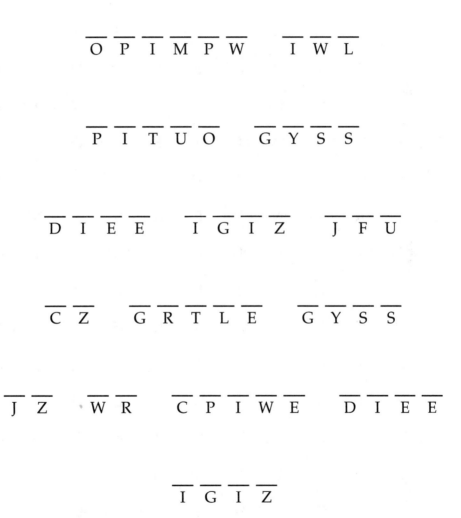

O P I M P W   I W L

P I T U O   G Y S S

D I E E   I G I Z   J F U

C Z   G R T L E   G Y S S

J Z   W R   C P I W E   D I E E

I G I Z

*T*he Apostle Paul traveled extensively carrying the gospel to cities in Asia Minor and Europe. In the box of letters, find the names of 18 cities that Paul visited before looking up the locations in the Scripture pool.

W D E R J E R U S A L E M C B

T O P J N I M O L C P A L E H

S E S I L O P O C I N T I L C

R S A T I O H E R N U P L O O

P U T E O L I I C O N I U M I

I C E M W O L A E L O H W E T

H A P O L E I M S A E T R Z N

A R T R I W P E A S N N E A A

L Y S T R A P M E S R I O D I

U S W I C N I L O E B R E D S

S U N C P L A A R H V O E A G

W A E R E B O T H T K C O I N

W E R T S E A H D L O R I N G

L S U S E H P E R A T H C Y T

I S C O R T E N O P E N M I X

P N I Y C Z G S R H E G I U M

Scripture Pool

Acts 12:25; 14:1,6; 15:35; 16:11-12; 17:13,16; 18:1; 20:15,17; 28:12-13,16;

Titus 3:12; Philippians 4:16

STAR OF DAVID

*T*he six-pointed star is the widely recognized symbol of Judaism and the central motif of the Israeli flag. It is for Jews what the cross is to Christians, the primary symbol of their faith. However, the origin of its use as a symbol for Judaism is not certain. For many years, the hexagram was simply a decoration and was used in Christian, Muslim, and Jewish design. It is believed to have been first officially used as a symbol for Judaism in Prague sometime between the fourteenth and sixteenth centuries. Since then its use has increased, and it is now universally regarded as the sign of the Jewish people. In Hebrew, the name for the Star of David is *Magen David*.

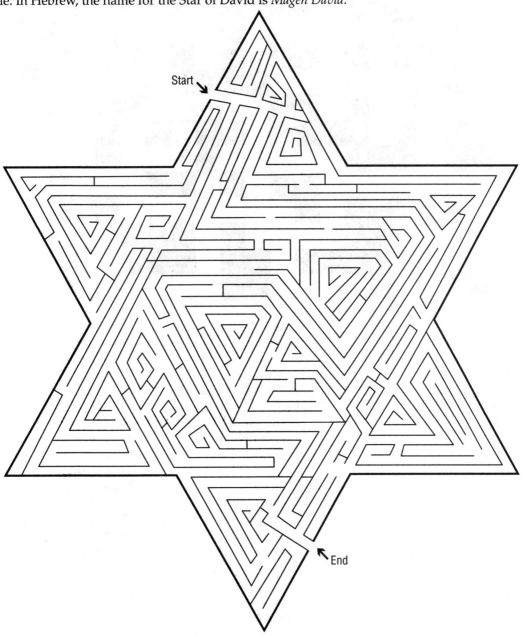

Most of the answers start with the letter "M."

Across

1 Professional organization of lawyers (abbr.)
5 Wound, disable
9 Stone for grinding wheat
10 Wonder, be awed
11 Kind of cheese
12 Miraculous meals for Israelites
13 Homes of lions
14 Female parent
15 Realm, province
17 Savior
18 Mustard seed's worth will do
19 Drink from leaves
20 Compassion
24 Wed
25 Biblical affirmative
26 Hearing organ
27 Marvel, oddity
29 The present
30 Riddle, enigma
31 Aroma
35 Entry way
36 New Testament prophetess
37 Not any
38 Edward's nickname
39 Gentle, compliant
40 Forbearance

Down

1 One who assists
2 Having no flavor
3 Donation
4 Alp
5 Personal pronoun, objective case
6 Elisha got Elijah's
7 A Great Lake
8 Animal protein
9 Concentrate on
10 Amplify, enlarge
12 Jesus' mother
14 Melody
16 Disciple and tax collector
17 Creator
20 Hero in death
21 Weep
22 Water to wine event
23 Numerous
24 Repair
27 Stars' companion
28 Imprint
30 Ridicule
32 Accomplish
33 First number
34 A primary color
36 Expert

*T*ry to complete the equation below without consulting the Scriptures!

The number of Jesus' apostles		_____
The number of the tribes of Israel	+	_____
The number of times Peter thought he should forgive those who wronged him	−	_____
The number of times Peter denied that he knew Jesus	−	_____
The number of sheep the shepherd had before he lost one	+	_____
The number of books in the Bible	−	_____
The number of times Jesus was tempted in the Wilderness	÷	_____
	=	_____

NOW . . . add these two digits together to get . . .

The number of times Elisha told Naaman to wash in the
Jordan River   _____

*U*nscramble as many of these names (of people and individuals) as you can without consulting the Scripture pool. Then, unscramble the circled letters to see their relationship to God's chosen ones.

MOMANTSIE __ __ __ __ __ __ __ __ ◯

HARHAPO __ __ __ __ __ __ __

GO __ __

MEAALK __ ◯ __ __ __ __

OLENG __ __ __ __ ◯

ELJEZBE __ ◯ __ __ __ __ __

ATOHBI __ __ __ __ __ __

DNCEBNUAHEZAZR __ __ __ __ __ __ __ __ __ __ __ __ __

BAZAD __ __ __ __ __

AGIOTLH __ __ __ ◯ __ __ __

DIMNAITISE __ __ __ __ __ __ __ __ ◯ __

ASANBTLAL __ __ __ __ __ __ __ __ __

TISIILHPNSE __ __ __ __ __ __ __ __ __ __

DABAZOHEJ __ ◯ __ __ __ __ __ __ __

__ __ __ __ __ __ __

Scripture Pool

2 Chronicles 20:1; 24:26   Deuteronomy 3:1   Exodus 1:22; 17:8   Genesis 26:18   Jeremiah 39:1

Judges 3:12,13   1 Samuel 17:23   1 Kings 18:13   Nehemiah 2:10   Numbers 25:17,18

ICHTHUS

*T*he sign of the fish came into use as a symbol of Christ in the second century. The symbol may have derived from the acrostic IXOYE (the Greek word for fish), with the letters standing for Jesus Christ, Son of God, Savior. Or the acrostic may have come from the symbol.

The fish is sometimes used as a symbol of baptism. Tertullian writes of new Christians as being little fishes following the Fish in the second birth that occurs in the waters of baptism.

The fish is sometimes a symbol of the Eucharist. Catacomb paintings of the fourth and fifth centuries frequently include the fish symbol in combination with bread and wine.

From early times, fish—especially dried fish—took the place of meat on days of fasting. The symbol of the fish is thus sometimes associated with the separation of Christians from the world.

In recent times individuals and organizations have used the fish symbol to testify to their identification with Christ.

Start

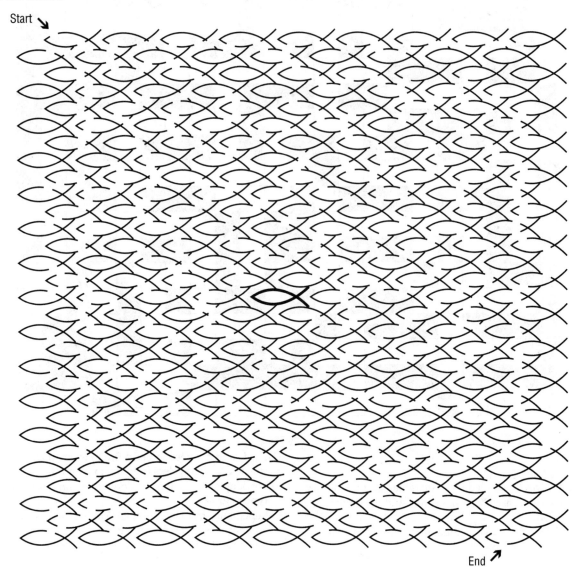

End

*A*nd sometimes, it pours.

Across

1 A property of rain

2 #19 Down mingled with fire rained on this country

4 This man stretched out his rod, and the downpour began

10 Heavy rain was one thing that caused the men of the ____ to tremble

11 The island natives kindled a fire to warm the shipwrecked travelers from the rain and the ____

13 The king's son shall come down like rain upon this type of grass

15 Repentance from having these kinds of wives was another reason these men were shaking

16 Men used to listen to Job, they opened their ____ wide, as for the spring rain

17 Those whose strength is in God make the #42 Down of _____ a spring

20 Elijah drew water from this brook

21 God would change rain to powder if the Israelites did not observe these

22 He knew how to float a boat when it seemed the rain would never end

24 In Isaiah, God promised a _____ for shade, a place of refuge, and a shelter from storm and rain

26 Floods, hailstones, fire, and brimstone would rain down on this king as judgment

27 Job said his _____ settled on men as dew

29 The fury of God's _____ will rain on the wicked while he eats

32 Moses said, "Let my _____ drop as rain"

34 An umbrella wouldn't have helped; he left home and moved to #57 Across

36 When Elijah did this earnestly, there was no rain for three and a half years

37 The captives were _____ from fear and chilling rain

40 Interdict

41 Job's speech _____ on them like early morning moisture (NKJ)

42 God's _____ failed Him, so He would command the clouds not to rain on it

43 You and me

45 Showers of rain and grass in the _____ (Zech. 10:1)

46 God made a _____ for the rain (Job 28:26)

49 The great I _____

51 What rain is

53 Not she

55 When God closed these, there was no rain

56 God does _____ things, such as sending rain (Job 5:9,10, NKJ)

57 The "little city" to which #34 Across escaped before there was a hot time in his old town (Gen. 19:23)

58 There was no need for rain in the Garden of Eden; this rose from the ground to water the plants

59 After 40 days and nights, God _____ the rain so the waters could recede (Gen. 8:2)

60 It won't be a tea party for the wicked. Rain consisting of fire and brimstone shall be the portion of their _____ (Psa. 11:6)

Down

1 Two of these have power to close the skies so that no rain falls (Rev. 11 :3-6)

3 God made a _____ for the thunderbolt (Job 28:26)

5 "Fire and brimstone" were forecast for this city because or sin (Gen. 19)

6 Wicked, depraved

7 Without wind or rain, God used these to fill the land with water (2 Kings 3: 17)

8 God rained down food on the Israelites in the wilderness. One food was _____ (Ex. 16:4,31)

9 When the wicked man is about to fill his _____, God will rain His fury on him while he eats (Job 20:23)

11 The wicked can also expect God to rain _____ upon them; they have to take their lumps (Psa. 11:6)

12 Does the rain have one of these? (Job 38:28)

14 There was #28 Down and rain on the day of this harvest, because the Israelites' wickedness was great in asking for a king (1 Sam. 12:17)

18 David said there would be no rain on the mountains of _____ (2 Sam. 1:21)

19 God gave #2 Across this for rain (Ex. 9:23)

23 If His people would _____ His commandments, God said, He would send early and latter rains (Deut.11:13,14)

25 The early rain comes in this season

27 God said the _____ had been withheld, because Israel was unfaithful (Jer. 3:3)

28 You hear it during a storm

30 When #4 Across lifted this to the sky, God didn't spare the Israelites' taskmasters (Ex. 9:23)

31 #4 Across wanted to be heard "as raindrops on the tender _____" (Deut. 32:2)

33 #5 Down's partner in crime

35 This island was chilly and rainy, but Paul's hosts offered a warm welcome (Acts 28:1-2)

38 God says to the snow, "Fall on the _____," likewise to the gentle and heavy rains (Job 37:6)

39 Were there any among the _____ of the nations that could cause rain? (Jer. 14:22)

41 If the Israelites disobeyed, God warned that He would _____ up the skies (Deut. 11:17)

42 #17 Across is one of these, unlike #18 Down

44 To love and _____ God was the way for the Israelites to receive the rain they needed (Deut. 11:13)

47 God saw and declared _____, after devising, "rules" and "routes" for the rain and thunderbolts (Job 28:26-27)

48 A king's _____ is like a cloud of the latter rain (Prov. 16:15)

50 In the wilderness, God rained #8 Down and _____ on His people for them to eat (Ex. 16:8)

52 David wanted no rain to fall on the mountain where Saul died, and also no _____ to drop (2 Sam. 1:21)

54 Refusing to follow God's commandments would result in rain of powder and _____ (Deut. 28:24)

Christianity makes some unequivocal claims.

Clue: MESSIAH *is* WPFFSOQ

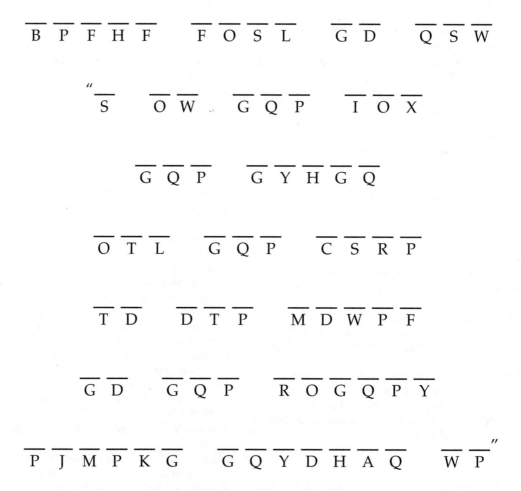

B P F H F   F O S L   G D   Q S W

" S   O W   G Q P   I O X

G Q P   G Y H G Q

O T L   G Q P   C S R P

T D   D T P   M D W P F

G D   G Q P   R O G Q P Y

P J M P K G   G Q Y D H A Q   W P "

MAILMAN

*A*s the children of Israel traveled through the desert for forty years, they were a mighty throng of people. Since Moses led them out of captivity in Egypt, the people brought him all their problems for judgment and resolution. This was a daunting task that would have surely led to Moses' collapse had it not been for the wise counsel of his father-in-law, Jethro. At Jethro's suggestion, Moses appointed a chain of command within the tribes that placed the resolution of tribal problems at the "local" level.

As Exodus 19:7 demonstrates, Moses was able to give and receive information from throughout the entire nation via the elders of the nation. This organization could be seen in the very setup of the encampments as they traveled. In a sense, a messenger delivering information down the line from Moses was an Israelite "mailman."

On the way to Moses' tent in the middle, you must pass through all the other tribal tents . . . but only once.

Start ↓

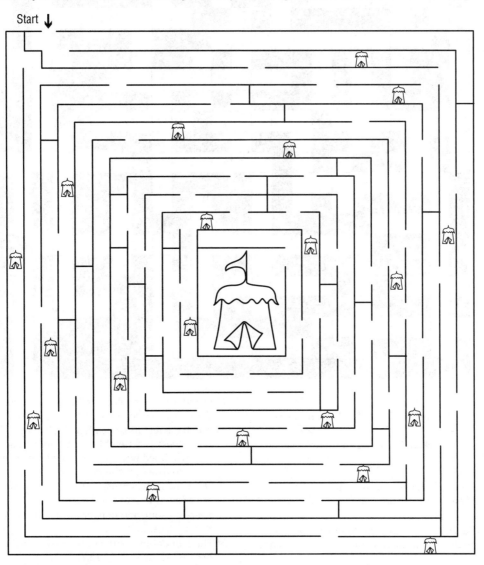

*T*he Psalms were written centuries ago, but the emotions they express are as current as our times. As we read through this book, we find ourselves caught up in the celebrations and heartaches of the writers—the times when God convincingly trounced the enemy, as well as those dark nights of the soul when God seemed very far away. Fill in as many answers as you can before consulting the chapter and verse given at the end of each clue. Refer to the New King James Bible.

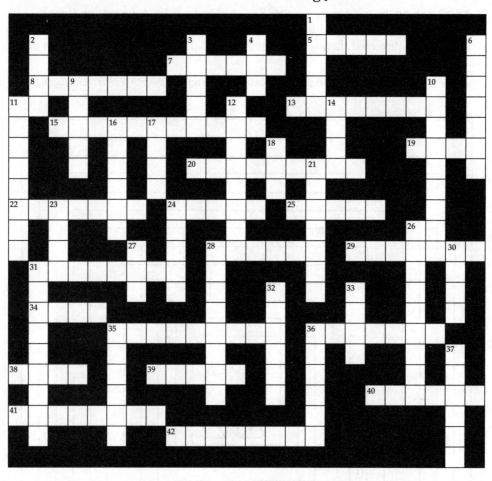

Across

5 "____ is he who has the God of Jacob for his help" (146:5)

7 In front of the wicked, David was mute with silence. He held his peace, even from good, and his ____ was stirred up (39:2)

8 "Trouble and ____ have overtaken me, yet Your commandments are my delights" (119:143)

11 Physician (abbr.)

13 David said that God had heard his vows, and had given him the ____ of those who #2 Down His name (61:5)

15 David asked God not to rebuke him in His #24 Down, "nor chasten me in Your hot ____" (6:1)

19 When the terrors of death had fallen upon him, and fearfulness and trembling, and horror had overwhelmed him, David longed for the wings of a ____, to fly away and be at rest (55:4-6)

20 "I see the treacherous, and am ____, because they do not keep Your word" (119:158)

22 Keep my soul, and deliver me; let me not be ____, for I put my trust in You (25:20)

24 The foundations of the hills quaked and were shaken, because He was ____ (18:7)

25 "Why does Your #24 Down _____ against the sheep of Your pasture?" (74:1)

26 A nurse's initials

28 Should David's enemies "escape by iniquity?" In #24 Down cast down the _____, O God!" (sing.) (56:7)

29 The man who avoids the ungodly, sinners, and the scornful finds _____ in the #27 Down of the Lord (1:1.2)

31 "Turn Yourself to me, and have mercy on me, for I am _____ and afflicted" (25:16)

34 The #36 Down and the deceitful fought against David without a cause. In return for his _____, they were his accusers. But he gave himself to prayer (109:2-4)

35 "My flesh trembles for #2 Down of You, and I am afraid of Your _____" (119:120)

36 "For they persecute the ones You have struck, and talk of the #9 Down of those You have _____" (69:26)

38 Mountains with more than one _____ fumed with #17 Down because God chose to dwell in the mountain of Bashan forever (68:16)

39 David moaned noisily because of the enemy and the oppression of the #36 Down. "For they bring down trouble upon me, and in _____ they #23 Down me" (55:2,3)

40 "Lord, all my _____ is before You; and my sighing is not hidden from You" (38:9)

41 The Israelites provoked God to #24 Down with their high places, and moved Him to _____ with their carved images (78:58)

42 The fate that David wished for God's enemies: "Let them be confounded and _____ forever; yes, let them be put to #1 Down and perish," that they might know God is the Most High over all the earth (83:17)

Down

1 "Because for Your sake I have borne reproach; _____ has covered my face" (69:7)

2 "The secret of the LORD is with those who _____ Him, and He will show them His covenant" (25:14)

3 The workers of iniquity are in great #2 Down, for God has scattered the _____ of him who encamps against God's people (53:5)

4 "In Your presence is fullness of _____" (16:11)

6 When the #36 Down sees the honor heaped upon the #26 Down man, he will be _____; he will gnash his teeth and melt away (112:10)

9 David said his eye "wastes away" because of this; his eye grows old because of all his enemies (6:7)

10 "You #34 Across all _____ words, you deceitful tongue," David said, referring to the man who boasts in evil (52:4)

11 "Why are you _____, O my soul? And why are you disquieted within me? Hope in God." (Two words, reverse order) (43:5)

12 Asking God to protect, or save, David said,"_____ my life from #2 Down of the enemy" (64:1)

14 "Arise, O LORD, in Your #24 Down; lift Yourself up because of the _____ of my enemies" (7:6)

16 "As a father _____ his children, so the Lord _____ those who #2 Down Him" (103:13)

17 When this emotion was felt against Moses and Aaron, the earth opened up and swallowed Dathan, and covered the faction of Abiram. A fire burned up the #36 Down (106:16-18)

18 God's people will #2 Down Him as long as the _____ and moon endure (72:5)

21 If he could have flown like a bird, David could have fled the terrors of death and the fearfulness, trembling, and horror that overwhelmed him. He could have escaped from the windy storm and _____ (55:4-8)

23 What right do the #36 Down have to declare God's statutes? They _____ instruction and they cast God's words behind them (50:16.17)

24 "There is no soundness in my flesh because of Your _____, nor any health in my #3 Down because of my sin" (38:3)

26 The man who boasts in evil will be destroyed by God forever. The _____ also shall see and #2 Down and laugh, saying, "Here is the man who did not make God his strength" (52:5-7)

27 "I #23 Down the double-minded, but I #34 Across Your _____" (119:113)

28 "Make vows to the LORD your God and pay them; let all who are around Him bring _____ to Him who ought to be feared" (76:11)

30 "When you eat the labor of your _____, you shall be #5 Across, and it shall be well with you" (sing.) (128:2)

31 "Let me not sink; let me be _____ from those who #23 Down me, and out of the deep waters" (69:14)

32 "The #2 Down of the LORD is the beginning of _____" (111:10)

33 "Come and bear, all you who #2 Down God, and I will declare what He has done for my _____" (66:16)

35 "Let the heavens rejoice . . . let the field be _____, and all that is in it. Then all the trees of the woods will rejoice before the LORD" (96:11,12)

36 When Asaph saw the prosperity of the _____, he was envious. But then be saw that God set them "in slippery places. . . . Oh, how they are brought to desolation, as in a moment! They are utterly consumed with terrors" (73:18.19)

37 Because God was his shield, David said, "I will not be _____ of ten thousands of #28 Across who have set themselves against me all around. . . . Salvation belongs to the LORD" (3:6.8)

EYEWITNESSES

On their way to the tomb that Easter morning, the women wondered how they would roll away the stone so they could anoint the body of Jesus with spices and oil. Little did they realize they were soon to be eyewitnesses to the greatest event in history. The Gospel accounts differ as to who was in that early-morning group, but there is no dispute as to the significance of the event—Jesus, Son of God, was dead and is alive again! Death has been overcome!

Start

End

*A*fter the multitude left, the disciples asked Jesus to explain the parable of the wheat and the tares. The words below are some of the words Jesus used in that parable. Fill in the blanks to find Jesus' explanation. Then, using the same code, fill in the blanks for His final word to the twelve.

1. F __ __ __ D is the __ __ __ __ D
    4 2 5   11 7 8 5

2. G __ __ D __ __ __ D __ are the __ __ N __ __ F
    7 7   9 2 2 9   9 7   9   7

   __ __ __ K __ N G D __ __
   10 3 2   4   7 6

3. __ __ __ __ __ are the __ __ N __ __ F __ __ __
   10 1 8 2 9   9 7   9   7   10 3 2

   __ __ C K __ D __ N __
   11 4   2   7   2

4. __ N __ __ Y is the D __ V __ __
   2   2 6   2   4 5

5. __ __ __ V __ __ __ is the __ N D __ F __ __ __ __ G __
   3 1 8   2 9 10   2   7   10 3 2 1   2

6. __ __ __ P __ __ __ are the __ N G __ __ __
   8 2 1   2 8 9   1   2 5 9

Jesus' word of admonition to the disciples:

__ __ __ __ __ __ __ __
3 2   11 3 7   3 1 9

__ __ __ __ __ __ __ __ __ __ ,
2 1 8 9   10 7   3 2 1 8

__ __ __ __ __ __ __ __ __ __ !
5 2 10   3 4 6   3 2 1 8

Noah is well-known for his floating menagerie, but another Old Testament character is well acquainted with animals as well. Look up the scriptures if you need to, to find the names of fifteen animals in the book of Job.

```
B  I  O  S  H  C  I  R  T  S  O  P  N  A  X  R
Q  P  N  L  X  M  G  I  A  O  P  N  W  O  A  R
S  I  K  W  A  H  T  O  O  L  R  A  D  N  P  R
N  O  P  Q  A  T  L  O  G  L  D  L  N  O  P  Y
R  E  G  A  N  O  O  I  N  Q  I  N  O  P  E  R
O  S  N  K  L  M  O  P  I  W  R  O  I  K  A  N
O  R  N  Q  L  E  V  I  A  T  H  A  N  C  A  N
S  O  K  N  W  H  O  X  T  R  U  O  S  B  L  E
N  H  Y  E  T  E  K  U  N  A  D  E  E  R  Q  A
J  K  N  W  A  B  O  R  U  P  T  E  B  A  S  U
Q  N  L  G  O  E  Q  A  O  N  K  L  P  V  K  L
O  I  L  O  C  U  S  T  M  T  R  E  N  E  O  I
S  E  N  O  M  K  L  P  Q  A  S  E  G  N  E  D
```

Scripture Pool
JOB 38:39, 41; 39:1, 5, 9, 13, 19–20, 26–27; 40:15; 41:1

"Mountaintop experiences" are what we call life-changing, significant experiences in our lives. For some people in the Bible, that was literally true—they had significant experiences on top of real mountains. For example, Moses on Mount Sinai, Abraham on Mount Moriah, and Elijah on Mount Carmel. In the letter box below find the names of mountains mentioned in the Bible.

```
M  N  O  G  I  L  E  A  D  S  P  O  W  N
T  A  R  A  R  A  N  X  P  E  R  Q  N  M
O  H  R  S  A  P  O  M  N  I  Q  D  C  I
N  S  O  A  Q  M  M  B  N  R  O  H  B  Z
C  A  R  M  E  L  R  D  L  P  A  Q  W  I
Z  B  O  I  B  R  E  U  S  I  Q  P  P  R
I  X  G  A  A  S  H  O  R  P  G  X  I  E
O  P  Q  N  L  P  Z  O  L  I  V  E  S  G
N  E  B  O  Q  P  M  P  B  N  M  G  G  A
O  N  S  T  T  A  B  O  R  P  Q  N  A  G
S  I  N  A  I  Z  T  S  N  P  G  R  H  W
```

Scripture Pool

GENESIS 8:4   PSALM 68:15   1 KINGS 18:19   DEUTERONOMY 27:13   JUDGES 2:9
2 SAMUEL 1:6   JOSHUA 13:11   NUMBERS 34:7   GENESIS 22:2   DEUTERONOMY 34:1
MATTHEW 24:3   NUMBERS 21:20   2 KINGS 19:31   JUDGES 4:6   GENESIS 14:5–6
EXODUS 19:11   JUDGES 7:3   DEUTERONOMY 11:29

*S*tay in a humble frame of mind to decipher this one.

Clue: MESSIAH *is* EBFFJCA

U K B F F B V   C L B

M A B   E B B X'   T R L

M A B P   F A C K K

J Y A B L J M   M A B

B C L M A.

*A*lthough not commonly recognized, the Bible is a book in which laughter and joy are abundant!

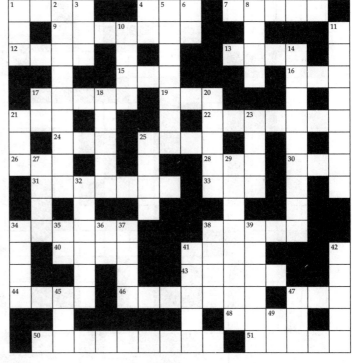

Across

1 Colored
4 Verb of being
7 Grin
9 Giggled
12 Silly smile
13 He made Ruth smile
15 Gone by
16 Everyone
17 He danced for joy before the Lord (2 Samuel 6:14)
19 Sacred initials on a communion table
21 God was not laughing at him in spite of what this man said (Job 9:23)
22 He laughed at the incredible word of the Lord (Genesis 17:17)
24 Ms. Peron
25 Some people will shed one when they laugh OR when they cry
26 Still
28 Pie ____ mode
30 Destruction caused from dampness
31 Chortle
33 Between waist and thigh
34 Evening meal
38 John the Baptist immersed Him (Matthew 3:13)
40 Money/goods exchange
41 Alone
43 Swing around
44 Doe's mate
46 Teacher of sorts
47 Happy's opposite
48 Boulder
50 Pleased

51 Between shoulders and hips

Down

1 Embrace
2 News of Mary's expectation gave her joy (Luke 1:42)
3 One of Jacob's boys (1 Chronicles 2:1–2)
4 Sound of pleasure
5 Take great joy
6 Short for editor
8 Night light
10 Happy
11 "I will laugh at your ____" (Proverbs 1:26)
14 He rejoiced at the naming of his son, John (Luke 1:63–64)

17 With I, a phrase for bride and groom
18 His parents laughed at the thought he could even be born (Genesis 17:17; 18:12)
20 Mom's name (see #18 Down) (Genesis 17:19)
21 Happiness
23 This comes only if you sow
25 Informed
27 Tannish-white color
29 More full of energy
32 Empty the suitcase
34 Hunk or slice
35 Letter's end

36 Spanish article
37 Remainder
38 He leaped for joy in his mother's womb (Luke 1:41)
39 "____ is better than laughter" (Ecclesiastes 7:3)
41 Jesus sent demons into them (Mark 5:12–13)
42 Former (modern) Egyptian ruler
45 Performer's signal
47 Travel by skimming across the top
49 Big Sur state (abbr.)

Words to the would-be wise!

Across

1 "A ____ turns away wrath" (2 words)
(Proverbs 15:1)

5 "A ____ does not love one who corrects him"
(Proverbs 15:12)

10 "Fools despise ____ and instruction"
(Proverbs 1:7)

12 "Train ____ a child in the way he should go"
(Proverbs 22:6)

13 A virtuous wife is worth "far above ____"
(Proverbs 31:10)

14 "Like one who takes away a garment in ____
weather . . . is one who sings songs to a
heavy heart" (Proverbs 25:20)

17 Proverbs of ____

19 "____ is a little with the fear of Lord, than
great treasure with trouble" (Proverbs 15:16)

21 "Let your eyes ____ straight ahead"
(Proverbs 4:25)

22 "Keep your ____ with all diligence" (Proverbs
4:23)

23 One of six things the Lord hates: "a ____
look" (Proverbs 6:17)

24 "____ in the Lord with all your heart"
(Proverbs 3:5)

26 "It is easier for a ____ [pl.] to go through the
eye of a needle than for rich man to enter the
kingdom of God" (Matthew 19:24)

28 "Like one who binds ____ in a sling is he who gives honor to a fool" (2 words) (Proverbs 26:8)

31 "For the commandment is a lamp, and the law a ____" (Proverbs 6:23)

33 "____ for the upright, the establishes his way" (Proverbs 21:29)

34 "Do not ____ the bread of a miser" (Proverbs 23:6)

35 Three too-wonderful things: "the way of a ____ on a rock" (Proverbs 30:18–19)

37 "The ____ of the righteous is choice silver" (Proverbs 10:20)

40 "Let her own works ____ her in the gates" (Proverbs 31:31)

42 "For the ____ gives wisdom" (Proverbs 2:6)

44 Riches sometimes "fly away like an ____" (Proverbs 23:5)

46 "The LORD is the maker of them ____" (Proverbs 22:2)

47 "____ who go to her [evil] return" (Proverbs 2:19)

Down

1 "As iron sharpens iron, ____ a man sharpens the countenance of his friend" (Proverbs 27:17)

2 "Go ____ the ant, you sluggard!" (Proverbs 6:6)

3 Worthless persons . . . "____ [pl.] discord" (Proverbs 6:12, 14)

4 "He who spares his ____ hates his son" (Proverbs 13:24)

6 "A ____ rages and is self-confident" (Proverbs 14:16)

7 "He that regardeth ____ is prudent" (Proverbs 15:5, KJV)

8 "By me [wisdom] princes ____" (Proverbs 8:16)

9 Proof of payment made

11 "Fools despise wisdom and ____" (Proverbs 1:7)

14 "Do not despise the chastening of the LORD, nor detest His ____" (Proverbs 3:11)

15 "He who rolls a stone will have it roll back ____ him" (Proverbs 26:27)

16 "The hand of the ____ makes rich" (Proverbs 10:4)

18 "Where no ____ are, the trough is clean" (Proverbs 14:4)

19 "Earnestly desire the ____ gifts" (1 Corinthians 12:31)

20 "The ____ of the wicked are an abomination to the LORD" (Proverbs 15:26)

25 "The desire of the righteous is ____ good" (Proverbs 11:23)

27 "He who has a ____ hand becomes poor" (Proverbs 10:4)

29 "Will you ____ your eyes on that which is not?" (Proverbs 23:5)

30 "Wisdom . . . speaks her ____" (Proverbs 1:20–21)

32 "Seldom set foot in your neighbor's ____" (Proverbs 25:17)

36 "Ask . . . the birds of the air, and they will ____ you" (Job 12:7)

37 "Wise men ____ away wrath" (Proverbs 29:8)

38 To fail to heed God's proverbs

39 "Do not ____ your heart be glad when he [your enemy] stumbles" (Proverbs 24:17)

41 "Deceit is ____ the heart of those who devise evil" (Proverbs 12:20)

43 "____ you see a man hasty in his words? There is more hope for a fool than for him" (Proverbs 29:20)

45 "Do not ____ hastily to court" (Proverbs 25:8)

*U*nscramble the words below and then fit them into the grid. You'll reveal the name of the person to whom all these words are related!

HEAGI   IUPRM   EFSSAT

NEAUBQT   MAHAN   LAOGLSW

TVSAHI   HNSUSAH   HEZRES

MEDOARCI   AHSAURESU

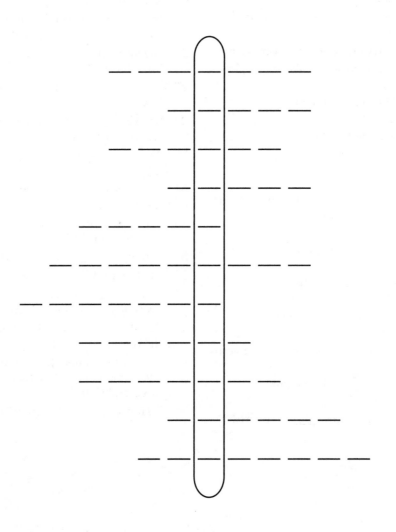

*L*ife might not seem fair, but God is just. He has shown us the way to eternal life . . . and leaves the decision making to us. The twenty-two words hidden in this puzzle are taken from the well-known story of Lazarus and the rich man in Luke 16, which illustrates the point.

```
I A T F L G C O N A D F P O S E W H
R O Y S T M N F R A G G E B U S I R
T E C T H O T E E I R N E T A G F M
O G R E M E N L N S A C L R D O C G
L R E H D K B G T I R G E I S D R E
A S M P B A J N U E L L P C U W U S
C G O O T V E H T E P H F H R S M Q
U U I R D P I A B R A H A M A O B B
K L D P E L W N U D H B K A Z J S T
H F A R J S V P E S L E G N A V L W
B S E S O M W S M B C L P U L N K A
U E D V D P D J D E D A U S R E P C
R E L A C R O S N T U S R U P A K O
```

Word Pool

MERCY SORES GULF DEAD MOSES TABLE
REPENT TONGUE LINEN WATER ABRAHAM PURPLE HADES ANGELS
PERSUADED RICH MAN LAZARUS DOGS CRUMBS GATE BEGGAR PROPHETS

GIANT VS. SHEPHERD

*T*he young shepherd David was dwarfed by the Philistine giant Goliath who stood six cubits and a span (over nine feet tall). Heavily armed, Goliath jeered his enemy's choice of David to battle with him in a showdown between Philistia and Israel in the valley of Elah.

It wasn't exactly that David was the Israelites' choice, it was more that David was the only willing volunteer. In fact, David was insulted at Goliath's challenge, and he asked, "Who is this uncircumcised Philistine, that he should defy the armies of the living God?" (1 Samuel 17:26).

What were David's fighting credentials? He told King Saul that he had slain a lion and a bear when they came after his flock of sheep. "This uncircumcised Philistine will be like one of them," (v. 36) he told Saul, convincing the king to let him go to battle for the army of Israel.

Besides having the tactical advantage of the long-range slingshot, David claimed the Lord gave him another advantage: "The LORD does not save with sword and spear; for the battle is the LORD's" (v. 47). After the stone flew out of David's sling, knocking Goliath to the ground, David ran over to the Philistine, drew Goliath's sword from its sheath, and cut off the giant's head.

Help David gather five stones for his battle against Goliath. Do not cross over a path that has already been used.

*F*ind your way to the foot of the cross!

Start

End

*Y*our spirit doesn't need to diet.

Clue: MESSIAH *is* CWAAZIP

BLESSED ARE THOSE

WHO HUNGER AND

THIRST FOR

RIGHTEOUSNESS'

FOR THEY SHALL

BE FILLED.

99

*A*ge is not a factor when it comes to God's kingdom. He is able to use all of us, no matter how young or old we are. This puzzle will given you a glimpse of how God's Word views age.

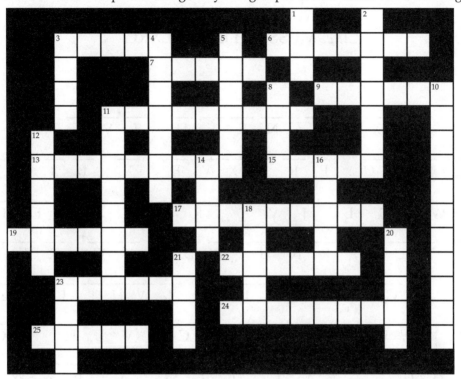

Across

3 God will carry this "house" till it's old (Isaiah 46:3–4)

6 Young men will see these (Acts 2:17)

7 Renew my youth, like this bird's (Psalm 103:5)

9 As a young man, you "took steps" where you wished (John 21:18)

11 These "good people" will still bear a harvest in old age (Psalm 92:12–14)

13 In Esther, the letter to these "cities" said kill all Jews, young and old (Esther 3:13)

15 An old wineskin might need one (Matthew 9:16–17)

17 Remember God in your youth, before "hard" days come (Ecclesiastes 12:1)

19 As a young man, you also "equipped" yourself (John 21:18)

22 Exalt your youth: be an example of "wholesomeness" (1 Timothy 4:12)

23 Don't despise this woman when she's old (Proverbs 23:22)

24 The glory of young men is their "power" (Proverbs 20:29)

25 Old men shall have this (sing.) while they are asleep (Acts 2:17)

Down

1 David: Don't remember the "follies" (sing.) of my youth (Psalm 25:7)

2 Better is a wise youth than a "silly" old king who won't listen (Ecclesiastes 4:13)

3 His book prophesied #6 and #25 Across (Joel 2:28)

4 Now old, David hadn't seen good people "beseeching" for bread (Psalm 37:25)

5 These "seniors" were first to die near Ezekiel's temple (Ezekiel 9:6)

8 Purge old leaven; be a new "chunk" (1 Corinthians 5:7)

10 The "posterity" of #4 Down

11 In a sound church, older women's behavior is "devout" (Titus 2:3)

12 Timothy's "essence" was to be an example to believers (1 Timothy 4:12)

14 From their youth, Israel and Judah did

"iniquity" before God (Jeremiah 32:30)

16 God was the psalmist's "belief" from his youth (Psalm 71:5)

18 The "harvest" of #11 Across

20 Because of his youth, he was afraid to offer Job advice (Job 32:6)

21 The old lion perishes for lack of "foood" (Job 4:11)

23 The young and old were slain in Ezekiel, but not those who bore this "label" (Ezekiel 9:6)

God's promise seemed almost beyond belief—but it proved true.

Clue: MESSIAH is NHLLXRG

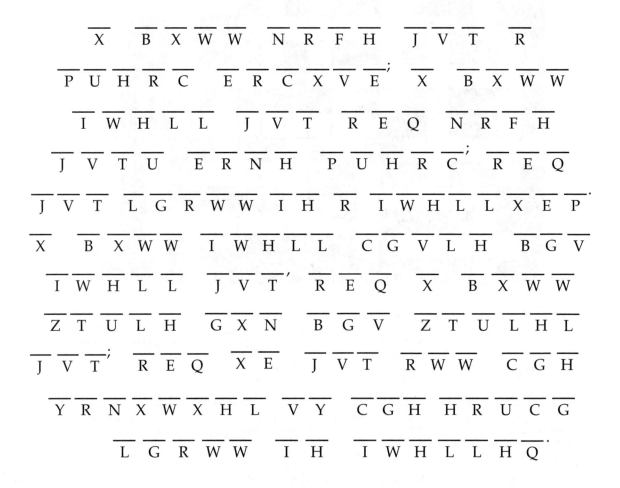

X B X W W   N R F H   J V T   R

P U H R C   E R C X V E ;   X   B X W W

I W H L L   J V T   R E Q   N R F H

J V T U   E R N H   P U H R C   R E Q

J V T   L G R W W   I H   R   I W H L L X E P .

X   B X W W   I W H L L   C G V L H   B G V

I W H L L   J V T '   R E Q   X   B X W W

Z T U L H   G X N   B G V   Z T U L H L

J V T ;   R E Q   X E   J V T   R W W   C G H

Y R N X W X H L   V Y   C G H   H R U C G

L G R W W   I H   I W H L L H Q .

"*B*ehold, a sower went out to sow...." Jesus taught about the kingdom of heaven by using parables. Fill in the clues from answers found in Matthew 13:3–23, to find the yield of good soil.

1. Example of one who sowed
2. Without roots, a person can easily "fall or trip"
3. Seed sown by the wayside can be easily "devoured" (2 words)
4. The birds in the parable (2 words)
5. Thorns
6. The soil or ground
7. Stony soil lacked this
8. The "crop" or harvest
9. The deceitfulness of riches can do this to the Word
10. Scorched by the sun
11. Seed (3 words)

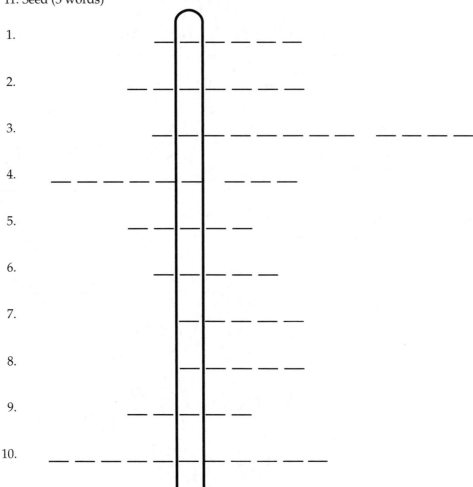

1. _ _ _ _ _ _
2. _ _ _ _ _ _
3. _ _ _ _ _ _ _   _ _ _ _ _
4. _ _ _ _ _ _ _ _
5. _ _ _ _ _
6. _ _ _ _ _
7. _ _ _ _ _
8. _ _ _ _ _
9. _ _ _ _
10. _ _ _ _ _ _ _ _ _
11. _ _ _ _ _ _ _ _

THE TRINITY CROSS

*T*he Trinity Cross—which honors the Father, Son, and Holy Spirit—is one of the most beautiful and elaborate of all cross designs. It is based on a double three-fold design—three of the three-petal fleur-de-lis designs on each arm of the cross.

This cross is one of a number of three-fold designs that are of Greek origin. The cross is frequently used as a church emblem on embroidered items that are hung or worn during the Trinity season of the liturgical church calendar.

Unscramble the words below and then place them in the grid. We've given you their common denominator as a starting point!

RHTIINGB
FENSOSCINO
NOITAERC
ENSEVSIGORF
OJY
ECNEPREATN
UMSINSBISO

CGLNEIASN
CIVNOCNOIT
TAHIF
EMODEFR
LANEEWR
NIAOSRTRTOE
ONNUI

__ R __ __ __ __ __

__ __ __ __ __ __ E __ __ __ __

C __ __ __ __ __ __ __ __ __

__ __ __ __ O __ __ __ __ __

__ __ N __ __ __ __ __ __

C __ __ __ __ __ __ __

__ I __ __ __ __ __

__ L __ __ __ __ __ __ __

__ __ I __ __

__ __ __ __ __ A __

__ __ __ __ T __ __ __

__ __ __ __ I __ __ __ __

__ O __

__ N __ __ __

Take His Easy Yoke

*J*esus said, "Take My yoke upon you and learn from Me, for I am gentle and lowly in heart, and you will find rest for your souls. For My yoke is easy and My burden is light" (Matthew 11:29–30).

Find your way through this maze by creating a string of *E*s.

```
E E E E E E E E E E E E E E E E E E E E E E E E E E R X B H W S R H F G
E R F E W F X D Y D R U H R F H K D B U K N Z F P E E E E E E E E E E E H
E Y G F X N H P P S F Z L G E E E E E E E E E D G P O B F B S F H N F S E F
E I F E E E E E E E E E E H B F H F W W K M B E E E E E E E E E E E P F H
E E E F O S F F H G K K P H K E E E E T U Y R F F H W P F B D T F A M H E E E    ← Start
F W F D P H E E E K R L B C D P G E E E E R T K H G Q L E E E V N P G B H F E
E E E E L K E F K E E E E E E K M F F P E U E E E K E R E E E E E E E E E    ← End
E S F E V U E G P E F P E K H F E C H J K F E M E P E N E H W M B E P E P F P
S E J E A L E H D E H R E P P H F E K P J E P P E K E F E D S C E E F E K H K
J E O E Z P E S R E D N E D R R N P E E E P T D E M E G E S B E N E U E J K M
Y E P E F M E N F E B U E R N E P O F E M J N B E B E H B F E S P E K E U B N
I E D E H N E V B K H L E T Y E L X H E C H V J E F E T F E P P H E L E Y E H
N E B E K A E E E E K D E Y T E T M P E G B F E E G E S E F G R R E N E T E R
V E W E L C F B H E M N E M E E X G N E R R E H L H E D G P E E E E B E R E G
C E F E F X G E E E O T E E C N N R S E T E B D P D E Z B D E Q B P D E F E H
S E Y F E Z H F B F A E G N L E E E E E Y E E E F S P E H R D C C L E F E H F
T E H E S E K L K P E N H P M E P F K F U F H E G N T F E S B V R E S F E E D
E E N E F F E E E E F R K R V E M H F E E E E E E E G P E E E E H P E C E C
E F V E U G W F K G H U S K R K F K G F K F N W H O M H N E T Z Y C L E X E S
E T Z E O V H S H K E E E E E E E E E E E E E E E U V J R E N U P H K E S E X
E N W E X B L R D D H F B H W F H F N F J F D P E T E E E E E E E E M E A E A
E V F E E E E E E E E E E E E E E E B H P E K B B B E V F F P E M P F F N E W E D
E D Y E R F Y F H B F F P B Q M F K R E S H H F E W H X N K G H H P D E T E G
E R E E N E E E E E E E K F E Y E P D E E E E E E E E E E E E E E E E E M E H
E K F T X E W T N H F E D H E R E R S F P R D R H F R K M N X F K R F F C E K
E E E E E E P N E K H E F N E T E Y Z P T K P F P G P F Y D G B D B P P X E M
F L F F Q F C B E D B E K C E P E E E E E E E E E E E E E E E E E E E E E E V
H C L U T S E C E R E E E E E S H N F V H F G H F H F R N F R N G F S S P E B
F E E E E E E D E E K F P E F C K H Y B E E E E E E H F B E E E E E E N K E C
E M F E N W F F E E P H D E E E E E E E E B K K H K E H H E H C H F D T D E P
E Z R E C K E E J E D M H E F C B H F S E E E E E K G E E E E E E E E E B E R
E F Z E E E F H K E N V K E H F K P K P F X L X M F P F D F B M Y F P E R E U
E B A P S U P L E E S B L E E E E E E E E E E E E E E E E E E E T P N U E Y E S
```

*B*y adding, subtracting, multiplying, and dividing the numbers found in the Gospel accounts of Jesus' miracles, you will arrive at the number of persons Jesus sent out to preach, teach, and heal in His name.

The number of men who were fed with the miracle multiplication
of the boy's lunch of loaves and fish (John 6:10) _____

Divided by . . .
The number of lepers who were cleansed and ÷ _____
healed by Jesus (Luke 17:12–14)

Multiplied by . . .
The number of days Jesus was in the tomb before × _____
His resurrection (Luke 24:7)

Divided by . . .
The number of years the woman suffered with the ÷ _____
issue of blood before she was healed (Matthew 9:20)

Plus . . .
The number of years the lame man laid by the + _____
pool of Bethesda (John 5:5)

Minus . . .
The number of waterpots filled with water that − _____
Jesus turned into wine (John 2:6–9)

Plus . . .
The number of friends who carried the paralytic + _____
man to Jesus to be healed (Mark 2:3)

Minus . . .
The number of sons of the widow woman who had − _____
a son who was raised from the dead (Luke 7:12)

Divided by . . .
The number of days Lazarus was in the tomb ÷ _____
(John 11:39)

Minus . . .
The number of demons cast out of Mary Magdalene − _____
(Luke 8:2)

Plus . . .
The number of blind men who received their sight as + _____
Jesus passed by (Matthew 20:30)

Multiplied by . . .
The number of men from the country of the × _____
Gergesenes who were delivered of demons (Matthew 8:28)

Equals . . .
The number of followers Jesus sent out two by two = _____
to minister in His name (Luke 10:1)

*F*aith in God can move mountains. Just ask the people who are singled out in Hebrews 11.

Across

2 Hannah offered him to the Lord before he was born

4 God's faithful servants subdued these "realms"

7 Cain's brother offered a better sacrifice, proving he was "virtuous"

14 Moses passed up the treasures of this country and instead chose the reproach of Christ

15 Some of the faithful wandered about in skins made from this animal

17 The faithful shall be made "without blemish" along with those faithful ones who came after them

19 Abraham was waiting for the "large town" whose builder and maker is God

20 When he was dying, he blessed each of the sons of Joseph

24 This Gileadite, though the son of a harlot, was a mighty man of valor; he defeated the Ammonites

25 By faith he offered a "more excellent sacrifice"

27 By faith, Abraham lived in Canaan as in a foreign "land"

28 He was the son Sarah prayed for

29 Moses refused to be called the "male child" of Pharaoh's daughter

30 This harlot received the spies from Israel with peace, and her life was spared

Down

1 Daniel was one who stopped the mouth of this wild animal

3 Because he was "taken away," he did not see death

5 Mister (abbr.)

6 Moses chose to suffer with God's people rather than enjoy the passing pleasures of "wrongdoing"

8 Some of the faithful endured this and refused deliverance, so as to obtain a better resurrection

9 From Abraham came descendants as innumerable as grains of this substance

10 The valiant faithful caused the armies of these "foreigners" to flee

11 The Sahara is an example of these places where the faithful wandered

12 The "censure" of Christ was more attractive to Moses than money

13 Faith caused the walls of this city to fall

16 This sea retreated at the advance of the Israelites

17 Jeremiah was one of these (pl.)

18 How many months Moses was hidden by his parents before being set afloat

21 Abraham and his family lived in these portable homes

22 Paul's and Silas's were loosed, and a jailer was converted

23 With Deborah's help, he defeated Sisera's army

26 He knew the dew would drop

Bonus:
Unscramble the circled letters to tell you
what our elders in the faith obtained through faith.

— — — — —   — — — — — — — —

*J*esus spoke these words from a mountain.

Clue: MESSIAH *is* TWQQBYI

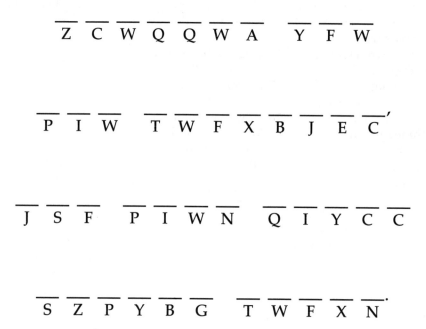

Z C W Q Q W A   Y F W

P I W   T W F X B J E C'

J S F   P I W N   Q I Y C C

S Z P Y B G   T W F X N.

RELUCTANT PROPHET

*W*hen he had time to think about it in the belly of the large fish, Jonah had a change of heart. Perhaps going to Nineveh wasn't as bad as the predicament he found himself in now. Jonah cried out to God, and God heard his prayer and delivered him from the insides of that great sea animal.

The Lord gave Jonah another chance to obey Him as He said to him again, "Arise, go to Nineveh, that great city, and preach to it the message that I tell you" (Jonah 3:2). This time, instead of fleeing from the Lord's presence, Jonah obeyed and "arose and went to Nineveh" (v. 3).

The city of Nineveh was known for its evil ways and violence (Jonah 3:8), plotting evil against the Lord (Nahum 1:11), being "full of lies" (Nahum 3:1), endless cruelty (Nahum 3:19, NIV), witchcraft and prostitution (Nahum 3:4, NIV), and exploitation (Nahum 3:16). It's no wonder Jonah was reluctant.

Jonah's decision to go to Nineveh is attributed more to his readiness to obey God than a love for the people of this wicked city. His message to the Ninevites was simple, "Yet forty days, and Nineveh shall be overthrown!" (Jonah 3:4). The Scripture says, "So the people of Nineveh believed God, proclaimed a fast, and put on sackcloth, from the greatest to the least of them" (v. 5). When God saw that they had turned from their

Start →

← End

All the clues in this puzzle begin with the same leTTer!

Across

1 ____ and obey

3 Lead us not into it, we pray (Matthew 6:13)

9 Blessed is the ____ that binds our hearts in love

10 Joseph of Arimathea gave his to Jesus (Mark 15:43–46)

11 It is not for us to know these or seasons (Acts 1:7)

13 "Whatever I ____ you in the dark, speak in the light" (Matthew 10:27)

14 Where this is, there your heart is
(Matthew 6:21)
15 Father, Son, and Holy Spirit
17 The Lord's fills the temple (Isaiah 6:1)
18 Doubting disciple
19 The apostle Paul left his cloak there
(2 Timothy 4:13)
20 These were made of potter's clay and iron,
in Daniel's vision (Daniel 2:41)
22 Judah, for example
25 ____ and fro
26 The number of men cast into
Nebuchadnezzar's fiery furnace
(Daniel 3:24)
28 The false shepherd will do this to the
hooves of his sheep (Zechariah 11:16)
30 Saul's hometown (Acts 9:11)
31 "____ shalt not kill" (Exodus 20:13, KJV)
32 John was imprisoned on the island of
Patmos for this (Revelation 1:9)
33 A place where the ram's blood was to be
applied (Exodus 29:20)
36 Jesus stood ____ before the Sanhedrin,
Herod, or Pilate
37 "Show me Your ways, O LORD; ____ me
Your paths" (Psalm 25:4)
38 "The thorn and ____ shall grow on their
altars" (Hosea 10:8)
40 "Jesus Christ is the same yesterday, ____,
and forever" (Hebrews 13:8)
42 Short for trumpet
43 Where our heavenly Father sits
(Revelation 3:21)
44 Jacob and Esau, for example
45 It makes us free (John 8:32)
47 Someday they will all be wiped away by
God (Revelation 7:17)
48 The apostle Paul's traveling companion;
he also received two letters from Paul
(Acts 16:1–4)
52 We are to let our requests to God be made
known with this (Philippians 4:6)
53 Jesus said the moneychangers had made
the temple a den of ____ (Mark 11:17)
56 The day He arose
58 Abraham gave these to Melchizedek
(Genesis 14:20)
60 The church in this city received two letters
from the apostle Paul
61 We are to do this to the spirits (1 John 4:1)

Down
1 "In the world you will have ____" (John
16:33)
2 The number of days Purim is celebrated
(Esther 9:26–27)
3 The one in which Moses conferred with
God was named "witness" (Numbers
17:7–8)
4 He came to Jesus in the wilderness
(Matthew 4:3)
5 The Lord's "eyelids ____ the sons of men"
(Psalm 11:4)

6 Zacchaeus's viewing place
7 Better invested than buried (Matthew 25:15)
8 Old and New
10 Adam and Eve were told neither to eat nor
____ the fruit of the tree (Genesis 3:3)
12 Abraham was sitting here when the Lord
appeared to him (Genesis 18:1)
13 ____ figuration or ____ gression
16 The wise woman makes this for herself
(Proverbs 31:22)
18 Judah's were called "whiter than milk"
(Genesis 49:12)
19 These appeared when the grain sprouted
(Matthew 13:26)
21 The place where a poor widow gave two
mites (Mark 12:41–42)
23 The way one discovers the Lord is good
(Psalm 34:8)
24 Let not your heart be so (John 14:1)
27 He who sat on a white horse was called
Faithful and ____ (Revelation 19:11)
29 "Do you not know that you are the ____ of
God and that the Spirit of God dwells in
you?" (1 Corinthians 3:16)
30 Huram came from here to do King
Solomon's bronze work (1 Kings 7:13)
34 The Lord's are of peace, to give a future and
a hope! (Jeremiah 29:11)
35 Every one of these will one day confess Jesus
as Lord (Philippians 2:11)
36 What Jesus did when He sat down in the
temple (John 8:2)
37 Jesus distributed the loaves after He had
given this (John 6:11)
38 The part of Jacob's ladder that reached to
heaven (Genesis 28:12)
39 The number of gerahs that make a shekel
(Exodus 30:13)
41 Jesus' mock crown was made of this
(John 19:5)
44 "Confidence in an unfaithful man in time of
trouble is like a bad ____" (Proverbs 25:19)
46 "Touch no unclean ____" (Isaiah 52:11)
49 The Lord said, "I will send a famine on the
land, not a famine of bread, nor a ____ for
water, but of hearing the words of the LORD"
(Amos 8:11)
50 The apostle Paul's "True son in our common
faith" in Crete (Titus 1:4–5)
51 Moses appointed some to be "leaders of
____" (Deuteronomy 1:15)
54 You, in old English
55 "The LORD will make you the head and not
the ____" (Deuteronomy 28:13)
57 Jesus said, "I am ____ light of the world"
(John 8:12)
58 Zacchaeus and Matthew were both
collectors of this
59 The number of lepers who cried to Jesus,
"Master, have mercy on us!" (Luke 17:12)

We know Him as Jesus Christ, the Son of the Living God, the Great Physician, the Author and Finisher of our faith. He is also known by a host of other names. Find as many names of Jesus as you can in this letter box.

```
R  E  A  M  R  E  S  U  R  R  E  C  T  I  O  N  G  S
S  W  L  E  P  A  M  O  V  B  G  D  R  X  S  J  B  E
C  A  M  I  V  K  O  E  F  I  L  F  O  D  A  E  R  B
E  N  I  V  F  D  H  U  S  I  A  K  X  D  D  L  I  H
P  Z  G  C  T  E  P  L  O  R  D  M  O  F  V  Q  D  A
T  S  H  T  U  R  T  N  E  S  L  G  B  N  O  G  E  I
E  J  T  Q  E  D  O  E  U  H  F  N  U  Z  C  M  G  S
R  B  Y  A  T  I  S  Q  W  O  V  T  R  B  A  I  R  S
K  A  C  J  R  R  T  A  B  O  I  C  E  F  T  C  O  E
W  I  T  N  E  S  S  M  B  R  A  N  C  H  E  G  O  M
H  L  N  V  P  E  A  O  Y  A  H  K  D  R  P  I  M  D
E  F  O  G  M  L  D  R  E  H  P  E  H  S  D  O  O  G
R  X  E  G  D  U  J  G  O  N  E  W  R  A  L  M  R  H
A  I  C  O  R  N  E  R  S  T  O  N  E  C  F  Y  U  P
```

Word Pool

I AM   MESSIAH   BRANCH   PROPHET   KING   LAMB OF GOD   JUDGE
BRIDGEGROOM   STAR   SCEPTER   CORNERSTONE   LORD   GOOD SHEPHERD
OVERSEER   ADVOCATE   WITNESS   LION   BREAD OF LIFE   DOOR
RESURRECTION   LIFE   WAY   TRUTH   VINE   ALMIGHTY

*P*salm 119 is divided into sections, each of which has been given a name. These names are provided for you below. Your challenge is to fit them into the grid! We've given you one name as a starting point.

Word Pool

ALEPH AYIN BETH DALETH GIMEL HE HETH
KAPH LAMED MEM NUN PE QOPH RESH TSADDE
SAMEK SHIN TAU TETH WAW YOD ZAYIN

*E*xcept for a few spectacular instances—a whirlwind taking Elijah to heaven and Phillip's mysterious trip to Azotus after baptizing the Ethiopian eunuch on the road to Gaza—transportation in Bible times was quite pedestrian. In the Word Pool, you'll find some of the ways that people traveled. Each of the words is hidden in the letter box below. Circle each word when you find it.

```
N  O  E  P  T  N  S  Q  N  E  R  T  K  L  J
N  L  O  P  N  C  K  A  I  R  P  L  A  N  E
M  E  S  R  O  H  P  M  N  X  L  A  Q  Z  T
O  P  I  Y  H  A  N  X  O  P  E  N  Q  I  O
E  M  N  O  P  R  O  L  O  O  B  O  A  T  W
N  C  A  R  R  I  A  G  E  L  O  J  H  G  E
A  X  A  M  N  O  S  U  B  M  A  R  I  N  E
L  S  A  R  O  T  M  N  X  R  A  P  O  I  T
P  H  O  X  T  J  K  L  F  X  O  C  N  L  W
O  I  M  N  L  P  T  O  O  F  E  D  M  N  Z
R  P  L  K  M  N  O  P  I  S  I  F  M  N  L
D  K  L  O  C  A  S  W  D  O  N  K  E  Y  X
Y  O  S  K  A  T  E  S  L  P  X  A  S  E  D
H  L  O  R  R  K  T  E  K  C  O  R  E  N  D
```

Word Pool

BOAT   CAMEL   CARRIAGE   CART   CHARIOT   DONKEY   FOOT
HORSE   SHIP   SKIFF

New Life

*E*ggs are one of the oldest, most recognized symbols of spring and fertility. For Christians, eggs are associated with Easter as a sign of new life and resurrection. In this symbolism, the shell of the Easter egg is compared to a rock tomb out of which emerges a new life.

The tradition of decorating Easter eggs is popular in many countries. Dyeing Easter eggs has been practiced since at least the fifteenth century and may have been practiced even earlier than that. In many countries eggs are dyed red to represent the shed blood of Jesus. Easter egg designs range from the elaborate Ukranian Easter eggs to the home-dyed Easter activity of many children. Decorated Easter eggs are often exchanged or given to friends and loved ones to signify the renewal of relationships.

Egg-rolling is a popular Easter event for children; the child who gets his or her egg to the finish line first without breaking it is the winner. Tradition claims that the egg roll is symbolic of the rolling away of the stone from the tomb on Easter morning.

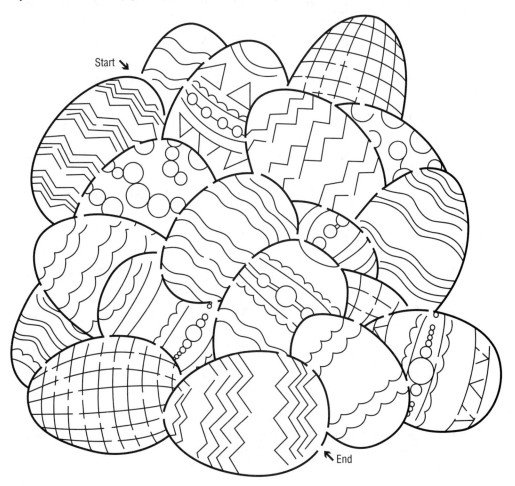

*I*n the letter box below are hidden words from the parable of the talents in Matthew 25:14–30.

```
U  S  O  P  G  P  L  Y  R  N  G  P  W  D
W  I  C  K  E  D  O  X  N  T  P  G  I  R
E  N  O  P  T  J  A  N  L  R  A  A  O  N
E  R  A  D  O  O  G  E  I  F  R  M  I  B
P  O  N  U  I  U  X  N  O  F  R  E  P  O
I  N  O  X  P  R  E  D  A  N  L  O  N  W
N  T  A  L  E  N  T  S  X  S  O  N  R  J
G  N  O  L  P  E  U  E  P  S  H  R  E  W
N  X  D  F  L  Y  O  R  S  E  H  I  T  E
A  T  O  I  N  S  U  V  O  N  I  E  N  S
E  W  I  V  J  T  L  A  R  K  N  O  E  G
W  O  N  E  T  R  U  N  A  R  O  O  M  G
N  L  I  L  U  F  H  T  I  A  F  D  O  N
D  R  L  O  B  N  I  M  P  D  E  A  N  G
N  K  W  R  O  N  G  F  A  D  E  S  E  N
E  N  O  D  L  L  E  W  H  S  D  I  Y  O
```

Word Pool

AFRAID DARKNESS ENTER FAITHFUL FIVE GNASHING GOOD JOURNEY
JOY LORD MONEY ONE SERVANT TALENTS TEN
TWO WEEPING WELL DONE WICKED

*A*rrange the events of the Exodus in correct chronological sequence, and line up the bold letters to reveal God's cry for His people.

WAT**E**R AND MANNA PROVIDED
M**O**UNT SINAI
CROSSING THE JORDAN RIV**E**R
MOS**E**S APPOINTED LEADER
PHARAOH DEFEATED
THE PR**O**MISED LAND
EGYPTIAN S**L**AVERY
FORTY YEARS IN THE WI**L**DERNESS
FREEDO**M**
PLAGUES AND DEA**T**H OF FIRSTBORN
CONQUERING CANAANITE KIN**G**S
REBELLION IN WILDERNESS OF **P**ARAN
ACROSS THE RED SEA ON DR**Y** GROUND

1. _____ ____ _____

2. _____ ____ _____

3. _____ ____ _____

4. _____ ____ _____

5. _____ ____ _____

6. _____ ____ _____

7. _____ ____ _____

8. _____ ____ _____

9. _____ ____ _____

10. _____ ____ _____

11. _____ ____ _____

12. _____ ____ _____

13. _____ ____ _____

*A*s the children of Israel traveled through the wilderness on the way to the promised land, the Lord gave Moses very detailed instructions to make a tabernacle so He could be among His chosen people. The clues below are based on the construction of the portable tabernacle.

Across

1 The bread of God's presence (Exodus 25:30)

6 Reconcile, make "at one" (Exodus 30:10)

10 The mercy seat is where God said He would ____ with Moses (Exodus 25:22)

12 One of the metals given to God for the tabernacle (Exodus 25:3)

15 Each cherub had two of these (sing.) (Exodus 25:20)

18 Made from stacte, onycha, galbanum, frankincense (Exodus 30:34–35)

19 By ____ God led the children of Israel by a pillar of cloud (Exodus 13:21)

20 The fabric of the tabernacle curtains (Exodus 26:1)

21 The wood of the table of the showbread (Exodus 25:23)

22 Precious metal that covered the ark of the covenant (Exodus 25:11)

23 Offering (sing.) for the anointing oil (Exodus 25:6)

25 This substance was put in the ark of the covenant to remind the children of Israel of God's provision for them (Exodus 16:33–34)

26 God ordered the tabernacle to be built as a place for Him to ____ among the people (Exodus 25:8)

28 The outer area surrounding the tabernacle; it measured one hundred by fifty cubits (Exodus 27:9)

29 Neuter pronoun

33 Oil made from this was burned for light (Exodus 27:20)

34 The people brought "____ rings and nose rings, rings and necklaces, all jewelry of gold" to offer to the Lord (Exodus 35:22)

35 The robe of the ephod was of this color (Exodus 28:31)

37 Color of thread other than gold, blue, and scarlet (Exodus 39:2)

38 ____ rings were set in the ____ corners of the ark so it could be carried (Exodus 37:3)

41 Made of stone, these contained God's law and were put in the ark of the covenant (Deuteronomy 10:5)

43 Pomegranates decorated the ____ of the priest's robe (Exodus 39:24)

44 The south and north sides of the court of the tabernacle were each ____ hundred cubits long (Exodus 27:9, 11)

45 The most sacred furnishing in the tabernacle; it was to remind the children of Israel of God's presence with them (Exodus 25:10)

46 Three bowls of the lampstand were fashioned like blossoms from this tree (Exodus 25:33)

49 God gave this leader His instructions to build the tabernacle (Exodus 25:1)

55 Candlestick (Exodus 25:31)

57 The part of the tabernacle behind the second veil, the Holiest of ____ (Hebrews 9:3)

58 These (sing.) were connected with clasps to couple the curtains together (Exodus 26:5)

60 The first hight priest of Israel (Exodus 28:1)

61 Gifted and talented in design and art (Exodus 31:4)

63 Strand of fiber used for loops (Exodus 26:4)

65 The people were restrained from bringing more material because they brought ____ much (Exodus 36:7)

66 Clothing (sing.) (Exodus 39:1)

67 The court of the tabernacle was fifty cubits ____ (Exodus 27:13)

68 Consecrated, sacred place (Exodus 25:8)

Down

2 Opposite of him

3 He was filled with the Spirit of God to design works of art (Exodus 31:2–4, KJV)

4 The stones on the ephod were ____ memorial stones for the sons of Israel (Exodus 28:12)

5 The ____ seat symbolized God's throne (Exodus 25:22)

7 Garments of ministry were made of blue, purple, and scarlet ____ (Exodus 39:1)

8 All the ____ and women whose hearts were willing were to bring material for the tabernacle (Exodus 35:29)

9 The tent of meeting; dwelling place (Exodus 40:2)

11 Each board was ____ cubits long (Exodus 26:16)

12 Aaron's rod that ____ was kept in the ark of the covenant (Hebrews 9:4)

13 One of the precious stones in the vestments of the priests (Exodus 25:7)

14 Moses met with God on this mountain (Exodus 24:16)

15 The priests were commanded to ____ the ephod, breastplate, tunic, turban, trousers, and sash, plate of the holy crown to minister in the holy place

16 Burnt offering and ____ offering were offered on the same altar (Exodus 40:29)

17 The gold cherubim were at the two ____ of the mercy seat (Exodus 25:19)

24 Winged creatures (Exodus 25:22)

27 The priests were to wash at the ____ before offering burnt offerings (Exodus 30:18)

28 Unit of linear measure equal to about eighteen inches (Exodus 25:10)

30 Portable dwelling place (Exodus 36:14)

31 God's chosen nation

32 Column; these supported the hangings around the court (Exodus 38:10)

33 A gift to the Lord (Exodus 25:2)

36 A priestly upper garment (Exodus 39:2)

39 An item used by the high priest to help determine God's guidance (Exodus 28:30)

40 The number of lamps on the lampstand (Exodus 37:23)

42 The ____s of badgers and rams were used as a covering for the tabernacle (Exodus 26:14)

47 Sweet incense was burned ____ the gold altar (Exodus 40:26–27)

48 One of the precious stones of the breastplate (Exodus 28:18)

50 Made from myrrh, cinnamon, cane, cassia, and olive oil to be used for anointing (Exodus 30:23–25)

51 The Lord said He would ____ with Moses about the commands He gave to the children of Israel (Exodus 25:22)

52 God told Moses to put water ____ the laver (Exodus 40:7)

53 The veil divided the holy ____ and the Most Holy (Exodus 26:33)

54 Set apart; sanctified (Exodus 26:33)

56 To pour out or apply oil as a ritual of consecration (Exodus 29:7)

57 There were two of these (sing.) in the tabernacle—one for burnt offerings and one for incense (Exodus 37:25; 38:1)

59 The ____ of the Lord filled the tabernacle (Exodus 40:34)

62 God told Moses, "No man shall ____ Me, and live" (Exodus 33:20)

64 The laver was set between the tabernacle ____ the altar (Exodus 40:30)

Sometimes starting at the bottom and working your way to the top is the key to finding truth. String together the letters in the box below to read one of the most famous statements made by Jesus in the New Testament.

E	N	A	E	E	Y	M
E	D	H	D	D	W	N
R	T	T	A	N	O	I
F	H	U	N	I	R	E
U	E	R	D	S	D	D
O	T	T	Y	E	Y	I
Y	R	E	O	L	O	B
E	U	H	U	P	U	A
K	T	T	S	I	A	U
A	H	W	H	C	R	O
M	S	O	A	S	E	Y
L	H	N	L	I	M	F
L	A	K	L	D	Y	I

O CHRISTMAS TREE!

*F*or most people who celebrate Christmas, a beautifully decorated Christmas tree is the center of festivities. Early Christmas tree decorations were simple, with strings of popcorn and cranberries, handmade paper ornaments, candy canes, apples, candies, cookies, and sweets. Candles added light to brighten the tree. Over the years, Christmas tree trimmings became increasingly ornate. Candles have been replaced by strings of electric lights, and the homemade ornaments have been replaced with tinsel and bright, glittering manufactured decorations.

The decoration of evergreen trees predates the use of the Christmas tree in Christian celebration. Primitive peoples believed that trees that remained green throughout winter months had special powers. The evergreen trees were used in ritual ceremonies and brought into homes to ensure the return of green vegetation.

Gradually, the decorated evergreen tree took its place in Christmas celebrations. In the fifteenth century the evergreen trees were used in German mystery plays depicting the stories of the Bible to teach Scripture. By the 1800s Christmas trees were used in the United States, brought to the U.S. by German immigrants.

*S*ometimes it is difficult in the twilight to tell when day ends and night begins. Find the verse hidden in the box of letters below (including reference).

I	D	M	A	U	Y	S	T
T	H	W	E	O	N	R	I
K	G	T	H	H	T	E	I
W	S	O	C	R	O	K	M
S	I	O	N	F	G	H	W
I	H	M	E	W	N	H	N
O	O	S	O	E	N	N	E
T	C	M	A	E	N	W	W
H	O	I	R	L	K	E	J
I	O	T	H	I	N	S	9:4

Complete the acrostic below that reveals how the Lord took care of His people as they wandered in the wilderness on the way to the promised land. Refer to Exodus 13:21; 15:22—17:16; 19:2, and Numbers 10; 12; 21.

1. It came from a rock

2. Name of place with twelve wells and seventy palm trees

3. The-Lord-Is-My-Banner was the name of the one Moses built after the victory at Rephidim

4. The way the Lord led the people by day

5. What Moses cast into the bitter waters to make them sweet

6. Place of bitter waters

7. The bread given by the Lord

8. When Moses held up his hand, the Israelites prevailed against them

9. Place where God gave the covenant

10. Name of wilderness between Elim and Sinai

11. What Moses did to reverse Miriam's leprosy

12. Amount of manna allotted per person

13. A fiery serpent was made of this and set on a pole

14. Signal announced by two silver trumpets

15. Place where Moses struck a rock and water rushed forth

16. Victory over them was marked by the defeat of king Og at Edrel

17. Type of bird that came in droves at evening to cover the camp

18. First place where water came from a rock

19. Place where the cloud settled after Sinai

1. __ __ __ __ __

2. __ __ __ __

3. __ __ __ __ __

4. __ __ __ __ __

5. __ __ __ __

6. __ __ __ __ __

7. __ __ __ __ __

8. __ __ __ __ __ __ __ __

9. __ __ __ __ __

10. __ __ __

11. __ __ __ __ __

12. __ __ __ __

13. __ __ __ __ __

14. __ __ __ __ __ __

15. __ __ __ __ __ __ __

16. __ __ __ __ __ __

17. __ __ __ __ __

18. __ __ __ __ __

19. __ __ __ __ __

*S*atan tempted Eve to become like God. She believed the tempter intead of God. The clues below all have to do with the Fall.

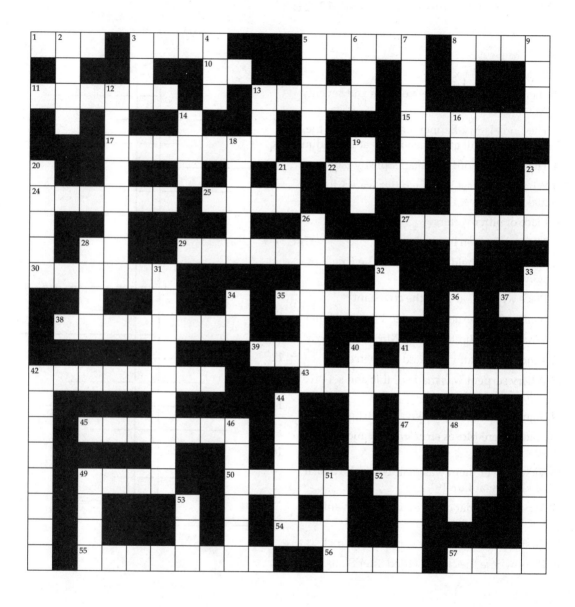

Across

1 The angels at the east of the garden guarded the ____ to the tree of life (Genesis 3:24)

3 Adam and Eve's first home (Genesis 2:15)

5 God made this for Adam and Eve to wear after they sinned (Genesis 3:21)

8 "She ____ of its fruit and ate" (Genesis 3:6)

10 "The man has become like one ____ Us" (Genesis 3:22)

11 This place was paradise for the first man and woman (Genesis 2:8)

13 The forbidden ____ (Genesis 3:2–3)

15 Trouble and sadness increased because of Eve's sin (Genesis 3:16)

17 Crafty; the serpent was more than most (Genesis 3:1)

22 Moral purity, virtue (Genesis 3:5)

24 Ill will; hostility (Genesis 3:15)

25 #5 Across was made of this (Genesis 3:21)

27 Fearful (Genesis 3:10)

28 "And ____ ate" (Genesis 3:6)

29 Sin brought this (Romans 5:16)

30 Gave attention to (Genesis 3:17)

35 To become aware (Genesis 3:5)

37 The serpent was cursed: "On your belly you shall ____" (Genesis 3:14)

38 Pleasing, agreeable; the tree of life was ____ to look at (Genesis 3:6)

39 Disobedience, wrongdoing; missing the mark (Romans 5:12)

42 Offspring (Genesis 3:16)

43 Because of their sin, Adam and Eve were denied access to this tree (3 words), and death entered the world (Genesis 3:24)

45 Adam to Eve (Genesis 3:6)

47 Necessary for sight (Genesis 3:7)

49 God said to the woman, "What is this you have ____?" (Genesis 3:13)

50 When Adam and Eve heard this, they went and hid (Genesis 3:8)

52 Middle (Genesis 3:3)

54 The serpent lied to Eve and told her, "You will not surely ____" (Genesis 3:4)

55 Weeds that grew after the Fall (Genesis 3:18)

56 "All the ____ of your life" (Genesis 3:14)

57 Suffering; this would accompany childbearing (Genesis 3:16)

Down

2 "In ____ all die" (1 Corinthians 15:22)

3 "Mother of all living" (Genesis 3:20)

4 Neither, ____ (Genesis 3:3)

5 Come in contact with (Genesis 3:3)

6 "You shall ____ eat of it" (Genesis 3:17)

7 Damned (Genesis 3:14)

8 "The woman whom You gave ____ be with me" (Genesis 3:12)

9 Perceived, understood (Genesis 3:7)

12 Beguiled (Genesis 3:13)

13 ____ leaves were the first clothing (Genesis 3:7)

14 "Through ____ man sin entered the world" (Romans 5:12)

16 "Till you ____ to the ground" (Genesis 3:19)

18 Bare, nude (Genesis 3:10)

19 "You will be like ____" (Genesis 3:5)

20 "____ reigned from Adam to Moses" (Romans 5:14)

21 ____ pain, ____ toil, ____ the sweat of your face (Genesis 3:16–17, 19)

23 Concealed, out of sight (Genesis 3:8)

26 The tempter of Eve (Genesis 3:1)

28 "You shall bruise His ____" (Genesis 3:15)

31 The tree was "____ to make one wise" (Genesis 3:6)

32 Feminine possessive pronoun (Genesis 3:6)

33 The result of judgment (Romans 5:18)

34 God placed #42 Down "____ the east of the garden" (Genesis 3:24)

36 Wickedness (Genesis 3:5)

40 The serpent was cursed to crawl on its ____ (Genesis 3:14)

41 Apparel (Genesis 3:7)

42 Angels (Genesis 3:24)

44 Earth, land (Genesis 3:17)

46 "Your ____ shall be for your husband" (Genesis 3:16)

48 Compass point (Genesis 3:24)

49 From ____ to ____ (Genesis 3:19)

51 "By the one man's offense many ____" (Romans 5:15)

53 In toil and sweat you shall ____ (Genesis 3:17–19)

*A*s our hearts go, so go our lives.

Start

End

*J*esus had a way with words. He could comfort, bless, admonish, forgive, and even raise the dead with His words. There was also another way that He used words to His listeners' benefit. Find all sixteen words and phrases hidden in the letter box, and determine what they have in common.

```
S  A  U  L  Y  O  L  I  V  E  C  S  M  A  R  T  E  F  L  E
R  D  K  P  E  E  H  S  T  S  O  L  U  O  F  W  A  S  Y  R
E  T  N  A  V  R  E  S  G  N  I  V  I  G  R  O  F  N  U  U
K  U  W  I  C  K  E  D  V  I  N  E  D  R  E  S  S  E  R  S
R  K  T  L  S  Y  U  P  O  F  A  C  S  C  S  O  T  V  K  A
O  D  E  A  H  O  B  A  S  T  I  S  P  X  H  N  I  A  N  E
W  E  N  T  I  E  W  U  K  Z  L  G  M  I  R  S  W  E  V  R
D  N  V  X  W  H  E  A  T  A  N  D  T  A  R  E  S  L  F  T
R  S  I  Q  D  R  T  R  H  J  R  E  A  R  U  E  N  A  D  N
A  E  R  A  E  M  U  S  T  A  R  D  S  E  E  D  W  N  J  E
Y  N  G  T  S  A  E  F  G  N  I  D  D  E  W  E  K  O  B  D
E  V  I  G  K  Z  R  N  R  I  F  O  B  L  H  I  M  E  S  D
N  O  N  E  J  O  E  O  W  S  T  N  E  L  A  T  C  G  Q  I
I  A  S  H  A  T  R  V  T  M  W  Y  I  E  L  A  N  O  M  H
V  Y  E  C  I  R  P  T  A  E  R  G  F  O  L  R  A  E  P  R
```

Word Pool

DRAGNET   FIG TREE   HIDDEN TREASURE   LEAVEN   LOST SHEEP   MUSTARD SEED
PEARL OF GREAT PRICE   SOWER   TALENTS   TEN VIRGINS   TWO SONS
UNFORGIVING SERVANT   VINEYARD WORKERS   WEDDING FEAST
WHEAT AND TARES   WICKED VINEDRESSERS

THE SOILS AND THE SEED

"*B*ehold, a sower went out to sow," begins the parable of the sower that Jesus told to His disciples (Matthew 13:3). Jesus went on to describe four types of soil in which the seed was planted. First, there was the seed that fell by the wayside and was eaten by the birds before it had a chance to take root. Then there was the stony soil where the seed grew shallow roots but soon withered in the scorching sun. The scattered seed also took root among the thorns, but the plants were choked out when the weeds grew up around them. But the seed planted in good soil yielded thirty, sixty, and a hundredfold.

The message of the parable of the sower is timeless. When a person hears the Word of God without understanding it, the wicked one will snatch it out of the hearer's heart. For the person who receives the Word with great joy but has no depth in his heart, that one does not survive tribulation or persecution. The Word sown in a heart preoccupied with the worries and cares of the world is choked out and bears no fruit. But the Word planted in a believing, receptive heart bears fruit many times over.

*W*hen God said "Go," Jonah said "No." But God had compassion on Jonah and the citizens of Nineveh. He spared Jonah's life, and when they repented, the Ninevites were spared the disaster that was coming to them. Find the answers to this crossword in the book of Jonah.

Across

1 Turbulence (Jonah 1:4)

4 God's command to Jonah (Jonah 1:2)

7 Jonah's nationality (Jonah 1:9)

9 Either, ____

10 Injury (Jonah 4:2)

11 Mad (Jonah 4:4)

14 Sea creature (Jonah 1:17)

15 Abyss (Jonah 2:3)

17 Still (Jonah 1:11)

18 The king of Nineveh proclaimed a fast, "Do not let them ____" (Jonah 3:7)

20 Length of Jonah's stay in the fish: ____ days and ____ nights (Jonah 1:17)

22 Jonah's mode of escape (Jonah 1:3)

23 Cinders (Jonah 3:6)

25 Center (Jonah 2:3)

27 Jonah was found fast ____ in the bottom of the ship (Jonah 1:5)

29 Chemical symbol for iron

30 Stomach (Jonah 1:17)

32 "The ____ of the Lord" (Jonah 1:1)

33 Gulp down (Jonah 1:17)

37 Sea ____ (Jonah 2:5)

39 Rescue

42 "The ____ of Nineveh believed God" (Jonah 3:5)

44 Freight (Jonah 1:5)

46 "____ have you done this?" (Jonah 1:10)

47 Number of days Nineveh residents had to repent (Jonah 3:4)

48 The Ninevites repented of this (Jonah 3:8)

50 "The ____ fell of Jonah" (Jonah 1:7)

51 More than adequate (Jonah 4:2)

53 That "great city" (Jonah 1:2)

55 First the cargo, then Jonah (Jonah 1:5, 15)

57 Ground (Jonah 1:13)

59 God's instructions to Jonah: "____ to Nineveh" (Jonah 1:2)

60 "____ is of the Lord" (Jonah 2:9)

61 "Roots" (Jonah 2:6)

Down

1 Jonah's intended destination (Jonah 1:3)

2 Die (Jonah 1:6)

3 "____ the Lord spoke to the fish" (Jonah 2:10)

5 "When my soul fainted within me, I ____ the Lord" (Jonah 2:7)

6 Shadow (Jonah 4:6)

7 Strenuously (Jonah 1:13)

8 You and I (Jonah 1:14)

9 "The belly ____ the fish" (Jonah 1:17)

12 "____, let every one turn from his evil way" (Jonah 3:8)

13 "You have brought ____ my life from the pit" (Jonah 2:6)

16 Seaport city (Jonah 1:3)

17 Stopped (Jonah 1:15)

19 "He went down ____ Joppa, and found a ship going ____ Tarshish" (Jonah 1:3)

20 Beverage made from leaves

21 Spoil

22 Place of the dead (Jonah 2:2)

24 Opposite of nights (Jonah 3:4)

26 Navigate or propel a boat with oars (past tense) (Jonah 1:13)

28 Weight, burden (Jonah 1:5)

29 "But Jonah arose to flee . . . ____ the presence of the Lord" (Jonah 1:3)

31 Jonah lamented: "It is better for me to ____ than to live" (Jonah 4:3)

34 Population of Nineveh: ____ hundred and twenty thousand persons and also much livestock (Jonah 4:11)

35 Jonah ____ faint when the sun beat on his head (Jonah 4:8)

36 God's attitude toward Nineveh (Jonah 4:11)

37 Evil (Jonah 1:2)

38 Regurgitate (Jonah 2:10)

40 Not wet (Jonah 2:10)

41 Sailing vessel

42 Proclaim (Jonah 3:2)

43 "As ____ dawned" (Jonah 4:7)

45 "God ____ ed from the disaster that He had said He would bring upon them, and He did not do it" (Jonah 3:10)

49 "Those who regard worthless ____ forsake their own Mercy" (Jonah 2:8)

51 Filled with fear (Jonah 1:10)

52 Deeds (Jonah 3:10)

54 Jonah sat on the ____ side of the city (Jonah 4:5)

55 ____ away (Jonah 3:9)

56 Creature that ate the plant that had sheltered Jonah from the sun (Jonah 4:7)

58 Lain ____ (Jonah 1:5)

*T*o find the names of plants and trees in the Bible, replace letters in the first word with letters from the same position in the second word. Then write the letters in the blank spaces. An example is given for you.

Ⓕ Ⓛ E A
H O Ⓐ Ⓧ

F L A X
‾ ‾ ‾ ‾

1. C A N A A N
   S U M M I T

— — — — — —

2. R E S T
   H O P E

— — — —

3. L A Z Y
  W I L L

— — — —

4. G R U B S
  H O A R D

— — — — —

5. M A N E
  T I L T

— — — —

6. F O X
  B I G

— — —

7. N O I S E
  A N G E L

— — — — —

8. G N O M E
  W R A P S

— — — — —

9. O L D E N
  D R I V E

— — — — —

10. P O E M
   T A L L

— — — —

11. B R I D E
   G L O O M

— — — — —

12. A P S E
   B L O W

— — — —

13. C L E A R
   M E D I A

— — — — —

14. M A P L E
   A P H I D

— — — — —

15. O A R
   I L K

— — —

16. H E A R T
   M A N N A

— — — — —

17. B O A R
   K E E N

— — — —

18. S H O A L
   W R E S T

— — — — —

19. M E L L O W
   W I C K E D

— — — — — —

20. A L L I E D
   D E M O N S

— — — — — —

21. A O R T I C
   G A L L O N

— — — — — —

You might think of these words of Jesus as referring to our Valentine for our Lord . . . and His gift back to us.

Clue: MESSIAH *is* ZRVVJKL

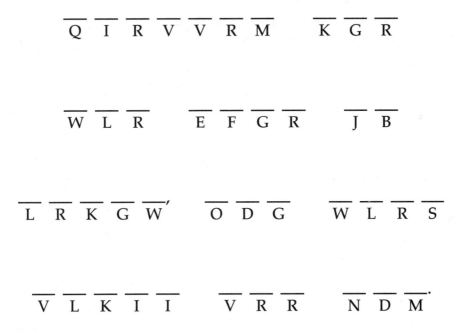

QIRVVRM KGR

WLR EFGR JB

LRKGW' ODG WLRS

VLKII VRR NDM.

*T*he Bible frequently gives us very precise "time markers" for days, weeks, and months. Using the numbers indicated by the clues, work the equation to come up with the answer.

Number of years children of Israel spent wandering in the desert (Numbers 32:13)

$=$ _____

Minus . . .
Number of months scorpion-like locusts are allowed to sting in the book of Revelation (Revelation 9:10)

$-$ _____

Plus . . .
Number of days two witnesses prophesy in Revelation before they are murdered (Revelation 11:3)

$+$ _____

Divided by . . .
Number of days before the murdered prophets arose (Revelation 11:11)

$\div$ _____

Minus . . .
Number of years Jeremiah prophesied Israel would serve the king of Babylon (Jeremiah 25:11)

$-$ _____

Divided by . . .
Number of days it took for God to complete His creation (Genesis 1:1–31)

$\div$ _____

Plus . . .
The day of the month that Noah's ark came to rest on Mount Ararat (Genesis 8:4)

$+$ _____

Minus . . .
Half the number of the jubilee year (Leviticus 25:10)

$-$ _____

Minus . . .
Number of months the dragon is allowed to blaspheme in Revelation (Revelation 13:5)

$-$ _____

$=$ _____

HAND OF RAIN

At a time of great famine in Samaria, God sent Elijah to challenge the prophets of Baal to prove before all of Israel that Elijah's God was the one true God. When the altars of Baal failed to burn and Elijah's altars were consumed, King Ahab and all of Israel rallied against the false prophets and they were executed.

Elijah had predicted God would end the devastating drought. So he sent a servant to look toward the sea for rain. When six trips produced no news of rain, Elijah sent the servant a seventh time. This time the servant reported he had seen a cloud the size of a man's hand. Elijah sent word to Ahab to ride his chariot to Jezreel to report the rain, but the spirit of God came upon Elijah and he ran on foot and beat Ahab to the city gate.

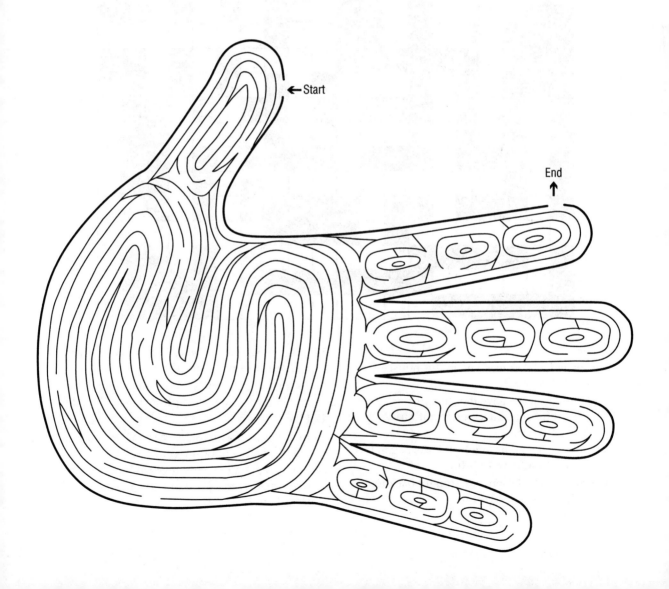

When it comes to learning more about God and receiving the blessings He has for us, it's best to sit at the feet of the Master.

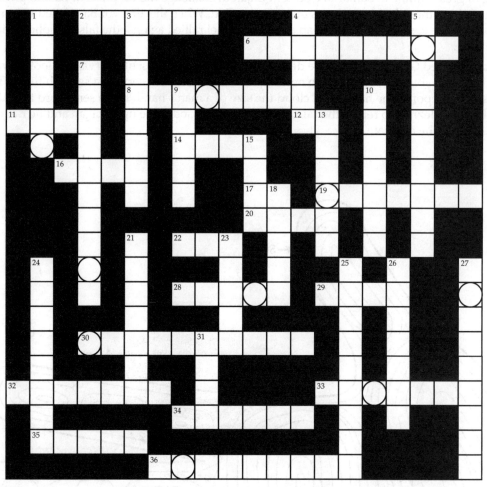

Across

2 Jesus did a lot of teaching in this house of God (Mark 12:35)

6 In this city, Jesus gave the chief priests, scribes, and elders a lesson in authority (Mark 11:27–33)

8 One of two regions in which Jesus began His ministry (Matthew 4:13–16)

11 A mother's only son was brought back to life in this city (Luke 7:11–15)

12 Not yes

14 Jesus ministered to Mary in this place, after His resurrection (John 20:11)

16 At this tax collector's home, Jesus taught that it's the sick who need a physician (Luke 5:29)

17 Like

19 In a certain "small town," Martha was taught what's really important (Luke 10:38)

20 In this region, the demon-possessed daughter of a woman from Canaan was healed (Matthew 15:21–28)

22 "But the Son of Man ____ nowhere to lay His head" (Luke 9:58)

28 Jesus healed great multitudes in this region beyond the Jordan (Matthew 19:1–2)

29 The wedding miracle took place in ____ of Galilee (John 2:1)

30 Jesus taught the devil a thing or two in this arid area (Matthew 4:1–11)

32 At Simon the leper's home in this town, Jesus taught that the poor will be with us always (Matthew 26:6–13)

33 Blind Bartimaeus was healed where Joshua once fought (Mark 10:46–52)

34 On the road to this village, Jesus opened the Scriptures to two men (Luke 24:13–35)

35 Jesus taught a lesson about healing on the Sabbath at a Pharisee ruler's "abode" (Luke 14:1–6)

36 After the demons left him for some swine, a man spread the word about Jesus in this district (Mark 5:20)

Down

1 The woman at the well learned about living water in this Samaritan city (John 4:5–10)

3 The Beatitudes were given to the disciples on one of these (Matthew 5:1–12)

4 In this type of field, the Pharisees were taught that Jesus is Lord of the Sabbath (Matthew 12:1–8)

5 The lesson in this garden was "watch and pray" (Matthew 26:36–41)

7 The sick begged to simply touch the hem of Jesus' garment in this land (Matthew 14:34–36)

9 This disciple's mother-in-law was healed in his home (Matthew 8:14–15)

10 In this country, Jesus preached that the kingdom of God was at hand (Mark 1:14–15)

13 Jesus taught His disciples the signs of the end of the age on this mountain (Matthew 24:3)

15 Jesus sat in one and taught the multitude that stood on the shore (Matthew 13:2)

18 After preaching and teaching in Galilee, Jesus healed many who lived in this province (Matthew 4:23–24)

21 The other region mentioned in conjunction with #8 Across; the two contain the town of Capernaum where Jesus dwelt (Matthew 4:13)

23 The other region connected to #20 Across; it's an ancient city of the Canaanites (Matthew 15:21)

24 In this town, Jesus claimed to be the fulfillment of Messianic prophecy (Luke 4:16–21)

25 In this people's country, Jesus healed the man whose unclean spirit was named "Legion" (Mark 5:1–9)

26 Passing through the midst of ____ and Galilee, Jesus met ten lepers and healed them; the one who thanked Him was from this city (Luke 17:12–19)

27 The Scriptures came to life when Jesus taught in this Jewish house of worship (Matthew 4:23)

31 In the Upper ____, Jesus taught His disciples the meaning of communion (Mark 14:15–25)

Bonus:
Unscramble the circled letters to find out where God meets us today.

___ ___ ___ ___ ___ ___ ___ ___ ___ ___

*J*esus comforted His disciples about His going away.

Clue: MESSIAH *is* JBEESDU

J I E Y   D E E N T B W R G'

S E D G   Y I   G I N'   U B   O U I

P B R S B F B E   S V   J B'   Y U B

O I T Z E   Y U D Y   S   W I   U B

O S R R   W I   D R E I;   D V W

C T B D Y B T   O I T Z E   Y U D V

Y U B E B   U B   O S R R   W I'

P B Q D N E B   S   C I   Y I

J G   L D Y U B T.

God had given us human beings the great gift of speech. That gift can be used to edify and encourage other people—or it can be misused to destroy or hurt people. The words in this puzzle concern Bible references to our misuse of speech—specifically, the ability to start small-scale and large-scale wars.

```
A R N S V K F X G B R E K J W D T O W P
D L O I D T C L U I E N R E P I V B I O
T Q I E K H Y G I C I S P S P C R N C A
E W T Q H I H C N V Q V S W O R D S K Z
C G A F N X Z E E S E J C O I B S Y E N
L M N G Q C L S T S R X L R S M R A D A
T F G Y S O U V R F M B P R O U A F N Z
Y K I V I O W E A R R O G A N C E K E Q
I E D V R G V O U A P S K L N H P J S M
M N N H J R O D Z J B I S E D I S V S V
P F I R E U H O D E S T R U C T I O N X
O R T P E G R U O C S L K N W M A Y M W
E K G X L E U Z J P Y D W F I B G N Z A
```

Word Pool

ARROGANCE ARROWS DESTRUCTION EVIL FIRE INDIGNATION KNIVES LYING
PERVERSE POISON RAZOR SCOURGE SMOKE SPEARS SWORDS
VIOLENCE VIPER WICKEDNESS

*T*he Israelites didn't know much about winning friends, but they definitely influenced people. This puzzle concerns many of the kings (and their nations) who fought the Israelites.

Across

1 The king of the land was hanged on a tree untill evening (Joshua 8:29)

3 One of the kings of Midian; the death of his daughter, Cozbi, stopped the plague in Israel (Numbers 25:6–15)

4 The king of this town was struck with the edge of the sword (Joshua 11:1, 10)

6 A town in the territory of Judah, near the place where David and Goliath fought (Joshua 12:15)

9 The king of Jarmuth (Joshua 10:3)

14 Another king of Midian; his name means "desirous" (Numbers 31:8)

15 A town near Mount Carmel; its name means "possession of the people" (Joshua 12:22)

16 The king of this country wouldn't let Moses and the Israelites pass through (Numbers 20:14–21)

18 King of Hebron (Joshua 10:3)

19 The king of this city wanted Rahab to squeal on the Israelite spies (Joshua 2:3)

21 This city of Canaan was captured by Joshua (Joshua 11:1–8)

23 King of Hazor (Joshua 11:1)

24 For example

27 Meaning "sacred place," this town in south Judah and its king were conquered by Joshua (Joshua 12:22)

28 Another king of Midian; his name means "friendship" (Numbers 31:8)

29 The king of this city met the same fate as the king of #19 Across (Joshua 10:28)

30 This city (and its king), conquered by Joshua, was later given to the Levites (Joshua 12:13)

Down

1 The king of this city fought against Israel and took some of them prisoner; the name means "fugitive" (Numbers 21:1)

2 A Canaanite town in the territory of Asher; its name means "habitation" (Joshua 11:2; 12:23)

4 Another king of Midian (Numbers 31:8)

6 How many kings of Midian were there? (Numbers 31:8)

7 A Canaanite city near Lachish; its name means "whiteness" (Joshua 10:29–30)

8 Military police (abbr.)

10 The king of Jerusalem in Joshua's time; his name means "My Lord is righteous" (2 words) (Joshua 10:1)

11 This king of Heshbon would not grant passage to the Israelites (Deuteronomy 2:30)

12 This city, "devoted to destruction," was destroyed by Israel (Numbers 21:1–3)

13 Meaning "pit" or "well," this town west of Jordan was another Israelite conquest (Joshua 12:17)

17 This king of Bashan fought Israel at Edrel (Numbers 21:33)

19 King of Lachish; his name means "may He (God) cause to shine forth" (Joshua 10:3)

20 A town near Samaria; its name means "delight" (Joshua 12:24)

21 This king fought with Israel in Rephidim; his name means "warlike" (Exodus 17:8)

22 A town in Judah; its name means "fence" (Joshua 12:13)

23 This king of Madon has a name that means "to call loudly" (Joshua 11:1)

25 Horam, this city's king, came to the aid of Lachish, but was struck down (Joshua 10:33)

26 Another king of Midian (Numbers 31:8)

Bonus:
Unscramble the circled letters to form four
words that tell of the ultimate victor all Christians are eagerly awaiting.

___ ___ ___   ___ ___ ___ ___   ___ ___   ___ ___ ___ ___ ___ ___

Safe Passage

Genesis 6:14—9:17 gives us a remarkable account of a man's faith in God in the face of seemingly ridiculous instructions. Not only did God tell Noah that it was going to rain (a phenomenon heretofore unknown), but that he was to save himself, his family, and a pair of every animal species by building a huge boat.

God was very specific about how the ark was to be built giving specific materials (gopherwood and pitch), size (450 feet long, seventy-five feet wide, and forty-five feet high), and arrangement (three decks, a door in the side with a window). Scholars have calculated that a vessel of this size would hold about forty-three thousand tons.

The rain lasted forty days and nights covering the earth with water for 150 days. Several accounts from the ancient world (other than the Scriptures) record stories of the Flood and some even recount versions of Noah's ark.

After almost a year on the water, the ark came to rest on Mount Ararat in what is now Turkey. Various attempts to locate the ark's remains have not uncovered indisputable evidence that the ark still exists. However, several archaeologists, who have braved shifting glaciers and dangerously unpredictable weather in their explorations, still claim that the ark may be caught beneath the ice.

*I*n this puzzle, you'll explore the ages of our long-lived biblical ancestors.

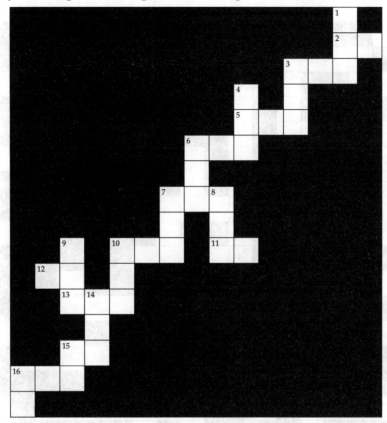

Across

2 The age of Isaac when Esau and Jacob were born (Genesis 25:25–26)

3 The age of Enosh at his death (Genesis 5:11)

5 The age of Cainan at his death (Genesis 5:14)

6 The age of Abraham at his death (Genesis 25:7)

7 The age of Sarah at her death (Genesis 23:1)

10 The age of Adam at his death (Genesis 5:5)

11 The age of Abram when he departed from Haran for the land God had promised him (Genesis 12:4)

12 The age of Abram when Hagar gave birth to Ishmael (Genesis 16:16)

13 The age of Jared at his death (Genesis 5:20)

15 The age of Isaac when he took Rebekah as a wife (Genesis 25:20)

16 The age of Joseph at his death (Genesis 50:26)

Down

1 The age of Enoch when he "walked with God" (Genesis 5:23)

3 The age of Noah at his death (Genesis 9:29)

4 The age of Mahalalel at his death (Genesis 5:17)

6 The age of Lamech when Noah was born (Genesis 5:28)

7 The age of Adam when Seth was born (Genesis 5:3)

8 The age of Lamech at his death (Genesis 5:31)

9 The age of Methuselah at his death (Genesis 5:27)

10 The age of Seth at his death (Genesis 5:8)

14 The age of Noah when the floodwaters came on the earth (Genesis 7:6)

15 The age of Esau when he took Judith and Basemath as wives (Genesis 26:34)

16 The age of Joseph when God gave him dreams of his destiny (Genesis 37:2)

*T*hink "BiblES," and this one will be easier!

Across

1 Shem was the father "of all the children of ____" (Genesis 10:21)

3 Fourth foundation jewel of New Jerusalem (Revelation 21:19)

7 Paul said Jesus became obedient to "____ the death of the cross" (Philippians 2:8)

9 The Jews sought to kill Jesus because they perceived He made Himself "____ with God" (John 5:18)

10 Jacob hid them under the terebinth tree by Shechem (Genesis 35:4)

11 Age, in days, of a male child when he is to be circumcised (Genesis 17:12)

12 In Mary's song, the Lord sends the rich away in this state (Luke 1:53)

15 Unending

16 To expand is to en____

18 One of the five ministry callings set in the church (Ephesians 4:11)

20 King Ahasuerus' queen (Esther 2:7)

22 Priest and scribe; fifteenth book of the Old Testament

23 David made him an officer over the tribe of Judah (1 Chronicles 27:18)

24 New Testament letters

27 Paul called him a "fellow prisoner in Christ Jesus" (Philemon 23)

28 About a bushel, in Hebrew measurement

29 The one of a sword is to be avoided!

31 ____ and every one

32 "____ into His gates with thanksgiving" (Psalm 100:4)

33 The writer of Proverbs said, "Lend your ____ to my understanding" (Proverbs 5:1)

34 One of King David's wives (2 Samuel 3:5)

35 One of Aaron's sons, he ministered as a priest (Numbers 3:4)

37 High priest whom Samuel served (1 Samuel 1:25)

38 David and Goliath, for example

40 Phillip explained the Scriptures to a eunuch from this nation (Acts 8:27)

42 Another name for Elijah

43 Red; another name for Esau (Genesis 25:30)

44 "They shall fear You as long as the sun and moon ____" (Psalm 72:5)

45 Peter wrote, "You younger people, submit yourselves to your ____" (sing.) (1 Peter 5:5)

Down

1 First garden

2 The name of the month (Hebrew) in which Nehemiah's wall was finished (Nehemiah 6:15)

3 Adversary

4 Jesus prophesied they will be part of "the beginning of sorrows" (Matthew 24:7–8)

5 The psalmist said he lifted his to the hills "from whence comes my help" (Psalm 121:1)

6 A woman of Canaan said to Jesus, "Even the little dogs ____ the crumbs which fall from their masters' table" (Matthew 15:27)

7 Place with twelve wells and seventy palm trees (Exodus 15:27)

8 Land of bondage (Exodus 3:16–17)

12 The psalmist declared it is full of the Lord's possessions (Psalm 104:24)

13 Receiver of a double portion of Elijah's spirit (2 Kings 2:9)

14 King Saul asked a woman from here to conjure the spirit of Samuel (2 words) (1 Samuel 28:7)

15 Job said the white of one is tasteless (Job 6:6)

17 To make a mistake

18 The Lord taught us to pray for deliverance from "the ____ one" (Matthew 6:13)

19 It is called "the helmet for My head" (Psalm 60:7)

20 Direction from which the wise men came (Matthew 2:1)

21 His trip to heaven was via a fiery chariot and whirlwind (2 Kings 2:11)

22 "From the ____ of the earth I will cry to You" (Psalm 61:2)

24 Ahasuerus made a decree "throughout all his ____" that wives are to honor their husbands (Esther 1:20)

25 Valley of great grapes (Numbers 13:23–24)

26 The Lord "placed cherubim at the _____ of the garden of Eden" (Genesis 3:24)

29 Judah's eldest son (Genesis 38:6)

30 Timothy's mother (2 Timothy 1:5)

31 City of Ephesians

33 David's hiding place (2 words) (1 Samuel 23:29)

35 His sons Hophni and Phinehas were killed when the ark of God was captured (1 Samuel 4:16–17)

36 Hire

37 After His resurrection, Jesus walked with two men on the road to this village (Luke 24:13)

39 Adam's helpmate (Genesis 3:20)

40 Mountain on which Joshua built an altar (Joshua 8:30)

41 Alpha and Omega, Beginning and _____ (Revelation 21:6)

43 Firstborn son of Judah and Shua (Genesis 38:3)

*H*elp is on the way.

Clue: MESSIAH *is* NGHHRST

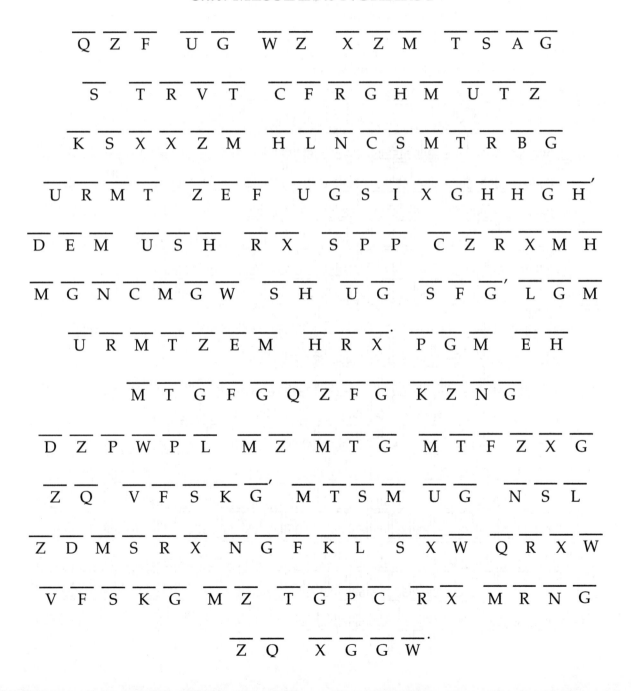

Q Z F   U G   W Z   X Z M   T S A G

S   T R V T   C F R G H M   U T Z

K S X X Z M   H L N C S M T R B G

U R M T   Z E F   U G S I X G H H G H '

D E M   U S H   R X   S P P   C Z R X M H

M G N C M G W   S H   U G   S F G ' L G M

U R M T Z E M   H R X   P G M   E H .

M T G F G Q Z F G   K Z N G

D Z P W P L   M Z   M T G   M T F Z X G

Z Q   V F S K G '   M T S M   U G   N S L

Z D M S R X   N G F K L   S X W   Q R X W

V F S K G   M Z   T G P C   R X   M R N G

Z Q   X G G W .

THE PATRIARCHAL CROSS

*T*his cross shape is an elaboration of the basic Latin cross, which has been adapted in more than four hundred ways as a Christian symbol.

The short arm at the top of the cross represents the placard on which Pilate wrote, "Jesus of Nazareth, the King of the Jews" (John 19:19). When used today, the short arm often bears the inscription "I. N. R. I." which stands for the Latin translation of his placard: "Iesus Nazarenus Rex Iudaeorum."

In early paintings, church patriarchs are frequently shown carrying this cross as a means of identifying with the cross of Jesus. The cross later became a symbol used by the cardinals and archbishops of the church. This cross shape is also associated with Peter and Philip.

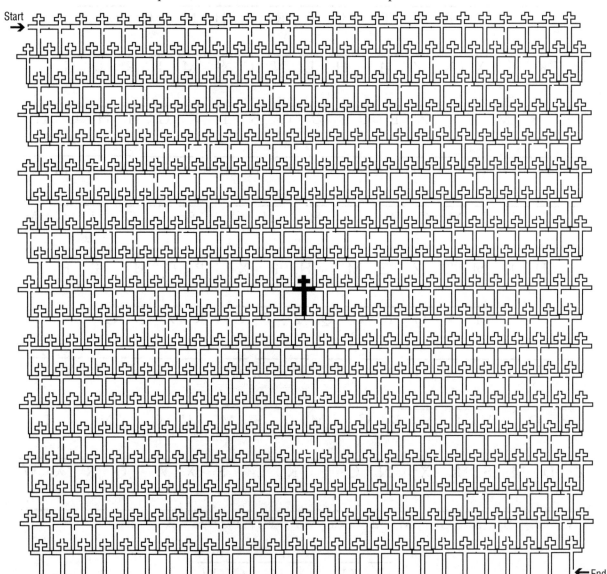

*E*xploring the possibilities . . .

Connect the letters—in all directions—to form a word string that gives one of the most famous quotes of Jesus.

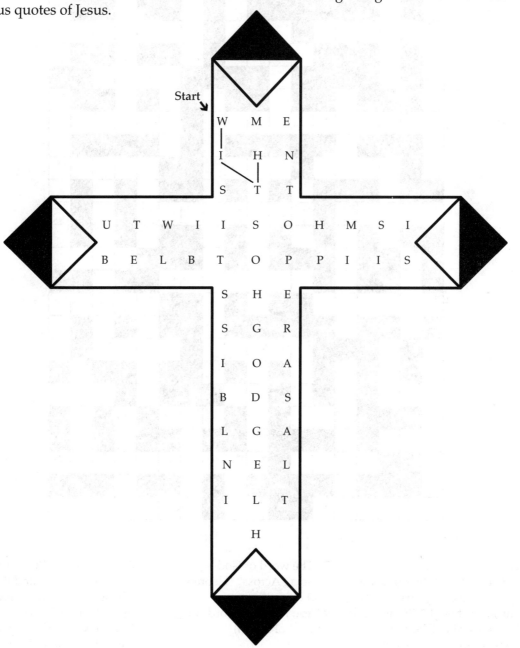

Start

*T*he words to complete this crossword are all about the Word of God.

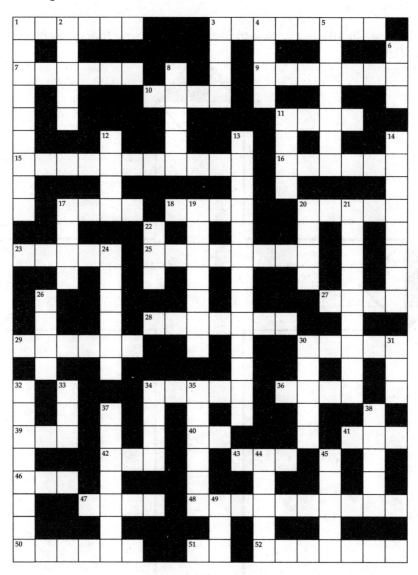

Across

1 "The words of the LORD are pure . . . like ____ tried in a furnace of earth" (Psalm 12:6)

3 "The word of God is #7 Across and ____" (Hebrews 4:12)

7 "The word of God is ____ and #3 Across" (Hebrews 4:12)

9 "You have the words of ____ life" (John 6:68)

10 "These are written that you may believe . . . and that believing you may have ____" (John 20:31)

11 "Receive . . . the implanted word, which is able to ____ your souls" (James 1:21)

15 "All Scripture is given by ____ of God" (2 Timothy 3:16)

16 "I will not ____ Your word" (Psalm 119:16)

17 "The ____ is the word of God" (Luke 8:11)

18 "The Holy Scriptures, which are ____ to make you wise for salvation" (2 Timothy 3:15)

20 "The word is near you, in your mouth and in your ____" (Romans 10:8)

23 "Your word is ____" (John 17:17)

25 "I rejoice at Your word as one who finds great ____" (Psalm 119:162)

27 "Be diligent to present yourself approved to God, a worker who ____ not need to be ashamed, rightly dividing the word of truth" (2 Timothy 2:15)

28 "How can a young man ____ his way? By taking heed according to Your word" (Psalm 119:9)

29 "Your word I have ____ in my heart, that I might not sin against You" (Psalm 119:11)

30 "The word of His grace, which is able to ____ you up" (Acts 20:32)

34 "Born ____ . . . through the word of God" (1 Peter 1:23)

36 "The word is ____ near you" (Deuteronomy 30:14)

39 "All Scripture is given . . . that the ____ of God may be complete, thoroughly equipped for every good work" (2 Timothy 3:16–17)

40 "____ that day the deaf shall hear the words of the book" (Isaiah 29:18)

41 "He wrote on the tablets the words of the covenant, the ____ Commandments" (Exodus 34:28)

42 "Your word was to me the ____ and rejoicing of my heart" (Jeremiah 15:16)

43 "If you #35 Down in Me, and My words #35 Down in you, you will ____ what you

desire, and it shall be done for you" (John 15:7)

46 "I will ____ forget Your word" (Psalm 119:16)

47 "The testimony of the LORD is sure, making ____ the simple" (Psalm 19:7)

48 "____ me according to Your word" (Psalm 119:28)

50 "Is not My word . . . like a ____ that breaks the rock in pieces?" (Jeremiah 23:29)

51 "If anyone loves Me, he will keep My word; and My Father will love him, and We will come ____ him and make Our home with him" (John 14:23)

52 "The word of God is . . . ____ than any two-edged sword" (Hebrews 4:12)

Down

1 "Your ____ according to Your word" (Psalm 119:41)

2 "If anyone ____ Me, he will keep My word" (John 14:23)

3 "Every word of God is ____" (Proverbs 30:5)

4 "'Do not mourn nor ____.' For all the people wept, when they heard the words of the Law" (Nehemiah 8:9)

5 "But the word of the LORD endures ____" (1 Peter 1:25)

6 "Speak . . . ____ the words that I command you to speak to them" (Jeremiah 26:2)

8 "Your word is . . . a ____ to my path" (Psalm 119:105)

11 "Hold me up, and I shall be ____, and I shall observe Your statutes continually" (Psalm 119:117)

12 "Is not My word like a ____?" (Jeremiah 23:29)

13 "The entrance of Your words gives light; it gives ____ to the simple" (Psalm 119:130)

14 "The ____ of the LORD are right" (Psalm 19:8)

17 "Piercing even to the division of ____ and spirit" (Hebrews 4:12)

19 "____ are those who keep His testimonies" (Psalm 119:2)

20 "Whoever . . . does not ____ your words . . . shall be put to death" (Joshua 1:18)

21 "His word was with ____" (Luke 4:32)

22 "Your words were found, and I ____ them" (Jeremiah 15:16)

24 "Forever, O LORD, Your word is settled in ____" (Psalm 119:89)

26 "My word . . . shall not return to Me ____" (Isaiah 55:11)

30 "Man shall not live by ____ alone; but . . . by every word that proceeds from the mouth of the LORD" (Deuteronomy 8:3)

31 "To____ this Scripture is fulfilled in your hearing" (Luke 4:21)

32 "Do not ____ a word" (Jeremiah 26:2)

33 "Rivers of water run down from my eyes, because ____ do not keep Your law" (Psalm 119:136)

34 "My words will by no means pass ____" (Matthew 24:35)

35 "If you ____ in Me, and My words ____ in you" (John 15:7)

37 "I ____ at Your word" (Psalm 119:162)

38 "Great ____ have those who love Your law" (Psalm 119:165)

44 "Direct my ____ by Your word" (Psalm 119:133)

45 "Christ also loved the church and gave Himself for her, that He might sanctify and cleanse her with the washing of ____ by the word" (Ephesians 5:25–26)

49 "Cut ____ tablets of stone . . . and I will write on these tablets the words" (Exodus 34:1)

The letter grid below contains twelve words associated with salt in the Bible. See how many you can find before consulting the Scripture Pool.

```
C  E  Y  T  R  A  E  S  P  V  T  S  Y
S  H  R  E  C  F  I  G  I  A  F  T  O
S  A  T  X  I  Y  C  N  F  L  I  B  G
H  W  C  R  A  L  L  I  P  L  L  P  F
C  L  E  R  A  P  D  R  T  E  S  A  L
E  O  B  N  I  E  L  E  N  Y  I  L  V
E  P  D  O  E  C  I  F  I  R  C  A  S
P  R  I  F  L  A  V  F  N  A  L  V  C
S  T  I  P  L  N  B  O  W  L  E  E  H
```

Scripture Pool

GENESIS 14:3   GENESIS 19:26   LEVITICUS 2:13   DEUTERONOMY 29:23
JOSHUA 15:62   2 SAMUEL 8:13   2 KINGS 2:20   ZEPHANIAH 2:9   MATTHEW 5:13
MARK 9:49   COLOSSIANS 4:6

A diplomat's heritage?

Clue: MESSIAH *is* PSWWJGR

Y F S W W S H   G N S   U R S

V S G T S P G Q S N W ' I E N

U R S L   W R G F F Y S

T G F F S H   W E O W

E I Z E H.

TAX COLLECTING

Luke 19 gives us an unusual account of a man named Zacchaeus. He was the chief tax collector in the city of Jericho. Tax collectors, in general, were hated, since their "salaries" were collected along with the taxes. Most tax collectors were considered little better than extortionists. Zacchaeus, as the chief collector, was probably one of the most hated, but he was also probably one of the richest men in the city.

Knowing his own reputation, Zacchaeus only hoped to catch a glimpse of Jesus as He passed by. Because he was short, Zacchaeus ran ahead of the crowd and climbed into a sycamore tree to get a better vantage point. Imagine the shock of the crowd—and Zacchaeus, too—when Jesus stopped beneath the tree and bade Zacchaeus to come down, and informed him that He should be Zacchaeus's guest. Jesus' action caused a dramatic change in the life of Zacchaeus and his family. He distributed much of his wealth to the poor, sought to right past wrongs, and began to follow the Master.

Jesus said, "The Son of Man has come to seek and to save that which was lost" (Luke 19:10).

Beginning at Zacchaeus, travel to each house to collect taxes. You must pass through each house to the adjacent street to continue the task. You can only go to each house once and you cannot double back or cross over the path you have already taken. Then finish up at the tree.

A nice place to visit? Not these cities and towns. Not if you worshiped the one true God and didn't go in for idolatry, fornication, and other commandment breakers.

Across

4 Another name for #17 Across (Jeremiah 46:14)

6 This city was "the beginning of sin" to the daughter of Zion (poss.) (Micah 1:13)

9 After seventy years, this city will commit fornication with all the kingdoms of the world (Isaiah 23:17)

12 In Abraham's day, the outcry against this city was great (Genesis 18:20)

13 The sword of the Lord is filled with blood; there's a great slaughter in this land (Isaiah 34:6)

15 The young men of this city and of Pi Beseth "shall fall by the sword" (Ezekiel 30:17)

16 It "will cease from being a city, and . . . will be a ruinous heap" (Isaiah 17:1)

17 This ancient capital of Egypt "shall be waste and desolate" (Jeremiah 44:1; 46:19; Hosea 9:6)

19 God will turn His hand against this Philistine city (Amos 1:8)

20 God will show the nations the nakedness of this city (Nahum 3:5–7)

22 The goddess Astarte was worshiped in this capital of Og, land of giants (Deuteronomy 1:4; Joshua 13:12)

24 Solomon foolishly worshiped Ashtoreth, the goddess of this city (1 Kings 11:5; Isaiah 23:12)

Down

1 Manasseh allowed the Canaanites to remain in this town just north of Caesarea; its king was conquered by Joshua (Judges 1:27)

2 Though "exalted to heaven," it will be "brought down to Hades" (Matthew 11:23)

3 The Philistine idol Dagon was worshiped here (1 Samuel 5:1–2)

4 New York (abbr.)

5 Eating things sacrificed to idols was one sin in this Revelation city (Revelation 2:12, 14)

7 #12 Across's partner in crime

8 "The beauty of the Chaldeans' pride" will never be inhabited after God is through with it (Isaiah 13:19–20)

10 Joy and gladness are taken from this land (Jeremiah 48:33)

11 Jesus renounced this city for its unbelief (Matthew 11:21)

14 God will make it "a heap of ruins in the field" (Micah 1:6)

15 God appointed His sword against this Philistine city and "against the seashore" (Jeremiah 47:7)

18 It didn't turn to persecuting Christians in a day (Acts 28:16)

21 Another name for Ava, a people who worshiped Nibhaz and Tartak (2 Kings 17:24, 31; 18:34)

23 Another name for Aven and Heliopolis, it means the opposite of "off." Its people were sun worshipers (Genesis 41:45, 50)

The prophetess Deborah sat under her own palm tree as Israel made its way to her for judgments. (See Judges 4.)

Start

End

The apostle Paul rarely traveled or ministered by himself. In the box of letters below, find the names of thirteen men and women who worked alongside Paul in the spreading of the gospel and the founding of the early chruch. (See Acts 12:25; 13:2, 5; 15:40; 18:18; 19:22, 29; 20:4 for help.)

```
A  S  U  H  C  R  A  T  S  I  R  A  S  P  K
R  H  O  P  O  R  T  E  I  U  Q  O  S  R  A
I  A  C  P  N  S  C  J  O  H  P  A  A  I  M
S  R  S  U  A  U  A  U  I  A  G  M  L  S  Y
A  S  E  U  N  T  H  B  T  L  L  A  I  C  H
T  Q  U  D  C  P  E  R  A  S  T  U  S  I  T
R  M  U  A  D  I  O  R  C  N  P  B  A  L  O
A  S  U  I  A  G  H  U  E  H  R  I  R  L  M
M  B  A  R  L  R  N  C  S  O  I  A  U  A  I
A  A  L  I  S  A  D  T  Y  J  S  Q  B  N  T
R  S  U  M  I  H  P  O  R  T  A  S  U  B  A
```

Word Pool

AQUILA   ARISTARCHUS   BARNABAS   ERASTUS   GAIUS   MARK   PRISCILLA
SECUNDUS   SILAS   SOPATER   TIMOTHY   TROPHIMUS   TYCHICUS

*S*ustenance is available to those who obey God.

Clue: MESSIAH is VRCCGTW

V Z   H E E I   G C

Y E   I E   Y W R

L G F F   E H   W G V

L W E   C R O Y   V R '

T O I   Y E   H G O G C W

W G C   L E N U .

*E*VANGELIZING

*T*hese are some of the places Paul visited on his three missionary trips. On his first trip he visited Antioch, where he was rejected by the Jews. At the conclusion of that trip, he and Barnabas went to Jerusalem, where they testified before the council about all that God had done. The second trip included Philippi, where Lydia was converted, and Corinth, where he established a church. In Galatia, on the third trip, Paul worked to help build up the church.

Noah, Lot, Moses, David, Daniel, Shadrach, Meshach, Abed-Nego, and even Jesus Himself are among those who were rescued by God's mighty arm of deliverance in some very perilous circumstances. Fill in the grid below with words from those stories in the Bible.

Across

1 Grieved (Genesis 6:6)

4 "The Lord ____ that the wickedness of man was great in the earth" (Genesis 6:5)

9 Daniel's prayer posture (Daniel 6:10)

12 "Stand still, and see the ____ of the Lord," (Exodus 14:13)

14 Chosen to lead God's rescue of His people from Egypt (Exodus 3:4, 10)

16 God delivered the Israelites in battle against this army (Exodus 17:13)

17 "The Lord ____ all the firstborn in the land" (Exodus 13:15, KJV)

18 "There is no other God who can ____ like this" (Daniel 3:29)

24 Also known as (abbr.)

25 An angel warned Joseph in a ____ to escape with Mary and Jesus to Egypt (Matthew 2:13)

28 "Why ____ you cry to Me?" (Exodus 14:15)

29 Compassion (Genesis 19:19)

30 "Who is like ____, O LORD?" (Exodus 15:11)

31 Moses ____ down when his hands got heavy (Exodus 17:12)

33 Abraham's nephew saved from destruction of Sodom and Gomorrah (Genesis 19:29)

35 Those who were bitten and looked at the serpent on the pole "shall ____" (Numbers 21:8)

37 God's promise to Noah (Genesis 6:18)

39 Those who disobeyed King Nebuchadnezzar were sentenced to die in the ____ (Daniel 3:15)

40 Either, ____

42 God said He would "harden the ____ of the Egyptians" (Exodus 14:17)

43 Daniel's companions in the den (Daniel 6:16)

45 Nebuchadnezzar was so angry when his decree was disobeyed that "the expression on his ____ changed" (Daniel 3:19)

47 Leave out

48 Nourishment, sustenance (Genesis 6:21)

49 Where Lot was sitting when the angels came to Sodom (Genesis 19:1)

50 "Come ____ before the LORD" (Exodus 16:9)

51 To save his life, he hid in the Wilderness of Ziph (1 Samuel 23:14)

52 "Our God whom we serve is able ____ deliver us" (Daniel 3:17)

53 During the drought the ravens provided this prophet with food and water (1 Kings 17:1, 4)

54 City where Lot and his family escaped to (Genesis 19:22)

55 Noah and Moses built these structures (sing.) to remember the Lord's deliverance (Genesis 8:20; Exodus 17:15)

58 The number of men walking in the fire (Daniel 3:25)

60 "The children of Israel complained ____ Moses and Aaron in the wilderness" (Exodus 16:2)

62 The lions' mouths were closed, ____ that they might not hurt Daniel (Daniel 6:22)

63 When Lot looked toward Sodom and Gomorrah, he saw "the ____ of the land which went up like the ____ of a furnace" (Genesis 19:28)

64 Tendency

65 "My God sent His angel and ____ the lions' mouths" (Daniel 6:22)

68 "The children of Israel went out with ____" (Exodus 14:8)

71 Dried grape

72 The people complained against Moses that they would die of ____ in the wilderness (Exodus 17:3)

74 "When Moses held ____ his hand, . . . Israel prevailed" (Exodus 17:11)

76 Fermented dough (Exodus 12:15)

77 Noah ____ according to what God commanded him (Genesis 6:22)

78 God promised Noah that He would not again ____ every living thing (Genesis 8:21)

79 "They baked unleavened ____ [sing.] . . . because they were driven out of Egypt" (Exodus 12:39)

Down

1 King Darius said, "Your God, whom you ____ continually, He will deliver you" (Daniel 6:16)

2 Male sheep

3 Affirmative

5 "____ the LORD commanded" (Exodus 16:34)

6 The ____ (sing.) covered the chariots, horsemen, and Pharaoh's army (Exodus 14:28)

7 "At ____ ye shall eat flesh" (Exodus 16:12, KJV)

8 "The earth was filled with ____" (adj.) (Genesis 6:11)

9 "That the Egyptians may ____ that I am the LORD" (Exodus 14:4)

10 The houses marked with the blood of the ____ would not suffer the death of the firstborn (Exodus 12:5–7, 13)

11 God's provision of escape for Noah and his family (Genesis 6:14)

13 King Saul "conspired" evil toward David (present tense) (1 Samuel 23:9)

15 The thoughts of man's heart was "only ____ continually" (Genesis 6:5)

19 Land of bondage and oppression for children of Israel

20 Filled with raging jealousy, this Israelite king was obsessed with killing his apparent successor (1 Samuel 23:15)

21 The Israelite would eat in ____ with their sandals, belts, and staffs (Exodus 12:11)

22 The fire had no ____, because God delivered the Hebrew children (Daniel 3:27)

23 Pharaoh's words to the Israelites: "____ ____" (2 words) (Exodus 12:32)

26 "____ for your life!" (Genesis 19:17)

27 The sacrificial lamb was to be "a ____ of the first year" (Exodus 12:5)

32 Jewish festival commemorating God's deliverance of His people from slavery (Exodus 12:11, 14)

34 God's miraculous provision to the children of Israel and Elijah (Exodus 16:4; 1 Kings 17:6)

36 "Heed the ____ of the LORD" (Exodus 15:26)

38 Daniel's enemies could find no ____ in him (Daniel 6:4)

39 God caused the ____ in judgment against the evil and violence on the earth (Genesis 6:17)

41 "They [the serpents] ____ the people" (Numbers 21:6)

42 God's instrument of deliverance (Exodus 13:9)

43 Two of every ____ thing were brought in the ark (Genesis 6:19)

44 He "found grace in the eyes of the LORD" (Genesis 6:8)

45 The Lord granted the people ____ in the sight of the Egyptians (Exodus 12:36)

46 "____ the end of the hundred and fifty days the waters decreased" (Genesis 8:3)

48 "The LORD will ____ for you" (Exodus 14:14)

51 This Hebrew prince was miraculously delivered, but his enemies perished (Daniel 6:23–24)

52 God was glorified in a pagan nation because of the three Hebrew children's ____ in Him (Daniel 3:28)

56 When those who were bitten would ____ at the serpent on the pole, they would be healed (Numbers 21:8)

57 "But what ____ we, that you complain against us?" (Exodus 16:7)

58 God ordained the ____ of Unleavened Bread to be observed throughout future generations (Exodus 12:17)

59 Time and again God miraculously delivered His people, the children of ____ (Exodus 3:10)

61 "We have ____, for we have spoken against the LORD and against you" (Numbers 21:7)

62 At Horeb, water came out of the rock after Moses ____ it (Exodus 17:6)

66 The furnace was exceedingly ____ (Daniel 3:22)

67 "Now the blood shall be a ____ for you" (Exodus 12:13)

68 The king ordered his army to ____ the three Hebrew children (Daniel 3:20)

69 "The flood was ____ the earth forty days" (Genesis 7:17)

70 Daniel continued to ____ as was his custom, despite the king's decree (Daniel 6:10)

73 He helped hold up Moses' hands at Rephidim (Exodus 17:12)

75 "Do what ____ right in His sight" (Exodus 15:26)

In Acts 2:5 we read about how "there were dwelling in Jerusalem Jews, devout men, from every nation under heaven." The chapter goes on to list fifteen nations or regions from which these men came. These men heard the gospel spoken in their own lanuages on the day of Pentecost. See how many of the fifteen nations or regions you can find in the letter grid below before looking them up in your Bible.

```
E  I  G  Y  H  P  M  S  A  E  G  Y  L  I  B  C  P
D  L  M  E  S  O  A  I  L  O  P  A  D  A  C  O  T
E  A  E  E  P  A  I  S  A  B  Y  A  E  P  N  N  P
C  A  D  J  T  P  M  B  L  E  M  A  J  T  B  O  A
A  R  O  U  A  E  A  Y  P  A  G  E  U  I  E  A  R
D  A  J  P  S  Y  T  A  T  Y  I  S  D  N  T  R  S
U  B  U  A  L  G  O  C  M  R  H  P  E  I  U  O  C
J  I  D  M  E  L  P  A  R  T  H  I  A  T  A  M  P
C  A  P  P  A  D  O  C  I  A  C  R  E  Y  E  E  A
L  I  M  H  I  L  S  O  Y  S  A  T  B  H  P  L  R
Y  A  A  Y  B  I  E  R  I  L  J  I  P  C  R  Y  A
H  P  S  L  L  E  M  E  A  C  L  Y  R  G  H  P
O  E  P  I  J  U  D  B  T  P  G  E  S  I  G  P  A
M  M  Y  A  I  G  Y  R  H  P  T  O  D  O  S  E  M
```

*J*esus did not play favorites, but He gave special designations to some of His disciples. John is referred to by an expression we'd all like to have applied to us: "The one whom Jesus loved."

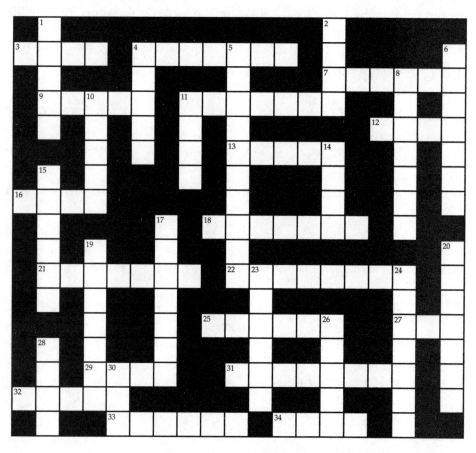

Across

3 Outside the Beautiful Gate, a man asked for these from Peter and John (Acts 3:3)

4 The man carrying this container of water showed Peter and John the Upper Room (Luke 22:10)

7 Sitting opposite this house of worship, His disciples asked questions about the end times (Mark 13:3–4)

9 John and two disciples extended this hand of fellowship to Paul and Barnabas (Galatians 2:9)

11 John was one of these "supporting structures" of the church (Galatians 2:9)

12 Jesus didn't want John and James to command this "flame" from heaven against #24 Down (Luke 9:54)

13 This former sorcerer wanted Peter and John to sell him some of God's power (Acts 8:18–19)

16 The man in #3 Across suffered from this condition

18 On Patmos, John heard a loud voice, sounding like this brass instrument (Revelation 1:10)

21 John's name is used on three of these (sing.)

22 The man in #4 Across was told that the "Instructor" (pl.) needed his guest room (Luke 22:11)

25 In #7 Across, John, Jesus, and three other disciples were siting on this mount (Mark 13:3)

27 John became a fisher of these (Luke 5:10)

29 "He who has the Son has ____," John wrote (1 John 5:12)

31 In #22 Across, they needed the Upper Room to observe this festival (Luke 22:8)

32 John also wrote, "He who ____ his brother is in darkness" (1 John 2:11)

33 On the cross, Jesus said to the disciple about Mary, His mother, "Behold your ____!" (John 19:27)

34 Peter and John told the Sanhedrin that they had to speak the things they had ____ and heard (Acts 4:20)

Down

1 James and John wanted to sit on either side of Jesus in His "majesty," in heaven (Mark 10:35–37)

2 John was mending one of these when he met Jesus (Matthew 4:21)

4 He was John's partner in missions after the Resurrection (Acts 3:1)

5 #13 Across wanted the ability to give this gift (2 words)—but only God can (Acts 8:18–19)

6 John's father (Matthew 4:21)

8 Peter and John were put into custody by these spiritual leaders, among others (Acts 4:1–3)

10 John, James, and Cephas perceived the "divine mercy" Paul had received, and approved (Galatians 2:9)

11 John, James, and Cephas wanted Paul and Barnabas to remember the "destitute" (Galatians 2:10)

14 Of one through ten, at which hour did Peter and John go to the temple? (Acts 3:1)

15 The man in #4 Across was the "lord" of his house (Luke 22:11)

17 The district where John came from (Matthew 4:18–21)

19 The "act of God" performed for the man in #3 Across put John and Peter in custody

20 Jesus called John and James the "Sons of ____" (Mark 3:17)

23 John and James referred to this prophet in #12 Across (Luke 9:54)

24 A village in this region rejected Jesus; John and James wanted to see it consumed (Luke 9:51–54)

26 Jesus said that not one "rock" would be left upon another in the end times (Mark 13:2)

28 John used this vessel in his former profession (Matthew 4:21)

30 Suffix meaning a doctrine or theory

*H*ow would *you* interpret these strange markings if they appeared on a wall while you were attending a king's banquet?

See Daniel 5:25 if you get stumped.

PRISON GUIDE

*T*hroughout the Scriptures we find angels performing some very special tasks for God. Sometimes they were tasks of a miraculous nature. Angels were sent to shut the lions' mouths against Daniel, to release Peter from prison, and to accompany the children of Israel as they crossed the Red Sea. At other times, angels appeared to change the direction a person was going. Balaam didn't see the angel his donkey saw that was sent to thwart Balaam's wicked purposes. Jacob wrestled all night with an angel and become lame from the struggle.

In most cases these beings probably didn't look anything like the traditional image of a winged figure with a halo. Indeed, we know that at least a few of them were mistaken for ordinary people until the extraordinary occurred. The angels that visited with Abraham dined and lodged with his family before they went to Sodom to warn Lot of the city's doom.

Begin at the right arm of the cross and end up back on the left arm of the cross on the angel's face.

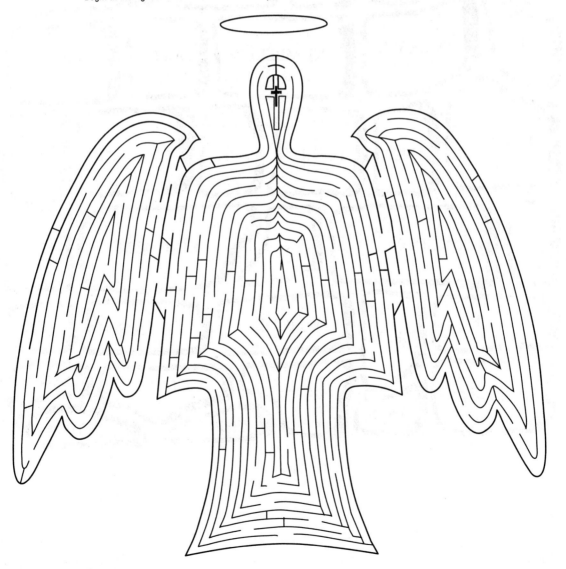

Connect the blocks below, which are based on a previous puzzle, to reveal the meaning of the message that appeared on King Belshazzar's wall during a feast in which he used the sacred vessels from the temple in Jerusalem. (See Daniel 5.)

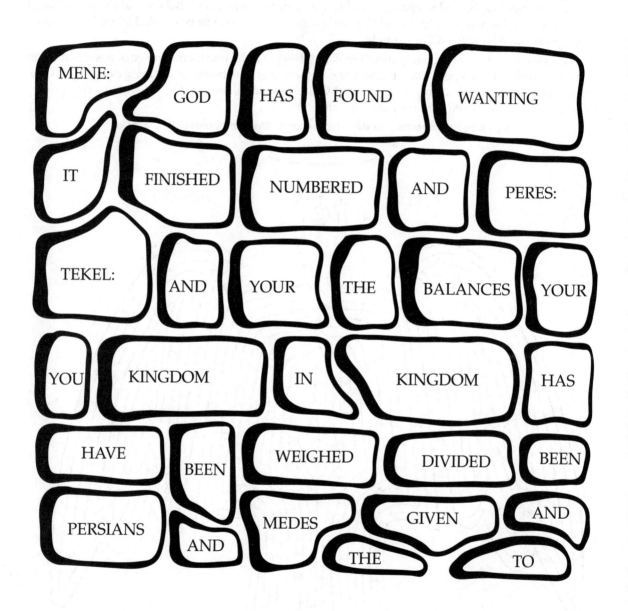

*E*arly Christians endured a lot more of this than modern-day Christians have.

Clue: MESSIAH *is* JTNNSFV

W Q T N N T G   F Y T   B V X N T

A V X   F Y T   O T Y N T U Z B T G

E X Y   Y S H V B T X Z N P T N N '

N F R T ' E X Y   B V T S Y N

S N   B V T   R S P H G X J

X E   V T F M T P .

THE SEVEN-POINTED STAR

*T*his star shape is also called the Mystic Star. It is an emblem that represents the sevenfold Spirit of God—seven being the biblical number for the perfection of God. In Revelation 3:1 we see the probable origin for this emblem: "These things says He who has the seven Spirits of God and the seven stars." Jesus Christ was frequently referred to by early Christians as the "Bright and Morning Star"—One who was fully aglow with the spirt of God. (See Revelation 22:16.)

When used as a church-related emblem, the star is red (flame color) to signify the penetrating, all-consuming power of God's spirit.

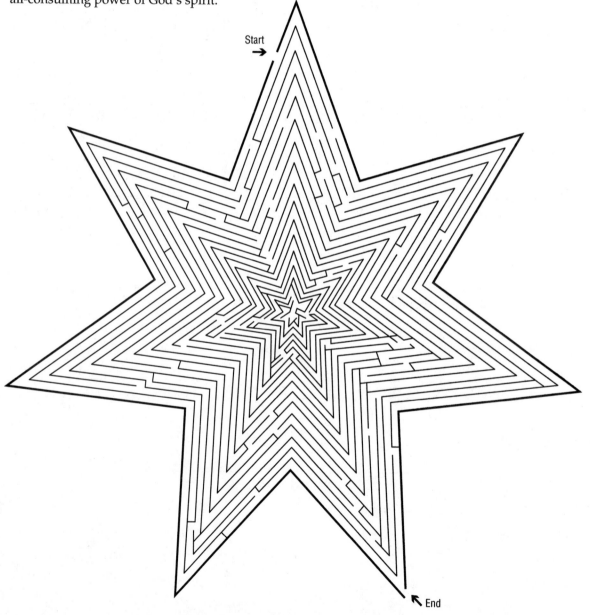

The story of Ruth in the Bible is a tragic story that has a happy ending. Some of the words in the crossword are from the book of Ruth.

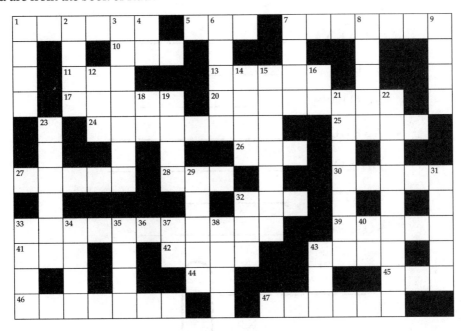

Across

1 Grain Ruth gathered (Ruth 2:17)
5 Before two
7 Boaz told the worker to allow her to work among these (Ruth 2:7)
10 Mesh or profit
11 Vietnamese holiday
13 Ruth's sister-in-law (Ruth 1:4)
17 Concubines and all
20 Union
24 Boaz to Naomi
25 "Ask not for whom the ____ #39 Across"
26 First lady
27 Love, a matter of the ____
28 Dined
30 Tree parts
32 Affirmative
33 Naomi to Ruth (3 words) (Ruth 1:14)
39 "Ask not for whom the #25 Across ____"
41 Mouths
42 Obtained by force
43 Ancient stringed instrument
44 Camper (abbr.)
45 Demure
46 Equilibrium
47 Sanctuary

Down

1 Ruth's beloved
2 Boaz's beloved
3 "____ me not to leave you" (Ruth 1:16)
4 King James "you"
6 Person Ruth would not leave (Ruth 1:22)
7 Luminary
8 Saying
9 "You are the ____ of the earth" (Matthew 5:13)
12 "He who has an ____, let him hear what the Spirit says" (Revelation 2:7)
14 Rant's partner
15 See ahead of time
16 Slang greeting
18 Spanish "the"
19 Name Naomi called herself because of her grief (Ruth 1:20)
21 Skill
22 Naomi's husband and Boaz's family name (Ruth 1:2; 2:1)
23 Shaking
29 Male voice
31 Impudent or cheeky
32 Asian ox
33 Country of Ruth's birth (Ruth 1:4)
34 Short's opposite
35 Equal
37 Third person, neuter
38 Ruth's motivation (Ruth 4:15)
40 Either's partner
43 Nickname for Louis

*U*nscramble the names of these seven key Bible figures and place them in the grid below to reveal a response they all had in common.

HRABAAM   __ __ __ __ __ __ __

SEUA   __ __ __ __

BCOJA   __ __ __ __ __

ASELUM   __ __ __ __ __ __

JEPSOH   __ __ __ __ __ __

SAAIIH   __ __ __ __ __ __

SOMSE   __ __ __ __ __

1.   __ __ __ __ __ __

2.   __ __ __ __ __

3.   __ __ __ __ __ __ __

4.   __ __ __ __ __ __

5.   __ __ __ __ __ __

6.   __ __ __ __ __

7.   __ __ __ __ __

*S*ome things are too HOT to handle!

Find eleven items in the letter grid below that the Bible describes as being HOT. (See how many you can find before consulting the Scripture Pool.)

```
O  N  A  N  G  E  P  O  A  L  S  T  D
R  F  O  P  O  V  E  N  S  I  D  O  I
I  U  T  H  S  I  D  P  O  A  O  N  S
A  R  I  O  E  T  A  S  L  R  U  P  P
E  E  R  U  S  A  E  L  P  S  I  D  L
H  B  S  T  N  S  R  N  H  T  C  I  C
E  E  R  G  G  T  B  T  O  R  O  R  O
V  A  E  E  N  R  O  R  T  E  A  P  A
O  R  S  M  A  E  I  S  L  A  O  C  H
A  E  C  A  N  R  U  F  C  M  L  S  E
R  G  L  P  S  I  D  A  O  S  V  O  A
B  E  R  T  S  N  R  U  F  R  T  S  P
```

Scripture Pool

EXODUS 16:21 DEUTERONOMY 9:19 DEUTERONOMY 19:6 JOSHUA 9:12 JOB 6:15–17
PSALM 39:3 PROVERBS 6:28 EZEKIEL 24:11 DANIEL 3:22
HOSEA 7:7 1 TIMOTHY 4:2

Most of the words in this crossword begin with the letter "S."

Across

1 Abram's wife (Genesis 12:5)

4 Jonah was cast into the heart of it (pl.) (Jonah 2:3)

7 The Lord told Moses, "_____ the laver between the tabernacle of meeting and the altar" (Exodus 40:7)

9 Isaiah said we all have gone astray like _____ (Isaiah 53:6)

10 God said, "Let there _____ light" (Genesis 1:3)

12 As priest of Israel, he anointed both Saul and David to be kings (1 Samuel 10:1; 16:13)

14 Isaac's mother (Genesis 21:1–3)

17 Neither, nor; either, _____

18 Jesus sent out His disciples with only a staff, one tunic, and their _____ (Mark 6:7–9)

21 A prophet was formerly called this (1 Samuel 9:9)

22 Deep sadness

23 Bashful

25 Chief of the evil spirits

26 Stigmata

29 Emergency signal, literally meaning "save our souls"

32 The king asked Nehemiah, "Why is your face _____?" (Nehemiah 2:2)

33 Israel offered these at Beersheba (Genesis 46:1)

35 Behold, in Old English

36 A Jewish chief priest in Ephesus, his seven sons were attacked by an evil spirit (Acts 19:13–16)

37 The psalmist prayed, "Uphold my steps in Your paths, that my footsteps may not _____" (Psalm 17:5)

39 We are always to test them to see if they are of God (1 John 4:1)

41 Day of rest

43 Jesus' final words on the cross were, "_____ is finished" (John 19:30)

45 Lot's wife became a pillar of this (Genesis 19:15, 26)

46 Paul taught that the wages for these is death (Romans 6:23)

47 Jesus asked, "How can one . . . plunder his goods, unless he first binds the ____ ____?" (2 words) (Matthew 12:29)

49 Jonathan loved David "as his own ____" (1 Samuel 18:1)

50 After ascension (abbr.)

52 Daniel was called by the king, "____ of the living God" (Daniel 6:20)

54 Esau was called this, which literally means "red" (Genesis 25:30)

55 Eli fell off one backwards and died when he heard that the ark of God had been captured (1 Samuel 4:11–18)

57 Open-palmed blow to the face

58 He killed more enemy Philistines at the time of his death than in his entire life (Judge 16:30)

60 Jesus referred to Himself mostly as "the ____ of man"

61 John heard the Lord's voice as "the ____ of many waters" (Revelation 1:15)

62 The shaft of Goliath's was like a weaver's beam (2 Samuel 21:19)

63 Judas's kiss was one (2 words) (Matthew 26:48)

Down

1 Cry

2 Isaiah prophesied a highway from Egypt to here (Isaiah 19:23)

3 Jesus taught, "No one, when he has lit a lamp, puts it in ____ ____ place" (2 words) (Luke 11:33)

4 Sign to the wise men that a new King had been born

5 Paul wrote that to Abraham, circumcision was a "____ of the righteousness" of his faith (Romans 4:11)

6 Moses sent twelve men into Canaan to do this (Numbers 13:17)

8 Name of altar built by Jacob: ____ Bethel (Genesis 35:7)

9 Earth

11 Organ of seeing

13 Señora

14 What a sower goes out to do (Matthew 13:3)

15 Residue of a fire

16 Straw

19 He had an army of 580,000 men of valor, yet cried to the Lord, "We rest on You" (2 Chronicles 14:8, 11)

20 Color of sins before they are made white as snow (Isaiah 1:18)

24 Jesus said He was sent, "____ God so loved the world" (John 3:16)

26 First king of Israel

27 Certificate of Deposit (abbr.)

28 Mourning garment

29 Jesus said they sit with the Pharisees in Moses' seat and "they say, and do not do" (Matthew 23:2–3)

30 Paul taught we are reconciled by Jesus to be "holy, and blameless, and above reproach in His ____" (Colossians 1:22)

31 It was sent into the wilderness once a year as part of the atonement (Leviticus 16:6–10)

33 Jesus sent His disciples to be witnesses to "Jerusalem, and in all Judea and ____, and to the end of the earth" (Acts 1:8)

34 Moses commanded them not to be mistreated (Exodus 22:21)

38 David asked Saul's soldiers, "____ there not a cause?" (1 Samuel 17:29)

40 The Levites cried, "____ up and bless the Lord" (Nehemiah 9:5)

42 Sweltering

44 The number of men hidden by Rahab (Joshua 2:4)

45 Temple builder known for his great wisdom

47 Joseph told his brothers, "God sent me before you . . . to ____ your lives by a great deliverance" (Genesis 45:7)

48 The Son of man gave His life as one (Mark 10:45)

49 Prerequisite for harvests; given to sower by the Lord (pl.) (Isaiah 55:10)

51 A woman with a flow of blood only wanted to touch this part of Jesus' garment (Matthew 9:20)

52 Paul said, "As the truth of Christ is in me, no one shall ____ me from this boasting" (2 Corinthians 11:10)

53 The Lord said the morning stars did this as He laid the cornerstone of the earth (Job 38:6–7)

55 The trees of the Lord are full of it (Psalm 104:16)

56 A donkey; Balaam's spoke to him (Numbers 22:30, KJV)

59 Direction of Syria from Israel

Now unscramble the circled letters in the grid to reveal one of the foremost symbolic figures in the Bible:

___ ___ ___ ___   ___ ___ ___ ___ ___ ___ ___

(2 words)

Escape from Pharaoh

*H*aving been raised in an Egyptian household as the adopted grandson of the Pharaoh, Moses nevertheless was very aware of his Israelite heritage and eventually became very resentful of the slavery of his people.

One day Moses observed an Israelite slave being beaten. Moses' anger overcame him and he killed the Egyptian oppressor. This sealed his fate with Pharaoh, who would have had Moses put to death if he could have been apprehended. But Moses fled for his life. He left Egypt, headed into the Midian desert, and became a sheepherder. Forty years later, Moses returned to Egypt at God's direction to free the Israelites from slavery.

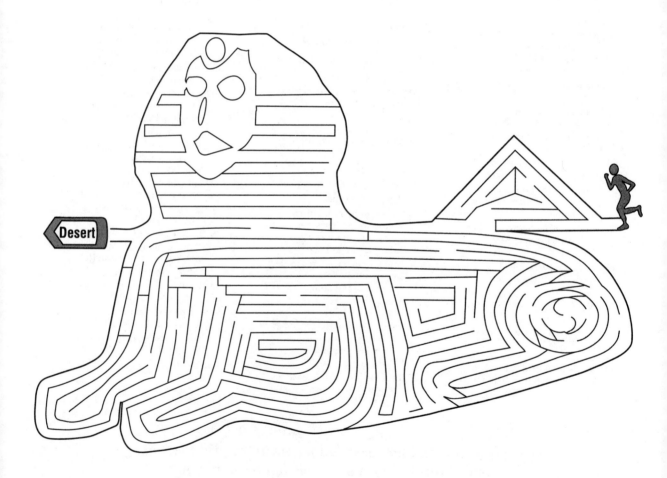

*H*ot on the heels of the previous puzzle. . .

Clue: MESSIAH *is* SSIAHME

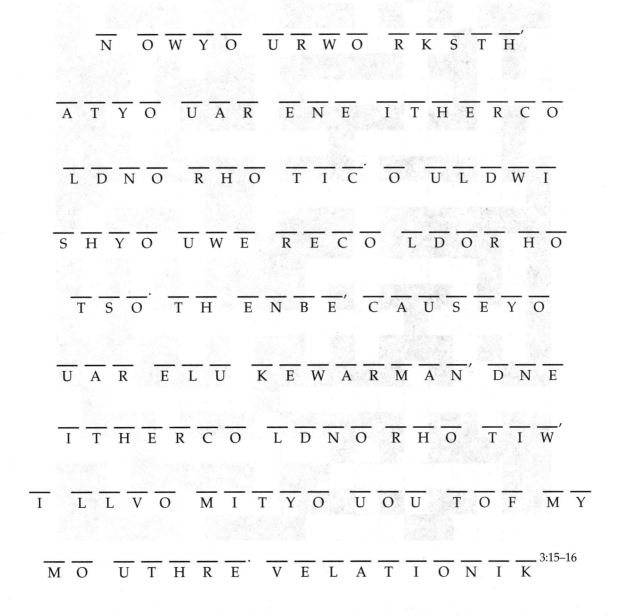

N O W Y O U R W O R K S T H '

A T Y O U A R E N E I T H E R C O

L D N O R H O T I C O U L D W I .

S H Y O U W E R E C O L D O R H O

T S O . T H E N B E ' C A U S E Y O

U A R E L U K E W A R M A N ' D N E

I T H E R C O L D N O R H O T I W '

I L L V O M I T Y O U O U T O F M Y

M O U T H R E V E L A T I O N I K . 3:15–16

The magnificent magnificat! Fill in as many of the words as you can from Mary's great praise song without consulting Luke 1:46–55.

And Mary said:

_____ _____ _____ the _____, and my _____ has rejoiced in _____
(36 down) (24 Across) (14 Across) (48 Across) (22 Across) (39 Down)

my _____. For _____ has regared the lowly _____ of _____ _____; _____
(11 Down) (34 Across) (25 Down) (34 Down) (37 Across) (45 Down)

behold, henceforth _____ _____ will _____ me _____. For He who is _____
(8 Across) (7 Down) (31 Across) (43 Across) (18 Across)

has done _____ _____ for _____, and _____ is His _____. And His _____
(7 Across) (3 Across) (36 Across) (4 Down) (28 Down) (26 Down)

is on those who _____ _____ _____ generation to generation. He has _____
(42 Down) (44 Across) (49 Across) (5 Down)

_____ with His _____; He has _____ the _____ in the _____ _____
(27 Across) (40 Down) (21 Down) (16 Down) (23 Across) (47 Down)

their _____. He has _____ _____ the mighty from their _____, and _____
(20 Across) (19 Across) (10 Across) (46 Across) (2 Down)

the _____. He has _____ the _____ with _____ things, and the _____ He
(6 Down) (29 Down) (38 Across) (9 Across) (33 Down)

has _____ away _____. He has _____ His _____ _____, in _____
(41 Down) (15 Across) (35 Down) (24 Down) (1 Across) (32 Across)

of His _____, as He _____ to _____ _____, to _____ and to _____
(26 Down) (12 Down) (17 Across) (29 Across) (13 Down) (44 Down)

_____ _____.
(30 Down) (45 Across)

Upper Room

*I*n remembering the Last Supper, we sometimes forget that the event was actually part of the Passover feast celebrated by all Jews. As recounted in Mark 14, Jesus' disciples were virtually blind to the real significance of the events of that week. The scribes were plotting to kill Jesus, but the fact that it was a holy week prevented them from carrying out their plans. A woman, having anointed Jesus' feet with expensive perfume, was severely criticized for the seeming waste of the costly oils. But Jesus described what she did as His anointing for burial.

Later the disciples inquired as to where Jesus might wish to celebrate the Passover feast. Jesus instructed them to go to a certain house where they were shown a large upper room, furnished and prepared for guests where they were to make ready the feast, which became the Last Supper.

End

Start ↗

*T*he reality of hell is the same for everyone. From the clues and scriptures below, find twenty words that are hidden in the letter box that tell us something about a place we want to avoid.

```
O  N  L  I  E  N  Y  O  I  S  C  O  R  P  I  O  N  S  H  O  T
H  I  N  Y  L  C  S  D  E  W  L  A  W  L  E  S  S  M  O  E  T
G  R  T  E  H  P  O  R  P  E  S  L  A  F  N  H  O  E  U  W  Y
N  O  H  I  I  L  O  R  M  E  N  G  A  E  O  D  D  U  N  O  R
I  P  R  S  A  J  I  O  X  P  D  O  R  L  F  O  E  N  B  P  A
K  E  W  T  N  E  M  H  S  I  N  U  P  B  O  R  K  O  E  Q  C
E  R  E  O  T  S  N  J  M  N  O  T  Q  A  H  I  C  R  L  P  S
E  R  N  O  P  O  N  O  T  G  R  E  E  N  O  P  I  H  I  A  C
S  C  C  O  I  R  P  O  N  L  K  R  O  I  Q  F  W  O  E  D  Z
F  N  O  I  T  C  U  R  T  S  E  D  O  M  F  Y  R  O  V  E  T
L  A  W  O  O  E  Z  S  W  C  U  A  O  O  B  O  I  B  I  A  E
E  G  A  O  O  R  I  G  N  A  S  R  E  B  L  O  E  P  N  T  W
S  O  R  R  Y  E  O  N  N  L  Q  K  O  A  P  A  O  S  G  H  O
E  I  D  T  S  R  A  I  L  O  A  N  O  P  S  Q  R  O  N  G  E
E  E  L  O  L  S  A  H  E  L  L  E  A  T  S  I  N  O  O  G  B
E  A  Y  I  D  O  L  S  O  P  R  S  W  I  T  C  H  E  M  O  P
R  E  V  I  L  P  R  A  T  O  E  S  R  E  R  E  D  R  U  M  T
B  E  T  E  O  Q  T  N  E  M  R  O  T  W  I  T  H  O  U  T  I
D  C  U  R  S  E  D  G  H  Y  P  O  C  R  I  T  E  S  W  O  E
```

What hell is like:
  Matthew 8:12; Revelation 19:20; Matthew 25:46; 2 Thessalonians 1:9
Who will be there:
  Psalm 9:17; Matthew 25:41; Romans 2:8; Revelation 19:20; Revelation 21:8
What will happen there:

*B*elow is the family tree of Abraham—his sons and grandsons by his wife, Sarah; his wife's servant Hagar; and his second wife Keturah.

Use these names to fill in the crossword grid on the next page.

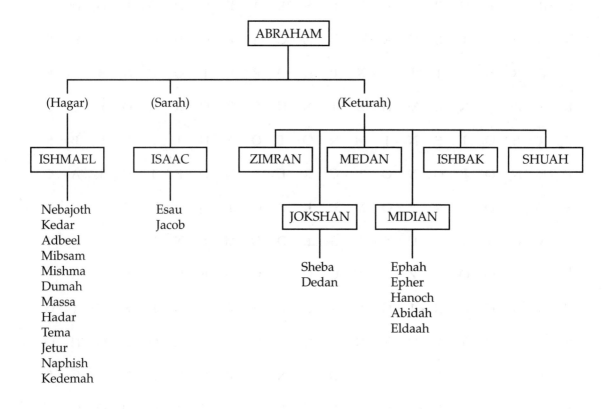

Across
1 Keturah's fifth son
3 Ishmael's tenth son
6 Ishmael's ninth son
7 Abraham's only son by Sarah
8 Keturah's third son
11 Ishmael's eleventh son
12 Midian's fourth son
14 Midian's second son
15 Jokshan's second son
16 Midian's first son
17 Ishmael's fourth son
21 Ishmael's twelfth son
22 Ishmael's fifth son
23 Ishmael's eight son

Down
2 Jokshan's first son
3 Keturah's second son
4 Isaac's firstborn twin
5 Isaac's secondborn twin
7 Abraham's only son by Hagar
8 Keturah's fourth son
9 Ishmael's first son
10 Keturah's first son
12 Ishmael's third son
13 Midian's third son
15 Ishmael's sixth son
16 Midian's fifth son
18 Keturah's sixth son
19 Ishmael's seventh son
20 Ishmael's second son

*T*he Church is not intended to be a destination point but a place a refuge, solace, training, and inspiration as we come and go from it as the Lord's witnesses in the world.

End

Start

SEVEN YEARS TO RACHEL

*T*he story of Jacob and Rachel, found in Genesis 29, is one of the great love stories of the Bible. After Jacob tricked his father, Isaac, into giving him the family blessing, Jacob fled from his angry brother, Esau, to take refuge with his uncle Laban. There, Jacob met and fell hopelessly in love with Laban's younger daughter, Rachel. Laban agreed to let Jacob marry Rachel in exchange for seven years of labor. So in love was Jacob that the years "seemed but a few days to him because of the love he had for her" (v. 20). But Laban tricked Jacob. Finding it necessary to marry off the elder daughter, Leah, before Rachel could marry, Laban allowed Jacob to wed Leah thinking she was Rachel. Eventually, Jacob was to marry his beloved Rachel, but not before Laban had extracted seven *more* years of labor for permission to marry her.

Jacob followed his heart through seven years of labor for Rachel. For Jacob to get to Rachel, go once through each of the seven grid boxes, but do not cross any lines without a heart.

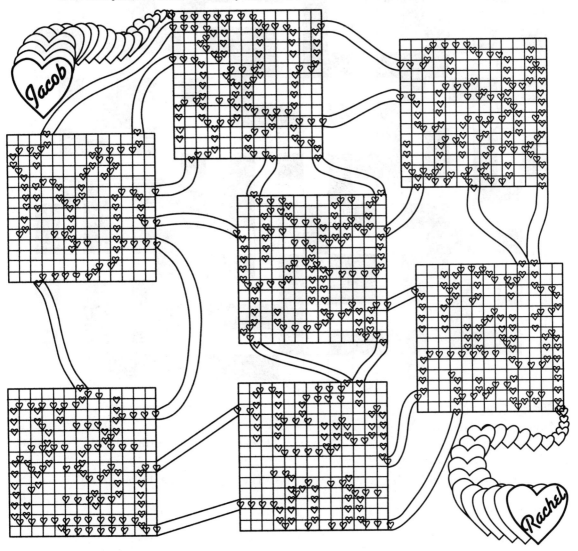

*L*ost . . . and found. In Luke 15 Jesus tells about three things that were lost and then found. Most of the answers for this crossword come from that chapter.

Across

1 Man's response who found his lost sheep (Luke 15:5)

5 "Your brother was dead and ____ alive again" (Luke 15:32)

7 The son who became angry (Luke 15:25)

11 Compensate

12 "I am no longer worthy to be____ your son" (Luke 15:19)

13 The ____ and nine (Luke 15:4, KJV)

16 Nourishment

17 The brother's complaint: "I ____ transgressed your commandment; . . . yet you ____ gave me a young goat" (Luke 15:29)

18 The younger son asked for his "allotment" of his inheritance (Luke 15:12)

20 Swine food (Luke 15:16)

24 Search (Luke 15:8, KJV)

25 See (past tense) (Luke 15:20)

26 Female spouse

27 Jesus said, "A certain man had two ____ " (Luke 15:11)

28 The shepherd, the woman, and the father each had something of value "disappear" (Luke 15:4, 8, 24)

30 Greater (Luke 15:7)

31 Opposite of alive (Luke 15:32)

33 At this moment (Luke 15:25)

36 The father expressed his affection to his son in this way (Luke 15:20)

38 Male parent (Luke 15:12)

41 Null and ____

42 "____ what woman" (Luke 15:8)

43 "Friends and ____ " (Luke 15:6, 9)

46 Sufficient (Luke 15:17)

48 The prodigal's confession: "I have sinned against heaven and in your ____ " (Luke 15:21)

50 "Distant" country (Luke 15:13)

51 The father ordered the servants to "bring out the best ____ " (Luke 15:22)

54 Yours and mine

56 "He began to be in ____ " (Luke 15:14)

57 Possessions (Luke 15:12)

59 Ceased living

61 When the son came home "they began to be ____ " (Luke 15:24)

63 "Safe and ____" (Luke 15:27)

64 Supreme being

65 Starvation (Luke 15:17)

66 "Rejoice with ____" (Luke 15:6, 9)

67 ____ merry; ____glad (Luke 15:24, 32)

68 A man who lost one of these searched until he found it (Luke 15:4)

69 "____ a lamp . . . and search carefully until she finds it" (Luke 15:8)

70 Discovers (Luke 15:4, 8)

71 The woman originally had ____ pieces of silver (Luke 15:8)

Down

1 To feel remorse and change your mind (Luke 15:7, 10)

2 Happiness (Luke 15:7)

3 Young cow (Luke 15:23)

4 "It was right that we should . . . be ____ " (Luke 15:32)

6 Brush clean (Luke 15:8)

7 "When he has found it, he lays it ____ his shoulders, rejoicing" (Luke 15:5)

8 The son's homecoming was celebrated with "music and ____ " (Luke 15:25)

9 Dashed (Luke 15:20)

10 The father's invitation to celebrate: "Let us ____ and be merry" (Luke 15:23)

12 The father's "mercy" (Luke 15:20)

14 "All #62 Down I have is____" (Luke 15:31)

15 The ____ famine meant there was not enough food (Luke 15:14)

19 Opposite of on (Luke 15:20)

21 To be in debt

22 Pigs (Luke 15:15)

23 Valuable items that the woman lost (Luke 15:8)

24 The prodigal son's was empty (Luke 15:16)

25 "____ he divided to them his livelihood" (Luke 15:12)

29 You (old English)

31 Wasted; consumed (Luke 15:30)

32 "I will ____ and go to my father" (Luke 15:18)

34 Having value (Luke 15:19)

35 " ____ came to himself"(Luke 15:17)

37 Rigid

39 The woman searched through her "dwelling" to find what was lost (Luke 15:8)

40 Jewelry to wear on a finger (Luke 15:22)

44 Prostitutes (Luke 15:30)

45 Traveled (Luke 15:13)

47 Playboy (Luke 15:13)

49 Where angels rejoice when sinners repent (Luke 15:7)

52 His father's servants had an adequate supply of this, but the son was without (Luke 15:17)

53 If she loses one coin, searches carefully "until she finds ____ ?" (Luke 5:8)

55 Object lesson (Luke 15:3)

58 One who sins (Luke 15:7)

60 Employed (Luke 15:17)

62 "All ____ I have is #14 Down" (Luke 15:31)

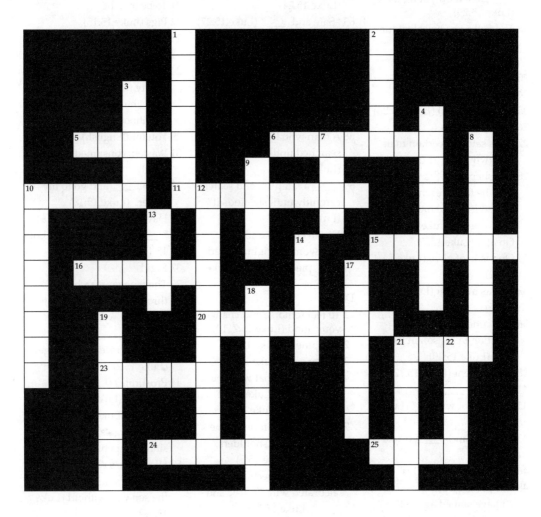

The people of the Bible appreciated oil because of its many practical and spiritual uses, but they had a love-hate relationship with vinegar. This puzzle illuminates some of the uses and abuses of these precious liquids.

Across

5 Job's steps were once bathed with this milky liquid, while the rock poured out rivers of oil (Job 29:6)

6 Taking away this piece of apparel is like vinegar on soda, says Proverb (Proverbs 25:20)

10 The psalmist was anointed with "new" oil (Psalm 92:10)

11 Taking the vow of one of these meant drinking no vinegar made from wine (Numbers 6:2–3)

15 In Exodus, the lamp burned with oil made from pressed ____ (Exodus 27:20)

16 They put sour wine on one of these and gave it to Jesus to drink (Matthew 27:48)

20 Luke says they mocked Jesus when they offered Him sour wine (Luke 23:36)

21 The woman poured costly oil on this part of Jesus' body (Mark 14:3)

23 These unleavened items (sing.) made of wheat flour were anointed with oil (Exodus 29:2)

24 He anointed the original tabernacle with oil (Leviticus 8:10)

25 These are with us always; His anointing was therefore proper (Mark 14:7)

Down

1 His servant lowered a debtor's bill to 50 measures of oil (2 words) (Luke 16:1–6)

2 #11 Across couldn't drink this fruit juice (Numbers 6:3)

3 Smoke to the eyes is like vinegar to these (Proverbs 10:26)

4 These altar "implements" were also anointed with oil (Leviticus 8:11)

7 She dipped her bread in vinegar at Boaz's table (Ruth 2:8, 14)

8 In John, Mary anointed Jesus' feet with this costly oil (John 12:3)

9 The "ill" should be anointed with oil (James 5:14)

10 The oil used in #21 Across was "pleasantly scented" (Mark 14:4)

12 David's "enemies" gave him vinegar to drink (Psalm 69:19, 21)

13 Two hundered and fifty shekels of this (sugar's "source") were used in the holy anointing oil (Exodus 30:23)

14 Timely rain meant the people could gather oil and "cereal" (Deuteronomy 11:14)

17 Some were foolish and some were wise as they took their lamps to meet the bridegroom (Matthew 25:1–4)

18 Jesus was anointed with this oil of "happiness" more than His companions (Hebrews 1:9)

19 The third item that could be gathered, from #14 Down (2 words) (Deuteronomy 11:14)

21 The type of plant used to convey sour wine to Jesus on the cross (John 19:29)

22 Moses sprinkled oil on this seven times to sanctify it (Leviticus 8:11)

*H*ope and healing for God's people.

Clue: MESSIAH *is* NFZZTVA

T R   N U   B F Q B E F   M A Q   V K F

G V E E F L   P U   N U   W V N F   M T E E

A C N P E F   J A F N Z F E I F Z'   V W L

B K V U   V W L   Z F F X   N U   R V G F'

V W L   J C K W   R K Q N   J A F T K

M T G X F L   M V U Z'   J A F W   T   M T E E

A F V K   R K Q N   A F V I F W'   V W L

M T E E   R Q K O T I F   J A F T K   Z T W

V W L   A F V E   J A F T K   E V W L.

THE THANKFUL ONE

It's hard to imagine forgetting to thank someone who literally hands you back your life. But this is exactly what happened to Jesus one day. Upon entering a certain village, ten men afflicted with leprosy cried out to Jesus for mercy. When these men realized they were healed, only one of them returned to thank Jesus and give glory to God.

Only one man's path will lead to Jesus in the corner. Begin at each man until you find the thankful one.

*S*ometimes doubts, worries, and cares overtake us. What's the solution? "Seek first the kingdom of God" (Matthew 6:33).

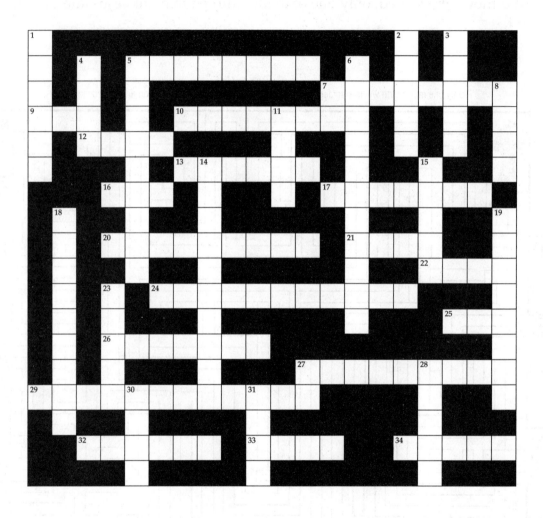

Across

5 They worry about food, drink, and clothing
(Matthew 6:31–32)
7 Don't have "fights" over doubtful things like
dietary laws (Romans 14:1)
9 She doubted God's word about the Tree of
Life (Genesis 3:4–6, 20)
10 They'll come in the last days and question
the Second Coming (2 Peter 3:3–4)
12 Can a risen _____ man persuade those who
doubted Moses and the prophets?
(Luke 16:31)
13 Cast your "problem" on the Lord
(Psalm 55:22)
16 With no doubt, you can wither a _____ tree
(Matthew 21:19–21)
17 "Be _____ for nothing" (Philippians 4:6)
20 "I want you to be without care," Paul said,
speaking of staying "single"
(1 Corinthians 7:32)
21 Let's _____ about Jesus
22 Don't worry; God is on our _____
24 Your heart can be "encumbered" by the cares
of this life (2 words) (Luke 21:34)
25 This king of Judah, perhaps doubting God's
support, allied with the king of Syria
(2 Chronicles 16:7)
26 Gideon still had doubts, even after squeezing
this much water from his fleece (Judges 6:38)
27 "Are You the 'Expected' ?" asked John's
disciples, displaying some doubt (2 words)
(Luke 7:20)
29 Does unbelief make the "loyalty" of God
ineffective? (Romans 3:3)
32 She was needlessly "worried and troubled
about many things," said Jesus (Luke 10:41)
33 Thomas, also known as the _____ , doubted
Jesus' resurrection (John 20:24–25)
34 Paul wanted men to pray without "ire" and
doubting (1 Timothy 2:8)

Down

1 His clan was the weakest in Manasseh—how
could he defeat the Midianites?
(Judges 6:11–17)
2 When this creature fastened itself onto Paul's
hand, the Maltese said, "No doubt this man
is a murderer" (Acts 28:3–4)
3 His doubt got him wet (Matthew 14:29–31)
4 The Israelites wouldn't "listen to" Moses;
they doubted a divine rescue (Exodus 6:9)
5 Paul had doubts about them; they seemed to
prefer the law (Galatians 3:1–2; 4:20–21)
6 Have compassion on some making a
"differentiation" (Jude 22)
7 Doctor (abbr.)
8 Doubting scribes and Pharisees needed a
"guidepost" from Jesus (Matthew 12:38)
11 Another word for worry (Psalm 37:7)
14 Worldly cares make us "unproductive"
(Matthew 13:22)
15 Jesus did fewer of these in His hometown
because of unbelief (Matthew 13:58)
18 He was made mute for doubting Gabriel's
word (Luke 1:18–20)
19 Doubt nothing, the Spirit told Peter. Go see
Cornelius in this city (Acts 10:1, 20)
23 Can worry add one _____ to your stature?
(Matthew 6:27)
27 First two initials of Narnia author
28 By believing, Martha would see the
"magnificence" of God (John 11:40)
30 Don't fret; it only causes "damage" (Psalm
37:8)
31 "But he who doubts is condemned if he
'feeds'" (Romans 14:23)

*P*roverbs 16:24 tells us, "Pleasant words are like a honeycomb, sweetness to the soul and health to the bones." See how quickly you can make your way through the honeycomb maze below!

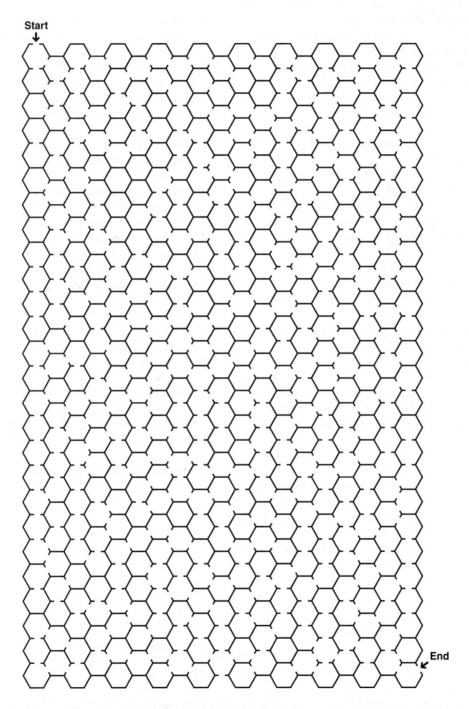

*P*rovide the names of the wives of the Bible men below to complete the acrostic, which gives us the name of the most cherished "wife" of all time and eternity.

1. Boaz and _____	(Ruth 4:13)
2. Jehoiada and _____	(2 Chronicles 22:11)
3. Heber and _____	(Judges 4:21)
4. Zacharias and _____	(Luke 1:5)
5. Er and _____	(Genesis 38:6)
6. Elimelech and _____	(Ruth 1:2)
7. Isaac and _____	(Genesis 24:67)
8. Abraham and _____	(Genesis 20:2)
9. Nabal and _____	(1 Samuel 25:3)
10. Lapidoth and _____	(Judges 4:4)
11. Moses and _____	(Exodus 2:21; 18:2)
12. Amram and _____	(Exodus 6:20)
13. Joseph and _____	(Genesis 41:45)

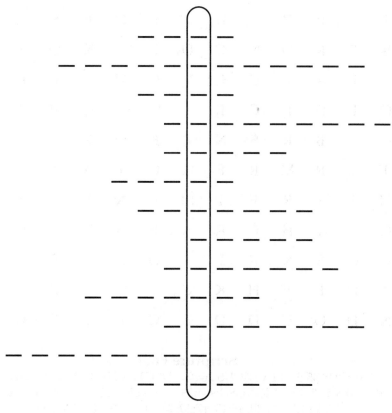

(Revelation 21:9)

*T*he Bible describes the human heart in many different ways. Find twenty of these "states of heart" in the box of letters below. (See how many you can find before you consult the Scripture Pool.)

```
S  E  A  B  R  O  A  E  D  E  C  E  I  T  F  U  L
L  O  H  C  W  F  R  O  S  N  C  D  O  U  P  R  U
V  W  E  S  O  S  F  D  I  W  U  O  N  N  L  F  F
E  I  A  E  R  N  U  E  L  P  R  O  U  D  I  U  R
M  L  V  R  R  S  F  C  L  C  E  W  S  E  W  S  A
E  L  B  U  O  D  E  U  K  S  I  Y  R  R  E  M  E
R  I  C  R  S  I  E  X  S  F  T  S  E  S  F  I  F
R  N  H  U  D  E  C  E  E  I  U  S  O  T  R  O  B
G  G  I  A  R  P  N  D  P  L  O  E  S  A  A  N  R
N  N  S  E  R  D  N  C  O  L  K  N  O  N  E  S  O
F  U  I  F  A  F  U  L  V  C  M  E  R  D  F  S  K
N  I  O  L  D  E  C  E  I  W  I  G  P  I  A  S  C
O  S  G  L  B  R  S  N  E  K  O  R  B  N  T  E  H
C  O  I  L  R  M  R  E  W  G  Y  A  I  G  S  N  I
U  W  N  I  Y  R  E  I  M  V  N  L  D  N  R  T  N
O  S  G  N  I  H  C  R  A  E  S  V  L  D  E  N  V
R  G  C  O  S  K  R  E  T  O  S  E  R  N  E  I  Y
R  W  I  U  E  P  H  K  C  I  W  S  E  U  R  A  L
O  S  N  D  O  U  D  D  E  C  E  I  S  U  F  F  L
```

Scripture Pool
EXODUS 35:5   LEVITICUS 26:36   DEUTERONOMY 28:28, 47, 65
JUDGES 5:15, 16   1 KINGS 3:9; 4:29   PSALMS 12:2; 34:18; 64:6; 101:5
PROVERBS 14:30; 15:13; 17:20; 25:20; 26:23   ISAIAH 35:4

Use the numbers under the letters to complete the passage below.

B L E S S E D   I S   T H E   M A N   W H O   W A L K S
1 2 3 4 5 6 7   8 9   10 11 12   13 14 15   16 17 18   19 20 21 22 23

N O T   I N   T H E   C O U N S E L   O F   T H E
24 25 26   27 28   29 30 31   32 33 34 35 36 37 38   39 40   41 42 43

U N G O D L Y,   N O R   S T A N D S   I N   T H E
44 45 46 47 48 49 50   51 52 53   54 55 56 57 58 59   60 61   62 63 64

P A T H   O F   S I N N E R S,   N O R   S I T S   I N
65 66 67 68   69 70   71 72 73 74 75 76 77   78 79 80   81 82 83 84   85 86

T H E   S E A T   O F   T H E   S C O R N F U L;
87 88 89   90 91 92 93   94 95   96 97 98   99 100 101 102 103 104 105 106

B U T   H I S   D E L I G H T   I S   I N   T H E   L A W
107 108 109   110 111 112   113 114 115 116 117 118 119   120 121   122 123   124 125 126   127 128 129

O F   T H E   L O R D,   A N D   I N   H I S   L A W
130 131   132 133 134   135 136 137 138   139 140 141   142 143   144 145 146   147 148 149

H E   M E D I T A T E S   D A Y   A N D   N I G H T.
150 151   152 153 154 155 156 157 158 159 160   161 162 163   164 165 166   167 168 169 170 171

___ ___   ___ ___ ___ ___ ___   ___ ___   ___ ___ ___ ___   ___
118 12   36 88 139 21 127   107 31   147 168 22 91   162

___ ___ ___ ___   ___ ___ ___ ___ ___ ___ ___   ___ ___   ___ ___ ___
83 102 151 6   65 2 56 74 156 114 161   1 50   124 11 134

___ ___   V ___ ___ ___   ___ ___   ___ ___ ___ ___ ___,   ___ ___ ___ ___
76 142   159 80 121   130 40   19 164 93 64 137   171 110 66 55

___ ___ ___ ___ ___ ___   ___ ___ ___ ___ ___   ___ ___ ___   ___ ___ ___ ___ ___
107 53 155 24 46 99   70 94 80 158 42   122 62 71   95 53 105 82 29

___ ___   ___ ___ ___   ___ ___ ___ ___ ___ ___,   ___ ___ ___ ___ ___
27 167   145 119 4   90 3 157 59 18 35   149 150 101 112 89

___ ___ ___ ___   ___ ___ ___ ___   ___ ___ ___ ___ ___   ___ ___ ___
106 37 92 104   128 38 9 25   5 133 20 127 49   15 69 26

___ ___ ___ ___ ___ ___;   ___ ___ ___   ___ ___ ___ ___ ___   V ___ ___
129 8 96 125 126 102   14 165 48   16 97 14 10 98   43 137

___ ___   ___ ___ ___ ___   ___ ___ ___ ___ ___   ___ ___ ___ ___ ___ ___ ___.
30 151   7 79 153 160   121 17 92 115 135   65 102 33 146 65 12 53

(Psalm 1:1–3)

*T*he noblest of women is described in Proverbs 31. The words that complete this passage are also the words you need for the crossword grid. See how far you can get before consulting your Bible.

Who can find a _____ wife? For her
_{18 Across}

_____ is far above _____. The _____
_{17 Across} _{16 Down} _{24 Across}

of her _____ safely _____ her; so
_{45 Down} _{15 Down}

_____ will have no lack of gain. She
_{19 Across}

does _____ _____ and not _____ all
_{45 Across} _{56 Down} _{5 Across}

the days of her life. She _____ _____
_{26 Down} _{44 Across}

and _____, and willingly works with
_{9 Down}

her hands. She is like the merchant

_____, she brings her _____ from
_{35 Across} _{48 Down}

_____. She also rises while it is _____
_{8 Across} _{58 Down}

_____, and _____ food for her house-
_{55 Across} _{11 Across}

hold, and a portion for her _____. She
_{27 Down}

considers a field and _____ it; from her
_{53 Across}

_____ she plants a _____. She _____
_{39 Down} _{29 Across} _{37 Across}

herself with strength, and _____ her
_{32 Down}

_____. She _____ that her _____ is
_{13 Across} _{1 Down} _{6 Down}

good, and her _____ does not _____
_{43 Down} _{37 Down}

_____ _____ night. She stretches out
_{62 Down} _{57 Across}

her hands to the _____, and her _____
_{46 Across} _{59 Across}

holds the _____. She extends her
_{30 Down}

_____ to the poor, _____, she reaches
_{21 Across} _{23 Down}

out her hands _____ the _____.
_{36 Down} _{2 Down}

She is not afraid of _____ for her
_{12 Down}

household, for all her household is

clothed with scarlet. She makes _____
_{36 Across}

for herself; her _____ is fine linen and
_{42 Across}

_____. Her husband _____ known
_{1 Across} _{63 Across}

_____ the_____, when he _____
_{7 Across} _{14 Across} _{4 Down}

_____ the elders of the land. She _____
_{47 Down} _{31 Across}

linen _____ and _____ them, and
_{22 Down} _{54 Down}

_____ _____ for the _____. Strength
_{50 Across} _{25 Across} _{20 Down}

and _____ are her clothing; she shall
_{52 Across}

rejoice in time _____ come. She _____
_{34 Across} _{49 Down}

her mouth with _____, and on her
_{28 Across}

_____ is the _____ of kindness. _____
_{10 Down} _{61 Across} _{33 Across}

watches over the ways of her house-

hold, and does not _____ the _____ of
_{51 Down} _{41 Across}

_____ness. _____ children rise _____
_{40 Down} _{59 Down} _{38 Across}

and call her blessed; her husband also,

and _____ praises her: "Many _____
_{65 Across} _{64 Across}

have _____ well, but you excel them
_{60 Down}

_____."
_{3 Down}

Loading the Boat

*N*oah was a "just man" who was righteous before God. For that reason, Noah and his family were saved from destruction when God decided to destroy all other life on dry land by a flood. God told Noah to build a large craft into which he was to gather his family and two of "every living thing of all flesh" so that the earth might be replenished when the flood waters receded (Genesis 6:19).

It is interesting to speculate whether or not this gathering of animals included fish and other sea creatures since they could have survived the flood on their own.

Help Noah with the complicated task of gathering *all* the animals into the ark. Do not cross over any of your paths.

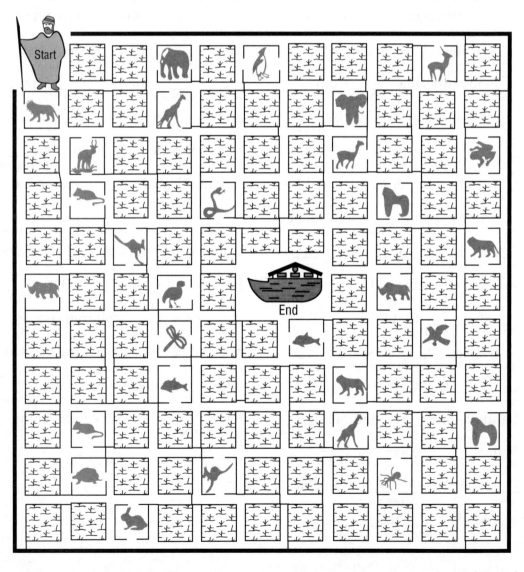

Solve the cryptogram below to reveal five specific commands that the apostle Paul gave to the Corinthians.

Clue: MESSIAH *is* 15 2 20 20 3 1 11

—— — —— — —— ,   —— —— — —— —   — — —— ——   — ——
23   1   21   7 11   20 21   1 16   8   9   1   20 21   3   16

—— —— —   —— — — —— —— ,   — —   — —— — —— — ,
21 11   2   9   1 3 21 11   6   2   6   19 1 22 2

— —   —— —— —— — —— —— .   —— — ——   — —— ——
 6   2   20 21 19   4 16 10   14 2 21   1 14 14

—— —— — ——   —— — —   — —   — —   — — —— —
21 11   1 21   25 4 5   8   4   6   2   8   4 16   2

—— — —— ——   —— — —— — .
23   3 21 11   14 4 22   2

THE GOOD SHEPHERD

*T*he symbolism of the Good Shepherd is found in both the Old and New Testaments. In Psalm 23, David asserts, "The LORD is my shepherd" (v.1). Jesus, too, used the example of the shepherd. In a parable, He told of the shepherd with one hundred sheep and he posed a question: If the shepherd loses one sheep, will he not leave the other ninety-nine to go and search for the lost one? Jesus' care for us, His sheep, is so profound, that He is in constant search of the lost sheep among us.

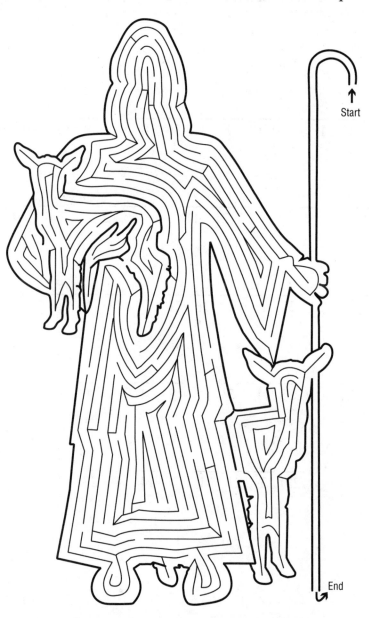

One of the most frequently repeated commands in the Bible is that to "Rejoice!" Complete these verses about rejoicing to discover a special theme they share in common.

1 "Let the _____ of those rejoice who seek the LORD" (1 Chronicles 16:10)

2 "You shall rejoice in your _____" (Deuteronomy 16:14)

3 "God had made them rejoice with great _____ " (Nehemiah 12:43)

4 "Break forth in _____ , rejoice, and sing praises" (Psalm 98:4)

5 "You shall rejoice in every _____ _____ which the LORD your God has given to you and your house" (2 words) (Deuteronomy 26:11)

6 "Then shall the virgin rejoice in the _____ " (Jeremiah 31:13)

7 "Let the _____ rejoice, and all that is in it" (1 Chronicles 16:32)

8 "You shall rejoice in all to which you have put your _____ " (Deuteronomy 12:7)

9 "Rejoice, O _____ , with His people; for He will avenge the blood of His servants, and render vengeance to His adversaries; He will provide atonement for His land and His people" (Deuteronomy 32:43)

10 "Let the _____ rejoice, and let the earth be glad" (Psalm 96:11)

11 "In Your _____ they rejoice all day long" (Psalm 89:16)

12 "My _____ shall greatly rejoice when I sing to You" (Psalm 71:23)

13 "Let Your saints rejoice in _____ " (2 Chronicles 6:41)

14 "The _____ shall rejoice and blossom as the rose" (Isaiah 35:1)

15 "I rejoice at Your _____ as one who finds great treasure" (Psalm 119:162)

16 "I will rejoice in Your _____ " (Psalm 9:14)

17 "But let the righteous be glad; let them rejoice before God; yes, let them rejoice _____ " (Psalm 68:3)

18 "In the shadow of Your _____ I will rejoice" (Psalm 63:7)

19 "The righteous shall rejoice when he sees the _____ [of the Lord]" (Psalm 58:10)

20 "Rejoice, O young man, in your _____ " (Ecclesiastes 11:9)

21 "Let all those rejoice who put their _____ in You" (Psalm 5:11)

1
2
3
4
5
6
7

AGAIN | I | WILL SAY, REJOICE!

8
9
10
11
12
13
14
15
16
17
18
19
20
21

The names of plants, birds, and animals in the Song of Solomon are the words you'll need to complete this crossword!

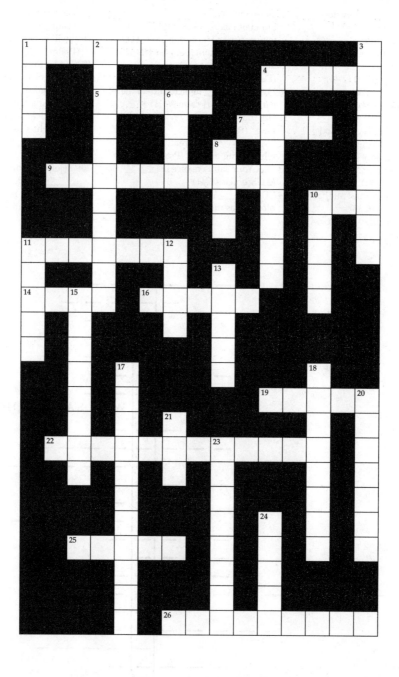

Across

1 Come with me from Lebanon . . . rom the mountains of the _____ (4:8)

4 Your teeth are like a flock of shorn _____ which have come up from the washing (4:2)

5 A bundle of _____ is my beloved to me (1:13)

7 Come with me from Lebanon . . . from the _____s' dens (4:8)

9 The time of singing has come, and the voice of the _____ is heard in our land (2:12)

10 The beams of our houses are cedar, and our rafters of _____ (1:17)

11 _____ and cinnamon (4:14)

14 My _____, my perfect one (5:2)

16 His locks are wavy, and black as a _____ (5:11)

19 Follow in the footsteps of the flock, and feed your little _____ beside the shepherds' tents (1:8)

22 With all the trees of _____, myrrh and aloes (4:14)

25 With all the trees of frankincense, myrrh and _____ (4:14)

26 They made me the keeper of the _____, but my own . . . I have not kept (1:6)

Down

1 Like a _____ among thorns, so is my love among the daughters (2:2)

2 Your temples behind your veil are like a piece of _____ (4:3)

3 Like an _____ among the trees of the woods, so is my beloved among the sons (2 words) (2:3)

4 _____ and saffron (4:14)

6 I am the _____ of Sharon (2:1)

8 I charge you, O daughters of Jerusalem, by the gazelles or by the _____ of the field (2:7)

10 Catch us the _____ . . . that spoil the vines (2:15)

11 The beams of our houses are _____, and our rafters of fir (1:17)

12 My beloved is like a gazelle or a young _____ (2:9)

13 His cheeks are like a bed of spices, banks of scented _____ (5:13)

15 They made me the keeper of the vineyards, but my own _____ I have not kept (1:6)

17 My beloved is to me a cluster of _____ _____ in the vineyards of En Gedi (2 words) (1:14)

18 I charge you, O daughters of Jerusalem, by the _____ or by the does of the field, do not stir up nor awaken love until it pleases (2:7)

20 Spikenard and _____ (4:14)

21 The _____ tree puts forth her green figs (2:13)

23 Calamus and _____ (4:14)

24 I have compared you, my love, to my _____ among Pharaoh's chariots (1:9)

*I*n Job 38–39, the Lord spoke to Job out of a whirlwind and asked him a number of questions. Transfer the words that complete the questions below to the acrostic grid, and discover what was revealed to Job through these questions.

1 "Have you given the horse _____ ?" (39:19)

2 "Have you seen the treasury of _____ ?" (38:22)

3 "Who has divided a . . . path for the _____ ?" (38:25)

4 "Do you know the _____ when the wild mountain goats bear young?" (39:1)

5 "Where were you when I laid the _____ of the earth?" (38:4)

6 "Who laid its [the earth's] cornerstone, when . . . all the sons of God shouted for _____ ?" (38:6–7)

7 "Who shut in the _____ with doors ...when I said, 'This far you may come, but no farther, and here your proud waves must stop!'" (38:8, 11)

8 "Who laid its [the earth's] cornerstone, when the _____ _____ sang together?" (2 words) (38:6–7)

9 "Have you seen the doors of the shadow of _____ ?" (38:17)

10 "And darkness, where is its place, that you may take it to its _____ ?" (38:19–20)

11 "Have you entered the treasury of _____ ?" (38:22)

12 "Who provides _____ for the raven?" (38:41)

13 "Who has divided a channel for the overflowing _____ ?" (38:25)

14 "Have you comprehended the _____ of the earth?" (38:18)

15 "From whose womb comes the _____ ?" (38:29)

16 "Have you . . . caused the _____ to know its place?" (38:12)

17 "Can you bind the cluster of the Pleiades, or _____ the belt of Orion?" (38:31)

18 "Who has put _____ in the mind?" (38:36)

19 "By what way is ... the east _____ scattered over the earth?" (38:24)

20 "By what way is _____ diffused?" (38:24)

21 "Can you send out _____ , that they may go, and say to you, 'Here we are!'?" (38:35)

22 "Who has given _____ to the heart?" (38:36)

23 "Where is the _____ to the dwelling or light?" (38:19)

24 "Have you entered the _____ of the sea?" (38:16)

25 "And the _____ of heaven, who gives it birth?" (38:29)

26 "Who has begotten the drops of _____ ?" (38:28)

1 — — — — — —
2 — — — —
3 — — — — — — — — —
4 — —
5 — — — — — —
6 — — —
7 — —
8 — — — — — — — —
9 — — —
10 — — — — —
11 — — —
12 — — — —
13 — — —
14 — — — —
15 — —
16 — — —
17 — — —
18 — — — — —
19 — — —
20 — —
21 — — — — — — —
22 — — — — — — —
23 — —
24 — — —
25 — — —
26

AN EXTRAVAGANT OFFERING

*A*fter encountering the Lord on Mount Sinai, Moses gathered all the children of Israel together and said, "These are the words which the LORD has commanded you to do" (Exodus 35:1). Moses went on to tell the people the Lord's plan for building a tabernacle, the ark of the covenant, and all the utensils and furnishings for the tabernacle.

The Scriptures tell us, "Then everyone came whose heart was stirred, and everyone whose spirit was willing, and they brought the LORD's offering for the work for the tabernacle of meeting, for all its service, and for the holy garments. They came, both men and women, as many as had a willing heart" (Exodus 35:21–22).

The people brought jewelry, yarn, fabrics, skins, and wood in such abundance that Moses eventually had to issue a proclamation, "Let neither man nor woman do any more work for the offering of the sanctuary" (Exodus 36:6–7). The people were restrained from bringing, for the material they had was sufficient for all the work to be done—indeed too much.

Start ↓

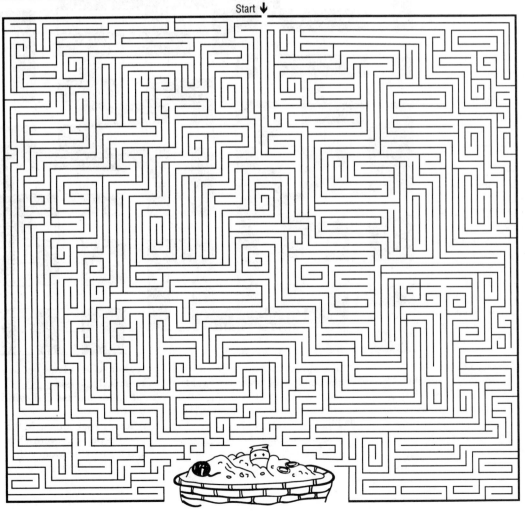

*O*h say, can you find the Bible *O* words to complete this crossword?

Across

5 One of Naomi's daughters-in-law; she stayed behind when Naomi and Ruth returned to Judah (Ruth 1:4, 8–9, 14)

6 Caleb's nephew, he is described as a "deliverer for the children of Israel," raised up by the Lord (Judges 3:9–11)

9 "_____ and perfume delight the heart" (Proverbs 27:9)

11 Paul asked the Ephesians to pray "that I may _____ my mouth boldly to make known the mystery of the gospel" (Ephesians 6:19)

13 Either, _____

15 Ancient measurement, "one-tenth of an ephah" (Exodus 16:36)

16 The thirty-first book of the Bible

18 In John's Revelation, Jesus calls Himself the "Root and the _____ of David, the Bright and Morning Star" (Revelation 22:16)

19 Paul rejoiced to see the "good _____ and the steadfastness" of faith shown by the Colossians (Colossians 2:5)

20 The first believers are described as being "of _____ heart and _____ soul" (Acts 4:32)

22 The king of Bashan defeated by the children of Israel; he was a giant with an iron bed nine cubits long (Deuteronomy 3:11)

23 Elder, opposite of younger; Joseph was Benjamin's _____ brother (Genesis 35:24)

24 A gift to God; a lamb or kid was used as a "sin _____ " by the children of Israel (Leviticus 5:5–6)

26 After the Last Supper, Matthew says the disciples sang a hymn and went to the Mount of _____ (Matthew 26:30)

27 "_____, that the salvation of Israel would come out of Zion" (Psalm 14:7)

28 One of Judah's sons who died in the land of Canaan (Genesis 46:12)

29 Jesus was displeased to find moneychangers selling "_____ and sheep and doves" in the temple (John 2:14–15)

31 The Lord saw that the thoughts of men's hearts—except for Noah's—were "_____ evil continually" (Genesis 6:5, 8)

32 Evil king of Israel, he bought the hill of Shemer and built a city called Samaria; Ahab was his son (1 Kings 16:16–28)

33 "The wings of the _____ wave proudly, but . . . God deprived her of wisdom" (Job 39:13, 17)

34 Opposite of off; also the name of one of Reuben's grandsons (Numbers 16:1)

35 As they walked in the wilderness, the children of Israel craved "the cucumbers, the melons, the leeks, the _____, and the garlic" of Egypt (Numbers 11:5)

37 Paul called the Gentiles "a wild _____ tree" grafted in among the Jews (Romans 11:17)

39 Paul wrote that Titus's "affections are greater for you as he remembers the _____ of you all" (2 Corinthians 7:15)

42 The Lord promised to heal the wounds of His people "because they called you an _____" (Jeremiah 30:17)

44 Jeremiah commanded the people not to "_____ the stranger, the fatherless, and the widow" (Jeremiah 7:6)

45 "God created man in His _____ image" (Genesis 1:27)

46 The Lord said to the church of Ephesus, "To him who _____ I will give to eat from the tree of life" (Revelation 2:7)

Down

1 A region known for its gold (Job 22:24)

2 Philemon's runaway servant (Philemon 10–11)

3 The psalmist said, "I have been young, and now am _____; yet I have not seen the righteous forsaken" (Psalm 37:25)

4 Jesus told His disciples to make disciples of all nations, "teaching them to _____ all things that I have commanded you" (Matthew 28:20)

6 The centurion believed the "_____ of the ship" more than Paul, and the ship sank as Paul had prophesied (Acts 27:9–44)

7 Fragrance, aroma from sacrifices

8 Alpha and _____, the Beginning and the End (Revelation 22:13)

10 "All who handle the _____, the mariners . . . will make their voice heard because of you" (Ezekiel 27:29–30)

12 A town of the tribe of Benjamin (Nehemiah 11:31–35)

13 The psalmist said, "You shall make them [enemies] as a fiery _____ in the time of Your anger" (Psalm 21:9)

14 A prophet of the Lord who cried out against the people of Judah's being taken captive (2 Chronicles 28:9–11)

17 Opposite of on

19 Jesus said it would be better for a person to have a millstone hung around his neck and be thrown into the sea than to "_____ one of these little ones" (Luke 17:2)

20 "Fatherless" children; "We have become _____ and waifs, our mothers are like widows" (Lamentations 5:3)

21 Type of stones engraved with the names of the twelve tribes of Israel and placed on the shoulders of the priest's holy garment (Exodus 39:6–7)

22 The prophet Samuel "took a flask of _____" and poured it over Saul's head to anoint him (1 Samuel 10:1)

23 Son of Naomi and Boaz, he was King David's grandfather (Ruth 4:13, 17)

25 Samuel said, "To _____ is better than sacrifice, and to heed than the fat of rams" (1 Samuel 15:22)

26 Paul said this man often refreshed him and was not ashamed of his prisoner's chains (2 Timothy 1:16)

29 The Lord "made the Pleiades and _____" according to the prophet Amos (Amos 5:8)

30 Ahithophel's evil advice to Absalom was regarded "as if one had inquired at the _____ of God"—but he hadn't! (2 Samuel 16:23)

32 All powerful; nature of God

35 Elijah asked the people, "How long will you falter between two _____?" (1 Kings 18:21)

36 "I made myself gardens and _____, and I planted all kinds of fruit trees in them" said the preacher in Ecclesiastes 2:5

38 "For men indeed swear by the greater, and an _____ for confirmation is for them an end of all dispute" (Hebrews 6:16)

40 The craftsman "takes the cypress and the _____; he secures it for himself among the trees of the forest" (Isaiah 44:14)

41 Place of refreshment and water in a desert

43 Sixth son of Jesse (1 Chronicles 2:15)

VISIT TO ELIZABETH

*W*hen the angel Gabriel came to Mary and announced to her, "You will conceive in your womb and bring forth a Son, and shall call His name Jesus," the angel also told Mary, "Elizabeth your relative has also conceived a son in her old age; and this is now the sixth month for her who was called barren. For with God nothing will be impossible" (Luke 1:31, 36–37).

After the angel departed, Mary went immediately to the hill country of Judah to the home of Zacharias and Elizabeth. When Elizabeth heard the greeting of Mary, the babe in her womb leaped and Elizabeth was filled with the Holy Spirit. She cried out to Mary, "Blessed are you among women, and blessed is the fruit of your womb! But why is this granted to me, that the mother of my Lord should come to me?" (Luke 1:42–43)

Both women received confirmation from the other about the miracle babies they were carrying.

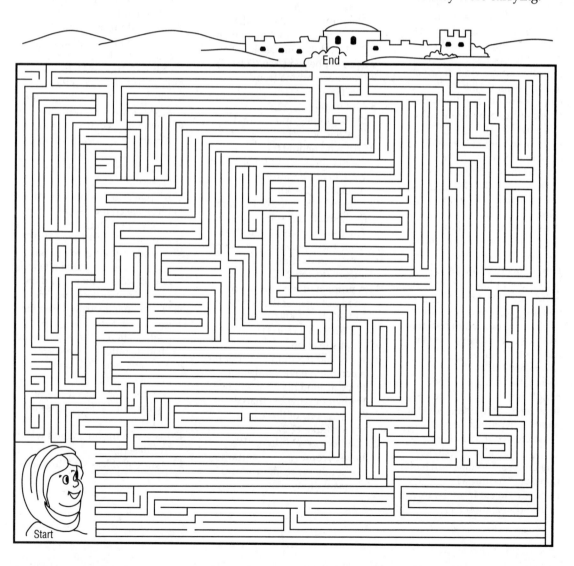

*J*esus is associated with various "numbers" of things, people, days, years, and "times" in His ministry. Complete the equation below to get to a major truth stated by the Lord. (Work down the first column; then continue to the second.)

The number of people Jesus fed
with five loaves and two fishes
(Luke 9:13–16)   = ____

Minus . . .
Number of people Jesus fed from
seven loaves (Mark 8:1–9)   − ____

Divided by . . .
Number of virgins who were
"wise" in parable (Matthew 25:2)   ÷ ____

Multiplied by . . .
Number of times Jesus said Peter
would deny Him (Matthew 26:75)   × ____

Minus . . .
Number of times Jesus said we are
to forgive (Matthew 18:22)
(____ × ____ =)   − ____

Minus . . .
Number of appointed ones sent
out by Jesus to Judean cities; they
returned saying "even the demons
are subject to us in Your name"
(Luke 10:17)   − ____

Multiplied by . . .
Number of apostles still alive at
the time of Jesus' resurrection
(Mark 16:14)   × ____

Minus . . .
Number of days Jesus fasted in the
wilderness (Matthew 4:2)   − ____

Divided by . . .
Number of sheep the shepherd
had before losing one (in parable)
(Luke 15:4)   ÷ ____

Multiplied by . . .
Number of lepers healed by Jesus
(Luke 17:12)   × ____

Minus . . .
Number of healed lepers who
returned to give thanks
(Luke 17:15)   − ____

Plus . . .
Number of years the man at the
Pool of Bethesda had been ill
when Jesus healed him (John 5:5)   + ____

Plus . . .
Number of disciples Jesus took
with Him to raise the daughter of
Jairus (Luke 8:51)   + ____

Minus . . .
Number of years a woman had a
flow of blood before being healed
by Jesus (Luke 8:43)   − ____

Minus . . .
Minimum return of good seed
planted in good soil: ____ fold
(Matthew 13:23)   − ____

Minus . . .
Number of years woman had been
bent over with an infirmity before
being healed by Jesus (Luke 13:11)   − ____

Minus . . .
Day of circumcision of newborn
son after birth (Luke 2:21)   − ____

Divided by . . .
Age of Jesus at the time He stayed
behind in Jerusalem to be about
His Father's business
(Luke 2:42–49)   ÷ ____

Equals . . .
The nature of Jesus and His Father
(John 10:30)   = ____

189

Fill in the blanks of Psalm 98 to complete this crossword!

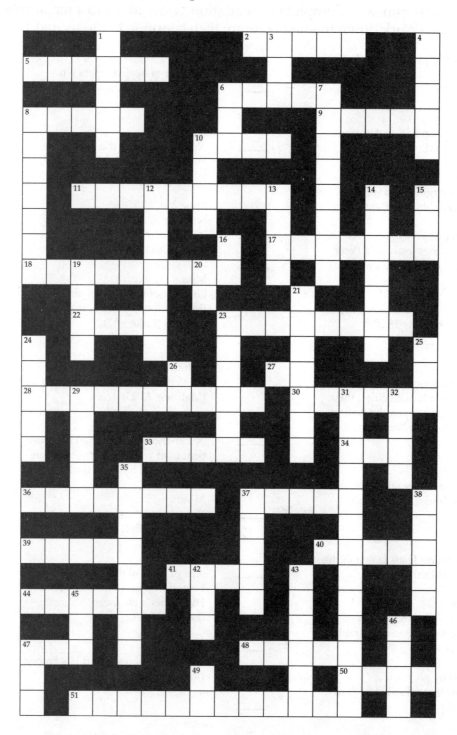

_____ , _____ _____ the LORD a
20 Down 50 Across 27 Across

new _____ ! For He has done _____
13 Down   11 Across

things; His _____ hand and _____
9 Across   15 Down

_____ arm have _____ _____
10 Down   44 Across 47 Down

the _____ . The _____ _____
12 Down   19 Down   47 Across

made known His _____ ; His
18 Across

_____ He has _____ in the _____
31 Down   23 Across   37 Across

of the _____ . He has _____ His
17 Across   28 Across

_____ and His _____ to the
29 Down   51 Across

_____ of _____ ; all the _____ of
33 Across 30 Across   32 Down

the _____ have seen the salvation of
4 Down

_____ _____ . _____ _____ to
42 Down 34 Across   6 Across 36 Across

the LORD, _____ the earth; break
25 Down

_____ in song, _____ , and sing
24 Down   21 Down

_____ . Sing to the LORD with the
8 Down

_____ , with the harp and the _____
10 Across   37 Down

of a _____ , with _____ and the
8 Across   7 Down

sound _____ a _____ ; shout
49 Down   41 Across

joyfully before the LORD, the _____ .
46 Down

Let the _____ _____ , and all
6 Down 22 Across

_____ _____ , the world and
45 Down 35 Down

_____ _____ _____ _____ it;
48 Across 3 Down 2 Across 16 Down

let the _____ clap their hands; let the
23 Down

_____ _____ joyful together
1 Down 26 Down

_____ the LORD, for He is coming to
43 Down

_____ the earth. With righteousness
38 Down

He _____ judge the _____ , and the
39 Across   40 Across

_____ with _____ .
14 Down   5 Across

Word Pool

ALL BE BEFORE DWELL EARTH ENDS EQUITY FAITHFULNESS FORTH FULLNESS
GAINED GOD HARP HAS HILLS HIM HIS HOLY HORN HOUSE IN ISRAEL
ITS JOYFULLY JUDGE KING LORD MARVELOUS MERCY NATIONS OF OH OUR
PEOPLES PRAISES PSALM REJOICE REMEMBERED REVEALED RIGHT
RIGHTEOUSNESS RIVERS ROAR SALVATION SEA SHALL SHOUT SIGHT SING SONG
SOUND THOSE TO TRUMPETS VICTORY WHO WORLD

*A*ccording to early church history, believers in Rome during the first century often met in the City's catacombs—a series of underground burial chambers and sarcophagi. How long will it take you to find your way to the meeting of Christians through this catacomb maze?

Start

The
Meeting

*S*ee if you can work out these words of Jesus before it's time to eat.

Clue: MESSIAH *is* PSHHQDN

P Z   C B B T   Q H   L B

T B   L N S   G Q E E   B C

N Q P   G N B   H S J L   P S '

D J T   L B   C Q J Q H N

N Q H   G B K I .

In the final days before His death and resurrection, Jesus instituted the Lord's Supper as a sign of the new covenant. Fill in the blanks below and the circled letters will tell you how we are to take the Lord's Supper.

1 "This is My _____ which is broken for you" (1 Corinthians 11:24)

2 This bread symbolized the continual presence of God (Exodus 25:30)

3 "Take, _____ "(Matthew 26:26)

4 The One who gives the true bread (John 6:32)

5 "He who eats My flesh and drinks My blood _____ in Me, and I in him" (John 6:56)

6 "My _____ is food indeed" (John 6:55)

7 "He took the cup . . . saying, '_____ from it'" (Matthew 26:27)

8 "I am the _____ bread" (John 6:51)

9 "Whoever eats My flesh and drinks My blood has _____ _____ " (2 words) (John 6:54)

10 Where the disciples ate the Last Supper (2 words) (Luke 22:12)

11 "Let a man _____ himself, and so let him eat of the bread and drink of the cup" (1 Corinthians 11:28)

12 "This is My blood of the _____ _____ " (2 words) (Matthew 26:28)

13 The bread we break is the _____ of the body of Christ (1 Corinthians 10:16)

14 "My _____ is drink indeed" (John 6:55)

15 "He who eats this bread will live _____ " (John 6:58)

16 This bread is eaten at Passover (Exodus 12:8)

17 "He who comes to Me shall never _____ " (John 6:35)

18 "For as often as you eat this bread and drink this cup, you _____ the Lord's death till He comes" (1 Corinthians 11:26)

19 "He took bread, _____ _____ and broke it"(2 words) (Luke 22:19)

20 The Last Supper was during the time of the _____ (Luke 22:1, 11)

21 "Unless you eat the flesh of the Son of Man and drink His blood, you have no _____ in you" (John 6:53)

22 "My blood . . . for the _____ of sins" (Matthew 26:28)

23 "Jesus took _____ , blessed and broke it, and gave it to the disciples" (Matthew 26:26)

*T*he answers to this puzzle will "ring true"... when you get them correct.

Across

1 Fact
6 The good news
11 Echo
13 Hawaiian feast
14 Sentinel
15 "And you shall know the truth, and the truth shall make you _____ " (John 8:32)
17 Arachnid
19 Velocity
21 Maple syrup state (abbr.)
22 Balance beam specialist
23 "_____ into all the world" (Mark 16:15)
25 Half of IV
26 Unlock
28 Respite
31 Russian ruler
33 "Just _____ I Am"
34 Behave
35 Place to find a needle?
38 Tribunal
41 Capital of Norway
42 Attention
45 Crowd
47 Pedro's aunt
48 Buckeye state
50 Winter sport
51 "The truth of the LORD _____ forever" (Psalm 117:2)
53 GB's presidential predecessor (initials)
54 Flush
55 "Rightly dividing the _____ of truth" (2 Timothy 2:15)

Down

1 Faith
2 _____ what you sow
3 Honorable
4 Nickname for a president or a bear
5 Half a laugh
6 Word listing
7 School in Norman, Oklahoma (initials)
8 Secure
9 Unsullied
10 Confederate leader, Robert E. _____
12 Oxidize
16 Brink
18 Give off
20 Kennedy book, _____ 109
21 Accuracy
24 Off's opposite
26 Dinner for a horse
27 A Bible book that includes many prayers
29 Short for finance course
30 Stammer
32 Large U.S. airline (initials)
36 One voice
37 Stew or bake
39 Horse restraint
40 Exchange
43 Wound
44 That was _____ ; this is now
46 Sparrow
49 Verb of being
52 Between T and W

194

*J*esus gave an important message about time to His disciples as they awaited the Day of the Lord.

Clue: MESSIAH *is* ZRFFVNU

U R N I R A   N A Q   R N E G U

J V Y Y   C N F F   N J N L '   O H G   Z L

J B E Q F   J V Y Y   O L   A B   Z R N A F

C N F F   N J N L .   O H G   B S   G U N G

Q N L   N A Q   U B H E   A B   B A R

X A B J F '   A B G   R I R A   G U R

N A T R Y F   V A   U R N I R A '

A B E   G U R   F B A '   O H G

B A Y L   G U R   S N G U R E .

CRUX ANSATA

*T*he Crux Ansata is of early Egyptian origin. It combines the Greek letter *tau* (which looks like a *T*) with a loop above it that symbolizes completeness or wholeness.

Start →

← End

Can you tell what time of day is being described from these clues? Do you know what is reported as happening in the Scriptures during that time period? (Remember that while the Jewish day began at dusk, the "first hour" in telling time at dawn was about 6 A.M.)

Clues

It was about opposite the time of day when Jesus walked on the water (Matthew 14:25).

Well before the time when Nicodemus came to see Jesus (John 3:2).

And even before Jesus went by Himself to pray after feeding the five thousand (Matthew 14:23).

It was well after, however, the time when the women came to the tomb after Jesus' crucifixion (Matthew 28:1).

And after the time when Jesus arrived in the temple to teach (John 8:2).

It was before the hour when Jesus was asked, "Where are You staying?" and the disciples remained with Him when He offered, "Come and see" (John 1:36–39).

But after the hour of His crucifixion (Mark 15:25).

In fact, it ended at the same hour when Jesus cried out from the cross, "My God, My God, why have You forsaken Me?" (Mark 15:34).

And began at the same hour when Jesus sat by the well at Sychar (John 4:6).

Answer

The time period is ⎯⎯⎯⎯⎯⎯⎯⎯⎯⎯⎯⎯⎯⎯⎯⎯⎯⎯

The event that happened during this time period was

⎯⎯⎯⎯⎯⎯⎯⎯⎯⎯⎯⎯⎯⎯⎯⎯⎯⎯⎯⎯⎯⎯⎯⎯

Easter Lilies

The word *lily* in the Scriptures may refer to a number of different flowers, from Madonna lilies to hyacinths. It may be a generic term for describing any brightly colored flower.

The lilies that decorated Solomon's temple were probably modeled after the water lily, or lotus. This was a common architectural motif in Egypt, Persia, and Assyria. (See 1 Kings 7:19–26.)

Jesus said, "Consider the lilies, how they grow: they neither toil nor spin; and yet I say to you, even Solomon in all his glory was not arrayed like one of these. If then God so clothes the grass, which today is in the field and tomorrow is thrown into the oven, how much more will He clothe you, O you of little faith?" (Luke 12:27–28). The lilies to which Jesus was referring were probably wild *Anemone coronaria*, a bright purple flower that still grows freely on the hillsides around the Sea of Galilee.

Lilies have become a common Easter symbol primarily because they are nearly always in bloom at Easter.

*I*n the words of the Fanny Crosby hymn, "Redeemed and so happy in Jesus, no language my rapture can tell." Redeemed! Redeemed!

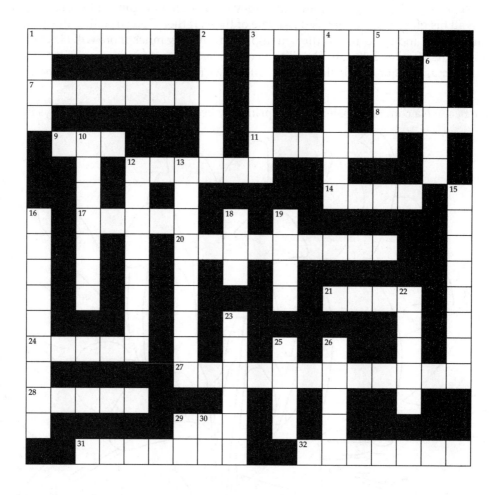

Across

1 In His mercy, God led forth the "populace" He redeemed from Pharaoh (Exodus 15:13)

3 His blood redeemed us and made us kings and _____ to our God (Revelation 5:9–10)

7 "Redeem Israel, O God, out of all their 'difficulties'" (Psalm 25:22)

8 He redeemed Naomi's land (Ruth 4:8–10)

9 God redeemed Israel with an outstretched _____ (Exodus 6:6)

11 In a period of "no food," He redeems us from death (Job 5:20)

12 The Lord brought the Israelites out with a "powerful" hand (Deuteronomy 7:8)

14 My _____ , which God has redeemed, will rejoice, said the psalmist (Psalm 71:23)

17 Christ redeemed us from the "plague" of the law (Galatians 3:13)

20 The Lord redeemed David's life from "affliction" (2 Samuel 4:9)

21 Every firstborn of a donkey was redeemed with a _____ (Exodus 13:13)

24 The "Heavenly Being" redeemed Israel from all evil (Genesis 48:16)

27 We weren't redeemed with "corruptible things, like _____ _____ _____ " (3 words) (1 Peter 1:18)

28 God redeemed the Israelites from slavery in this land (Deuteronomy 15:15)

29 Ephraim and Samaria, though redeemed, spoke "falsehoods" (sing.) against God (Hosea 7:13)

31 Zacharias said God had "called on" and redeemed His people (Luke 1:68)

32 The rich can't redeem this sibling (Psalm 49:6–7)

Down

1 He redeemed His children in His love and "compassion" (Isaiah 63:9)

2 He redeemed His people, the sons of Jacob and _____ (Psalm 77:15)

3 He redeemed us from lawless deeds and "refines" (sing.) for Himself His own special people (Titus 2:14)

4 Redeem my soul and deliver me because of my "foes," said David (Psalm 69:18)

5 Asaph urged God to remember the "clan" of His inheritance, which He had redeemed (Psalm 74:2)

6 The sons of Korah were redeemed from the power of the "burial plot" (Psalm 49:15)

10 Another word for redeemed (Psalm 136:24)

12 "Redeem me and be 'compassionate' to me," was David's plea (Psalm 26:11)

13 Moses pleaded, "Don't destroy those You redeemed through Your 'eminence'" (Deuteronomy 9:26)

15 The "bought back" of the Lord shall return and come to Zion, singing (Isaiah 51:11)

16 The Lord has redeemed this city of righteousness, Isaiah said (Isaiah 52:9)

18 _____ *Maria*

19 I'll redeem you from the "clutch" of the terrible, God told Jeremiah (Jeremiah 15:21)

22 "In Him we have redemption through His _____ " (Ephesians 1:7)

23 A man had a year to redeem a house he sold in this type of city (Leviticus 25:29)

25 "And the 'twelve months' of My redeemed has come" (Isaiah 63:4)

26 God redeemed His people by His great "strength" (Nehemiah 1:10)

29 Lieutenant (abbr.)

30 That is (abbr.)

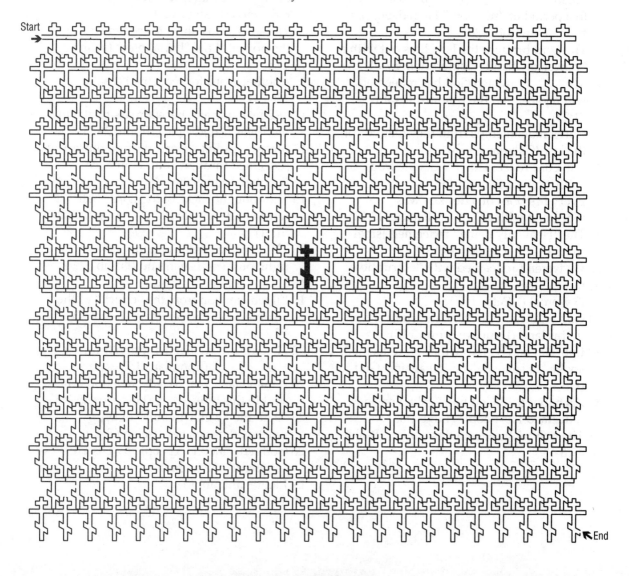

THE RUSSIAN CROSS

*T*he Russian Cross, also called the Eastern Cross or the Slavic Cross, appears on the tombs of the early czars and it also is seen frequently on the spire or dome of the Eastern Orthodox Church.

The upper bar indicates the inscription that Pilate wrote about Jesus, "JESUS OF NAZARETH, THE KING OF THE JEWS" (John 19:19). The lower slanted bar is said to have been the footrest of the cross. The Eastern Church believed that Jesus was crucified with His feet side by side, rather than one over the other, as seen in early paintings of the Western Church.

The reason for the slant of the lower bar is a mystery. One tradition says that the earthquake at the time of the crucifixion caused the bar to slant. A more probable theory is that the lower bar forms the shape of the Cross Saltire or St. Andrew's Cross (see *St. Andrew's Cross* maze). Andrew is the apostle who is believed to have introduced Christianity into Russia.

Start

End

*I*n the letter box below, find the "companion" word in these common groupings of words from the Bible.

Trust and _____
Adam and _____
Peter, James, and _____
The Law and the _____
The Way, the Truth, and the _____
Abraham and _____
Cain and _____
Jonathan and _____
Faith, Hope, and _____
Father, Son, and _____ _____ (2 words)

Kingdom, Power, and _____
Shadrach, Meshach, and _____
Samson and _____
Abraham, Isaac, and _____
Heaven and _____
Life and _____
Grace and _____
Now and _____
Body and _____
Good and _____

```
G  D  L  P  E  A  F  O  R  B  L  O  A  B  E  D  E
A  B  E  V  D  E  L  C  A  J  B  S  A  R  S  V  N
D  A  V  E  I  D  E  A  T  B  L  E  B  A  I  G  O
B  E  D  A  V  E  G  O  G  H  O  P  F  L  P  R  O
P  H  V  E  A  T  S  B  L  O  E  H  V  I  O  F  L
S  A  B  E  D  N  E  G  O  S  O  P  R  A  H  O  I
D  E  L  I  A  H  J  A  R  L  O  V  E  V  I  R  D
P  R  O  P  H  O  E  H  Y  T  S  F  J  A  P  E  C
E  B  O  C  A  J  A  S  A  C  I  J  O  H  C  V  H
E  H  V  E  O  B  P  E  Y  L  A  B  E  H  D  E  N
G  A  L  O  R  I  Y  H  O  L  E  S  E  T  P  R  I
I  R  I  T  R  S  L  O  V  Y  P  L  V  A  C  E  F
H  A  L  I  L  E  D  R  E  V  L  R  E  E  L  L  H
A  S  T  E  H  P  O  R  P  J  A  C  A  D  E  G  O
B  E  D  N  E  L  A  H  E  L  D  E  A  T  V  I  L
E  V  H  N  S  E  R  A  H  E  L  B  D  A  L  L  G
```

On especially stressful days, it's important to remember what the Bible says about "rest"—a scriptural concept that means not only relaxation but peace of spirit and freedom from oppression.

Complete the verses below—which reveal vital, stress-free benefits—and use the missing words to fill in the acrostic grid. You'll discover an important command of God worth remembering!

1 "My Presence will go with you, and I will give you _____" (Exodus 33:14)

2 "Then the churches throughout all Judea, Galilee, and Samaria had peace and were _____" (Acts 9:31)

3 "Go, return each to her _____ house . . . The LORD grant that you may find rest" (Ruth 1:8–9)

4 "When the LORD your God has given you rest from your _____ all around, . . . you will blot out the remembrance of Amalek" (Deuteronomy 25:19)

5 "Sit still, my daughter, until you know how the _____ will turn out" (Ruth 3:18)

6 "You shall pass before your _____ armed, all your mighty men of valor, and help them, until the LORD has given your _____ rest, as He gave you" (Joshua 1:14–15)

7 "And to whom did He swear that they would not enter His rest, but to those who did not obey? So we see that they could not _____ in because of unbelief" (Hebrews 3:18–19)

8 "In that day there shall be a Root of Jesse, . . . and His _____ place shall be glorious" (Isaiah 11:10)

9 "It is a righteous thing with God to repay with _____ those who trouble you, and to give you who are troubled rest" (2 Thessalonians 1:6–7)

10 "Tomorrow is a Sabbath rest, a _____ Sabbath to the LORD" (Exodus 16:23)

11 "Then the land shall rest and _____ its sabbaths" (Leviticus 26:34)

12 "Work shall be done for six days, but the _____ is the Sabbath of rest" (Exodus 31:15)

13 "I would have been _____ ; then I would have been at rest" (Job 3:13)

14 "If you would prepare your heart, and stretch out your hands toward Him; . . . you would be secure, _____ there is hope" (Job 11:13, 18)

15 "Return to your rest, O my soul, for the LORD has dealt _____ with you" (Psalm 116:7)

16 "Blessed is the man whom You instruct, O LORD . . . that You may give him rest from the days of _____" (Psalm 94:12–13)

17 "I am not at ease, nor am I quiet; I have no rest, for _____ comes" (Job 3:26)

18 "The LORD blessed the Sabbath day and _____ it" (Exodus 20:11)

19 "Oh, that I had wings like a _____ ! I would fly away and be at rest" (Psalm 55:6)

20 "Arise, O LORD, to Your resting place, You and the _____ of Your strength" (Psalm 132:8)

21 "Take My _____ upon you and learn from Me, for I am gentle and lowly in heart, and you will find rest for your souls" (Matthew 11:29)

1 — — — —
2 — — — — — — —
3 — — — — — —
4 — — — — — —
5 — — — — — —
6 — — — — — — —
7 — — — —
8 — — — — — —
9 — — — — — — —
10 — — — —
11 — — — —
12 — — — — —
13 — — — — —
14 — — — — —
15 — — — — — — —
16 — — — — — — — —
17 — — — — — —
18 — — — — — —
19 — — — —
20 — — —
21 — — — —

In each father-son pair below, the name of either the son or the father has been scrambled. Unscramble these names and then unscramble the circled letters to reveal an important scriptural bond in a father-son relationship.

FATHER	SON	
ABRAHAM	<u>CSAIA</u>	Ⓞ _ _ _ _
<u>HEUJ</u>	JEHOAHAZ	_ Ⓞ _ _ _
<u>ONHA</u>	SHEM	Ⓞ _ _ _ _
DAVID	<u>LOOMSNO</u>	_ _ _ _ _ _ Ⓞ
ASA	<u>SOEJHAHTAHP</u>	_ _ _ _ _ _ _ _ Ⓞ _ _
<u>MARAM</u>	MOSES	_ _ Ⓞ _ _
AMAZIAH	<u>AZIHARA</u>	_ _ _ _ Ⓞ _ _
<u>EHPETUL</u>	JOEL	_ _ Ⓞ _ _ _ _
AARON	<u>LEERAAZ</u>	_ _ _ Ⓞ _ _ _
ISAAC	<u>BAJCO</u>	_ _ Ⓞ _ _
<u>SEEJS</u>	DAVID	_ Ⓞ _ _ _

Unscrambled the circled letters here:

_ _ _ _ _ _ _ _ _ _ _

*T*his crossword is about one of the most valued entities in the Bible—both literally and spiritually—LIGHT!

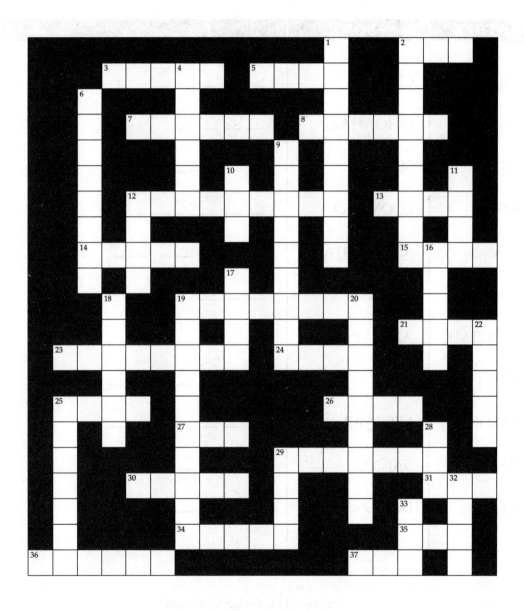

Across

2 Second Samuel 23:4 says that the Messiah "shall be like the light of the morning when the _____ rises"

3 "They _____ in the dark without light, and He makes them stagger like a drunken man," says Job 12:25

5 "Light is _____ for the righteous, and gladness for the upright in heart," says Psalm 97:11

7 Isaiah said of the Messiah, "The people who _____ in darkness have seen a great light" (Isaiah 9:2)

8 "The light of the _____ indeed goes out," says Job 18:5

12 God said, "Let there be lights in the _____ of the heavens to divide the day from the night" (Genesis 1:14)

13 The "lesser light" (Genesis 1:16)

14 "Truly the light is _____ , and it is pleasant for the eyes to behold the sun" (Ecclesiastes 11:7)

15 The arrival of day

19 After Mordecai's victory over Haman, Esther's people experienced "light and _____ , joy and honor" (Esther 8:16)

21 As Paul traveled to Damascus "at about _____ , suddenly a great light from heaven shone around" him (Acts 22:6)

23 Intermittent bursting of light

24 The best place for Light to shine

25 Shining heat

26 Jesus said true believers do not "light a _____ and put it under a basket" (Matthew 5:15)

27 Jesus taught, "The lamp of the body is the _____ " (Matthew 6:22)

29 Jesus said, "While you have the light, _____ in the light, that you may become sons of light" (John 12:36)

30 The flame of the wicked "does not _____ " (Job 18:5)

31 "God made _____ great lights; the greater light to rule the day, and the lesser light to rule the night" (Genesis 1:16)

34 A faint or brief glow of light (especially in the eyes)

35 Offering to be given for light in the tabernacle (Exodus 35:28)

36 Habakkuk said, "The sun and moon stood still in their habitation; at the light of Your _____ " (Habakkuk 3:11)

37 Opposite of night

Down

1 To fill or flood with light

2 "The light of the sun will be _____ , as the light of seven days," says Isaiah 30:26

4 The Lord led His people with a _____ of cloud by day and a _____ of fire by night (Exodus 13:21)

6 The Lord "knows what is in the _____ , and light dwells with Him" (Daniel 2:22)

9 During the plague of darkness, the Israelites in Egypt still had light in their _____ (Exodus 10:23)

10 Beam of light

11 During the Transfiguration, Jesus' clothes "became shining, exceedingly white, like _____ " (Mark 9:3)

12 God told Moses to take his sandals off his _____ in the presence of a bush that was burning but was not consumed (Exodus 3:1–5)

16 In the face of a night far spent, Paul encouraged the Romans to cast off the works of darkness, and "put on the _____ of light" (Romans 13:12)

17 The Lord asked Job where he was "when the morning stars _____ together" (Job 38:7)

18 In Isaiah's prophecy about the Messiah, he said that a light has shined on "those who dwelt in the land of the _____ of death" (Isaiah 9:2)

19 Habakkuk speaks of the sun and moon's standing still "at the shining of Your _____ spear" (Habakkuk 3:11)

20 The psalmist declared, "The LORD is my light and my _____ " (Psalm 27:1)

22 Opposite of day

25 A flicker of light

28 God began His creation by saying, " _____ there be light" (Genesis 1:3)

29 Shaft of sunlight or moonlight

32 Jesus said, " _____ while you have the light, lest darkness overtake you" (John 12:35)

33 After the defeat of Haman, the Jews had "light and gladness, _____ and honor" (Esther 8:16)

*F*ind ten items in the box of letters below that were carried in baskets in the Bible.

```
B  G  O  O  S  K  A  B  N  E  V  A  E  L  N  U  E
A  D  T  V  A  E  U  L  T  M  M  U  S  H  D  B  D
K  E  N  E  S  A  L  E  A  I  E  F  H  E  A  R  E
M  O  O  D  E  T  M  S  G  R  U  R  F  A  E  S  A
E  T  G  D  B  N  F  R  T  T  F  G  I  F  R  I  F
A  D  S  O  A  E  G  A  I  S  U  M  S  M  B  E  R
P  O  O  U  K  M  S  A  U  L  B  R  H  F  D  U  H
R  G  T  A  E  M  A  B  R  M  H  E  A  I  E  N  E
O  D  M  M  D  E  K  S  F  I  S  U  S  D  N  L  A
D  E  P  E  G  D  D  I  R  R  I  S  G  A  E  E  F
U  R  M  R  O  A  G  R  E  E  A  M  M  R  V  A  R
C  E  U  F  O  S  F  R  M  C  T  G  E  B  A  V  A
F  M  S  R  D  D  H  U  M  L  I  U  M  D  E  N  G
I  G  U  A  S  F  U  E  U  A  W  R  F  E  L  U  M
T  I  E  H  I  D  E  C  S  X  T  F  E  C  N  S  B
F  H  A  S  S  A  D  D  E  R  U  E  D  U  U  T  A
I  U  P  R  E  R  B  O  C  E  I  P  O  R  P  D  S
S  U  N  L  E  A  V  U  R  U  T  I  U  R  S  E  K
```

Scripture Pool
GENESIS 40:17   LEVITICUS 8:2   DEUTERONOMY 26:2   JUDGES 6:19
2 KINGS 10:7   JEREMIAH 24:1   AMOS 8:2   MARK 6:43; 8:19   ACTS 9:24–25

CROWN OF THORNS

*T*he crown of thorns is indicative of both the pain and the mockery associated with the crucifixion of Jesus.

The Scriptures tell us that Pilate's soldiers "took Jesus into the Praetorium and gathered the whole garrison around Him. And they stripped Him and put a scarlet robe on Him. When they had twisted a crown of thorns, they put it on His head, and a reed in His right hand. And they bowed the knee before Him and mocked Him, saying, 'Hail, King of the Jews!' Then they spat on Him, and took the reed and struck Him on the head. And when they had mocked Him, they took the robe off Him, put His own clothes on Him, and led Him away to be crucified" (Matthew 27:27–31).

Pilate commanded an inscription for the cross, "JESUS OF NAZARETH, THE KING OF THE JEWS," and had it written in Hebrew, Greek, and Latin (John 19:19). "Therefore the chief priests of the Jews said to Pilate, 'Do not write, "The King of the Jews," but, "He said, 'I am the King of the Jews.'"' Pilate answered, 'What I have written, I have written'" (v. 21–22).

Never was a crown more royal.

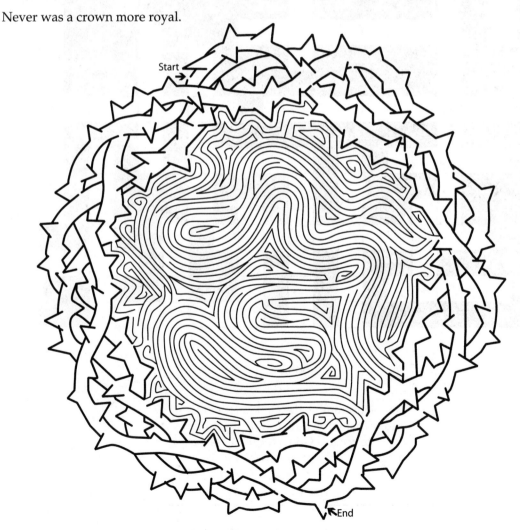

It's hard to forgive someone who has hurt us. But forgiveness from God makes us realize its importance.

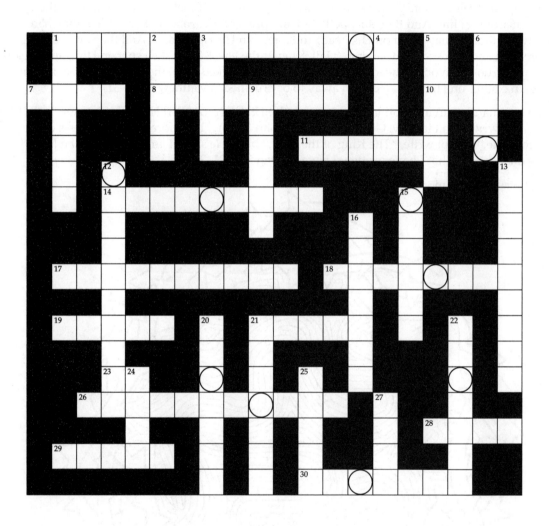

Bonus:

Unscramble the circled letters
to reveal what puts us into a position
to receive God's forgiveness.

__ __ __ __ __ __ __ __ __

Across

1 Forgive seventy times _____ (Matthew 18:21–22)

3 Joseph forgave them (Genesis 45:3–5)

7 God would "mend" Israel's backsliding (Hosea 14:4)

8 God "erases" our transgressions (2 words) (Isaiah 43:25)

10 "Look on . . . my 'discomfort,' and forgive all my sins," said David (Psalm 25:18)

11 God will abundantly "excuse" (Isaiah 55:7)

14 Hezekiah requested "redemption" for the people (2 Chronicles 30:18)

17 "Forgive men their _____" (Matthew 6:14)

18 Whoever "trusts" in Him receives forgiveness (Acts 10:43)

19 The people worship "images"; don't forgive them, said Isaiah (Isaiah 2:8–9)

21 Those whose lawless "acts" are forgiven are fortunate (Romans 4:7)

23 _____ Shaddai

26 The sins of the woman who poured this on Jesus were forgiven (2 words) (Luke 7:46–47)

28 Once forgiven, the paralytic did this (Luke 5:23–25)

29 God is "prepared" to forgive (Psalm 86:5)

30 This great city sought forgiveness just in time (Jonah 3:5–10)

Down

1 A martyr who forgave his killers (Acts 7:59–60)

2 Abigail, wife of _____ , begged David's forgiveness (1 Samuel 25:23–28)

3 Without shedding of this, there's no forgiveness (Hebrews 9:22)

4 If God marks iniquities, who can "remain upright"? (Psalm 130:3)

5 Ask for forgiveness (Acts 2:38)

6 We were dead in trespasses; now forgiven, we're _____ (Colossians 2:13)

9 This son of Gera confessed his sin to David (2 Samuel 19:18–20)

12 In His forbearance, God "crossed above" old sins (2 words) (Romans 3:25)

13 "Cancellation" of sins (Matthew 26:28)

15 Forgive others as God in _____ forgave you (Ephesians 4:32)

16 "Favored" is he whose sin is forgiven (Psalm 32:1)

20 The servant owing one hundred of these wasn't forgiven (Matthew 18:28)

21 The creditor forgave the "two who owed" him money (Luke 7:41–43)

22 He begged Moses and Aaron's forgiveness (Exodus 10:16–17)

24 If God's people repented, He would heal their _____ (2 Chronicles 7:14)

25 Peter told this sorcerer to repent (Acts 8:18–22)

27 It covers a multitude of sins (1 Peter 4:8)

*D*ecode one of the greatest statements in the Bible from the Great Shepherd to us, His sheep!

Clue: MESSIAH *is* EKGGUAL

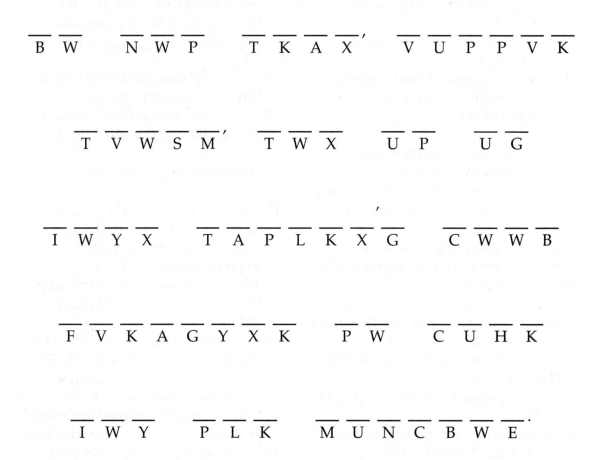

B W   N W P   T K A X '   V U P P V K

T V W S M '   T W X   U P   U G

I W Y X   T A P L K X G '   C W W B

F V K A G Y X K   P W   C U H K

I W Y   P L K   M U N C B W E .

When the bones were connected, they could walk around. Oh, hear the word of the Lord—as told in Ezekiel 37.

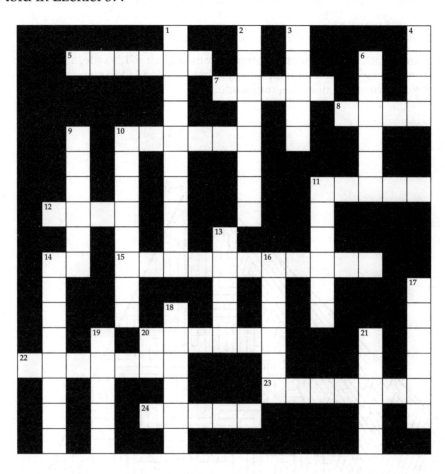

Across

5 Burial plots (v. 12)
7 Tranquility (v. 26)
8 Bones were dry, "optimism" was lost (v. 11)
10 The stick of Ephraim was in the hand of _____ (v. 16)
11 Abide (v. 25)
12 Royal leader (v. 22)
14 Registered nurse (abbr.)
15 Eternal (v. 26)
20 The son of #12 Across (v. 25)
22 Purify (v. 23)
23 Law (v. 24)
24 Rod (v. 16)

Down

1 Easy to hate (v. 23)
2 The people will have one "lamb leader" (v. 24)
3 God's servant, whose name means "supplanter" (v. 25)
4 Can these dead bones _____? Yes! (v. 3)
6 "I will be their God, and they shall be My _____ " (v. 27)
9 Republic (v. 22)
10 Ruling (v. 24)
11 Debase (v. 23)
13 The four winds breathed on the "killed" (v. 9)
14 Clattering (v. 7)
16 Tendons (v. 6)
17 Dale or dell (v. 1)
18 The dry bones hadn't drawn their last _____ , after all (v. 5)
19 The apple of God's eye (v. 24)
20 Postscript (abbr.)
21 The bones were the "family" of Israel (v. 11)

DOWN TO EGYPT

"Get out of your country, from your family and from your father's house, to a land that I will show you" (Genesis 12:1).

So said God to Abram, and so began Abram's journey to Canaan.

But there was a famine in Canaan sometime after Abram and Sarai, his wife, arrived. Abram decided to pack up and move to Egypt, at least temporarily. That decision led to some trouble, but God kept all His promises to this future "father of a multitude."

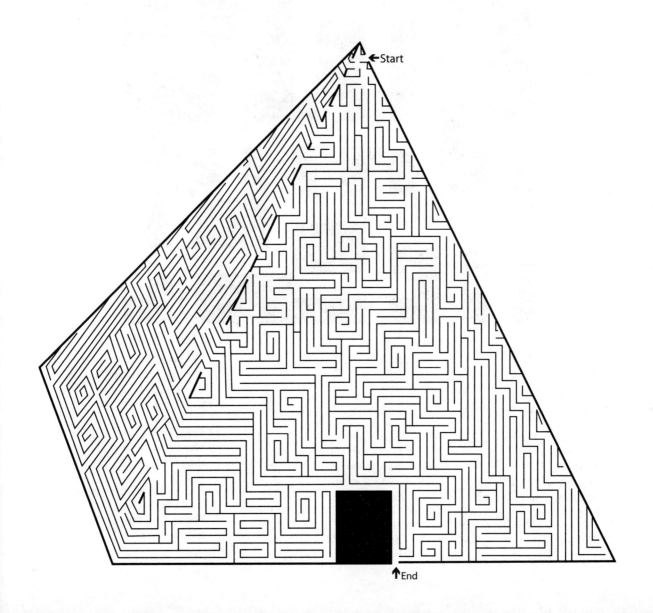

Use words reflecting prosperity from Deuteronomy 28:1–14 to complete the grid, and discover what they have in common from God's perspective.

Now it shall come to pass, if you diligently obey the voice of the LORD your God, to observe carefully all His commandments which I command you today, that the LORD your God will set you ____ above all nations of the earth. And all these blessings shall come upon you and overtake you, because you obey the voice of the LORD your God:

Blessed shall you be in the city, and blessed shall you be in the ____.

Blessed shall be the ____ of your body, the ____ of your ground and the increase of your ____, the increase of your ____ and the offspring of your ____.

Blessed shall be your basket and your kneading ____.

Blessed shall you be when you ____ in, and blessed shall you be when you ____ out.

The LORD will cause your ____ who rise against you to be defeated before your face; they shall come out against you one way and flee before you seven ways.

The LORD will command the blessing on you in your ____ and in all to which you set your hand, and He will bless you in the ____ which the LORD your God is giving you.

The LORD will ____ you as a holy people to Himself,

lust as He has sworn to you, if you keep the commandments of the LORD your God and walk in His ways. Then all peoples of the earth shall see that you are called by the name of the LORD, and they shall be afraid of you. And the LORD will grant you ____ of goods, in the fruit of your body, in the ____ of your livestock, and in the produce of your ground, in the land of which the LORD swore to your fathers to give you. The LORD will open to you His good ____, the heavens, to give the ____ to your land in its season, and to bless all the ____ of your hand. You shall ____ to many nations,

but you shall not borrow. And the LORD will make you the ____ and not the tail; you shall be ____ only, and not be beneath, if you heed the commandments of the LORD your God, which I command you today, and are careful to observe them. So you shall not turn aside from any of the words which I command you this day, to the right or the left, to go after other gods to serve them.

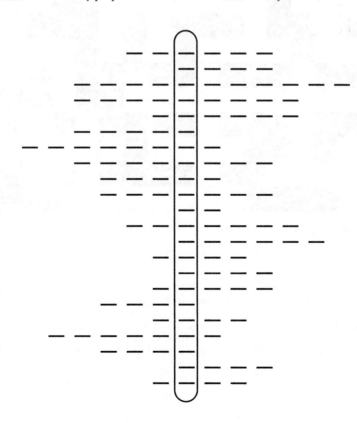

*T*he Bible has a great deal to say about learning, observing, studying, thinking, and meditating. Provide the missing words in the sixteen statements below to complete the crossword grid.

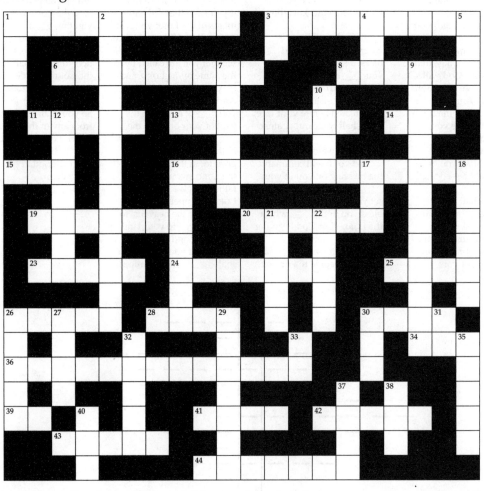

1 Take heed to yourself, and _____ keep yourself, lest you forget the things your _____ have seen, and lest they
                1 Across   28 Across

    _____ from your heart all _____ days of your life. And teach them to your children and your _____
    8 Across   4 Down   2 Down
    (Deuteronomy 4:9)

2 The Lord said to His people in Horeb: "Gather the people to Me, and I will let them hear My _____ , that they may
                                                                       11 Across

    learn to _____ Me all the days they live on the _____ , and that they may teach their children" (Deuteronomy 4:10)
    41 Across   43 Across

3 Moses called all Israel, and said to them: "Hear, O Israel, the statutes and judgments which I speak in your hearing

    today, that you may learn them and be careful to _____ them" (Deuteronomy 5:1)
                                             12 Down

4 He [the king] shall write for himself a copy of this _____ in a book, . . . and he shall read it all the days of his _____
40 Down · 25 Across

, that he may learn to fear the LORD his God and be careful to observe all the words of this law and these statutes,

that his _____ may not be lifted above his brethren, that he may not turn aside from the commandment to the right
32 Down

hand or to the left, and that he may _____ his _____ in his kingdom, he and his children in the midst of Israel
19 Across · 1 Down

(Deuteronomy 17:18–20)

5 I remember the days of _____ ; I meditate on all Your _____ ; I muse on the work of Your hands. I spread out my
38 Down · 26 Down

hands to _____ ; my soul longs for You like a thirsty land (Psalm 143:5–6)
14 Across

6 Learn to _____ _____ ; seek justice, rebuke the oppressor; defend the fatherless, plead for the _____ (Isaiah 1:17)
31 Down 37 Down · 35 Down

7 When you come into the land which the LORD your God is giving you, you shall not _____ to follow the _____ of
23 Across · 9 Down

those nations (Deuteronomy 18:9)

8 _____ the people together, _____ and _____ and little ones, and the stranger who is within your gates, that they
18 Down · 30 Down 26 Across

may hear and that they may learn to fear the LORD your God and carefully observe all the words of this law

(Deuteronomy 31:12)

9 Give me _____ that I may learn Your commandments (Psalm 119:73)
16 Across

10 _____ , by _____ spirit within me I will seek You early; for when Your judgments are in the earth, the inhabitants of
15 Across 3 Down

the world will learn _____ (Isaiah 26:9)
36 Across

11 Blessed is the man who walks not in the counsel of the _____ , nor _____ in the path of _____ , _____ _____ in the
16 Down · 7 Down · 29 Down 17 Down 5 Down

_____ of the scornful; but his _____ is in the law of the LORD, and in His law he _____ day and _____ (Psalm
10 Down · 24 Across · 3 Across · 21 Down

1:1–2)

12 Let my heart be _____ regarding Your _____ , that I may not be _____ (Psalm 119:80)
6 Across · 13 Across · 44 Across

13 You shall love the LORD your God with all your heart, with all your soul, and with all your _____ (Matthew 22:37)
30 Across

14 The preparations of the heart belong to man, but the _____ of the tongue is from the LORD (Proverbs 16:1)
20 Across

15 What I say to you, I say to all: _____ ! (Mark 13:37)
22 Down

16 The wise men who came from the East to present gifts to the young child Jesus are also called _____
27 Down

17 _____ he thinks in his heart, _____ is he (Proverbs 23:7)
33 Down · 39 Across

18 They _____ the wind, and reap the whirlwind (Hosea 8:7)
34 Across

19 We know that we are of God, and the whole _____ lies under the sway of the wicked one. And we know that the
42 Across

Son of God has come and has given us an understanding, that we may know Him who is true (1 John 5:19–20)

*A*ll parts of this equation are from the book of Numbers—*naturally!*

The year after the children of Israel came out of Egypt and the Lord said to Moses, "Take a census of all the congregation" (Numbers 1:1–2) = ____

Multiplied by . . .
Number of tribes included in the census (Numbers 1:47) × ____

Multiplied by . . .
Number of covered carts used to bring an offering to the Lord for the tabernacle (Numbers 7:3) × ____

Multiplied by . . .
The worth in shekels of silver in the platter given to the Lord (Numbers 7:13) × ____

Multiplied by . . .
The worth in shekels of the silver in the bowl given to the Lord (Numbers 7:13) × ____

Divided by . . .
Number of silver trumpets made for calling the congregation and directing the movement of the camp (Numbers 10:2) ÷ ____

Plus . . .
The worth in shekels of the gold pan filled with incense given to the Lord (Numbers 7:14) = ____

Multiplied by . . .
The animals in the peace offerings (Numbers 7:17)

Number of rams × ____

Number of male goats × ____

Number of male rams × ____

Number of oxen × ____ = + ____

Plus . . .
The number of animals for the burnt offering (Numbers 7:87)

Number of oxen = ____

Number of rams + ____

Number of male lambs + ____

The number of kid goats for the sin offering (Numbers 7:87) + ____ = ____

Multiplied by . . .
Number of days Miriam was shut out of the camp (Numbers 12:15) × ____ = + ____

Plus . . .
"Retirement" age of levitical priest (Numbers 8:25) = ____

Multiplied by . . .
The number of turtle doves for an atonement offering for a Nazirite who touched a corpse (Numbers 6:10) × ____ = + ____

Plus . . .
The day of the month of the celebration of Passover (Numbers 9:3) + ____

Equals . . .
The census of all "able to go to war" (from twenty years old and above) (Numbers 1:45–46) = ____

THE EIGHT-POINTED STAR

A star with eight points has long been an emblem of baptism, since eight is the biblical number used to symbolize the regeneration of man.

Jesus was given His name at the time of His circumcision when He was eight days old, and a Christian child receives his name at baptism. In early instances of adult baptism, new believers frequently changed their names at the time they were baptized. The changing of the name added to the symbolism of regeneration in baptism. In many churches, the base of the baptismal font is octagonal, or eight-sided.

The fact that eight souls were saved in the ark—Noah and his wife, and their three sons and their wives—has been associated with the symbol. The appearance of a new star in the sky at the time of Jesus' birth is also linked to the symbolism of the eight-point star.

Start →

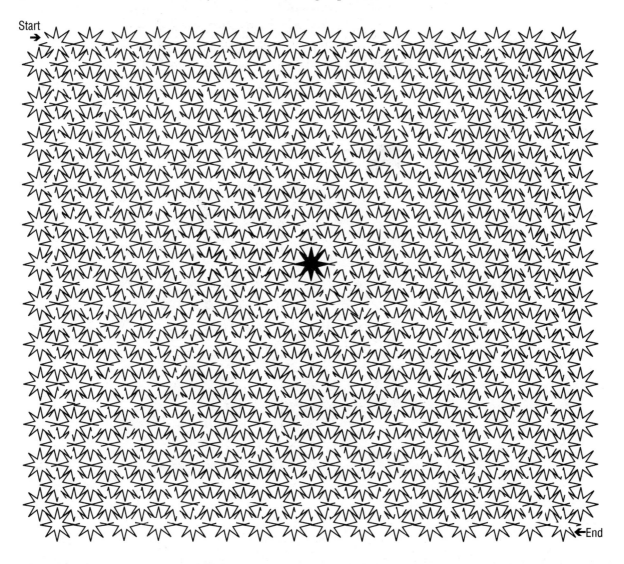

←End

PUZZLE ANSWERS

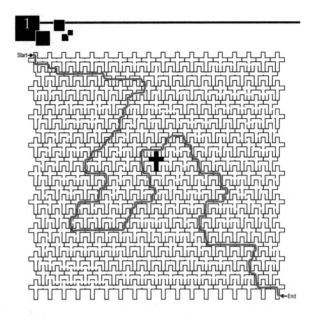

I will destroy this temple that is made with
hands, and within three days I will build
another made without hands. (Mark 14:58, NKJ)

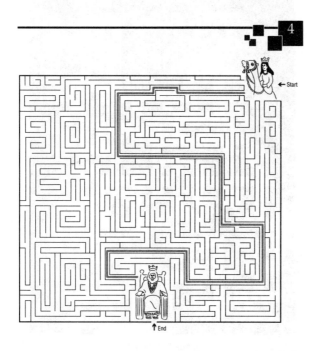

Starting at the top left, read every other letter on
every other line beginning with the first letter "Y"
until the message is complete.

Message: YE SHALL SEEK ME, AND FIND ME,
WHEN YE SHALL SEARCH FOR ME WITH ALL
YOUR HEART. (Jeremiah 29:13)

Starting at the bottom right and reading "back-
wards," you'll find this message interlocking with
God's command:
CIRCUMSTANCES and OUR SORROWS and
INCORRECT TEACHING and INACCURATE
KNOWLEDGE and A HARDNESS OF HEART and
PRIDE and DIVIDED LOYALTIES and LAZINESS
and THE LUSTS OF THE FLESH and THE ATTACKS
FROM OUR ENEMY

PUZZLE ANSWERS

Bonus "J" JUBILEE

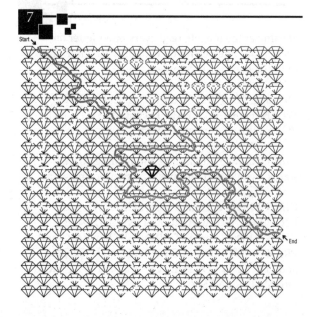

8

CEDAR
SHITTAH
OIL TREE
MYRTLE
FIR
PINE
BOX TREE
OLIVE
PALM
FIG

TREE OF LIFE

Many of these trees are mentioned in Isaiah 41:19.

9

Puzzle Answers

10

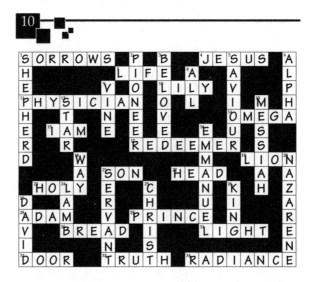

11

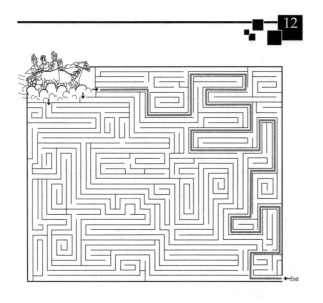

12

←End

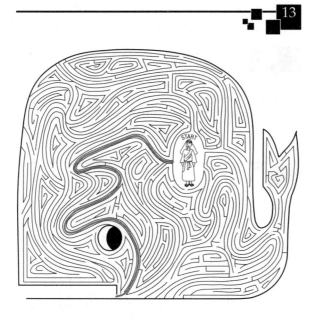

13

Puzzle Answers

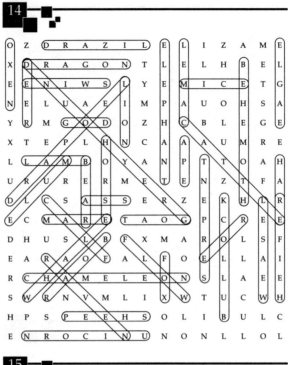

Watch ye and pray, lest ye enter into temptation. The spirit truly is ready, but the flesh is weak. (Mark 14:38)

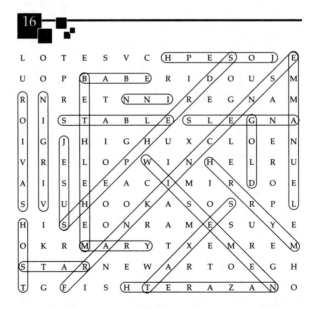

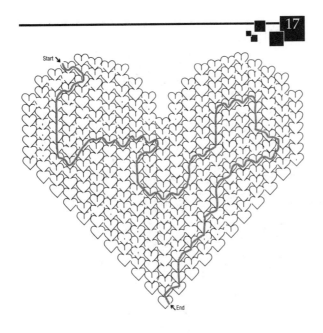

17

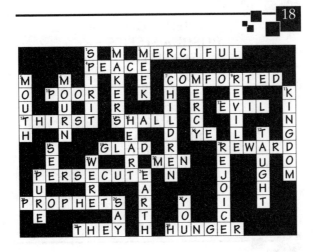

18

PUZZLE ANSWERS

19

Start→

←End

20

ABEDNEGO
(JOSHUA'S) SPIES
ISRAELITES
JOSEPH
MOSES
APOSTLES
JONAH
MORDECAI
PHILIP
ELIJAH
PAUL

21

This is my commandment, that ye love one another as I have loved you. (John 15:12)

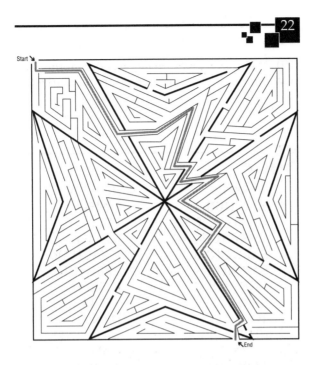

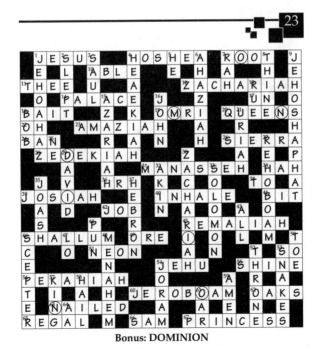

Bonus: DOMINION

PUZZLE ANSWERS

24

ZILPAH, Leah's handmaid, was the mother of Gad and Asher, whose games are all marked.

25

JASPER	REUBEN
SAPPHIRE	SIMEON
CHALCEDONY	LEVI
EMERALD	JUDAH
SARDONYX	ISSACHAR
SARDIUS	ZEBULUN
CHRYSOLITE	JOSEPH
BERYL	BENJAMIN
TOPAZ	DAN
CHRYSOPRASE	NAPHTALI
JACINTH	GAD
AMETHYST	ASHER
PEARL	

26

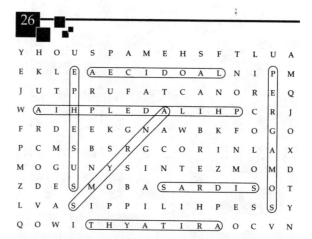

They are the locations of the seven churches that John wrote to in the Book of Revelation.

27

Start

End

28

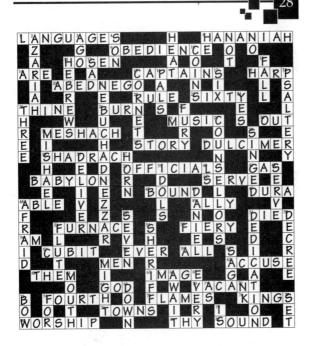

29

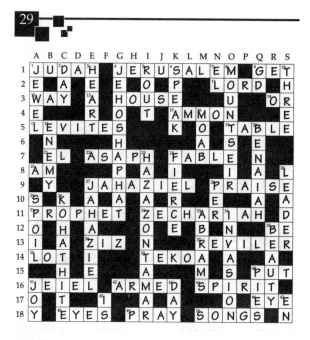

	A	B	C	D	E	F	G	H	I	J	K	L	M	N	O	P	Q	R	S
1	J	U	D	A	H		J	E	R	U	S	A	L	E	M		G	E	T
2	E		A		E		E		O		P			L	O	R	D		H
3	W	A	Y		A		H	O	U	S	E			U			O	R	E
4	E			R		O	T		A	M	M	O	N						E
5	L	E	V	I	T	E	S		K		O		T	A	B	L	E		
6		N			H				A		S		E						
7	E	L		A	S	A	P	H		F	A	B	L	E		N			
8	A	M		P		A		I		I			I		A				L
9		Y		J	A	H	A	Z	I	E	L		P	R	A	I	S	E	
10	S		K	A		A		A		R		E			A		A		A
11	P	R	O	P	H	E	T		Z	E	C	H	A	R	I	A	H		D
12	O		H	A		O		E		B		N					B	E	
13	I		A	Z	I	Z		N			R	E	V	I	L	E	R		
14	L	O	T		I		T	E	K	O	A		A		A				
15			H		E			A			M		S		P	U	T		
16	J	E	I	E	L		A	R	M	E	D		S	P	I	R	I	T	
17	O		T		I		A		A					O		E	Y	E	
18	Y		E	Y	E	S		P	R	A	Y		S	O	N	G	S		N

30

Stand ye still and see the salvation of the Lord.
(2 Chronicles 20:17)

31

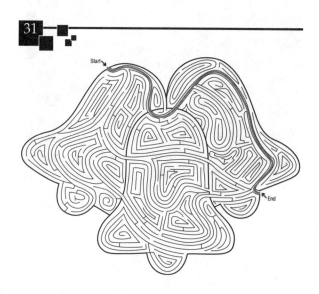

Nuts	Lentils	Vinegar
Almonds	Cucumbers	Mint
Butter	Melons	Anise
Milk	Fish	Dill
Honey	Onions	Cumin
Cheese	Garlic	Salt
Veal	Leeks	Locusts
Mutton	Manna	Pomegranate
Bread	Olives	Grapes
Wheat	Fitch	Olive oil
Barley	Grasshoppers	Goat
Flour	Wine	Ox
Corn	Raisins	Vension
Beans	Figs	Quail

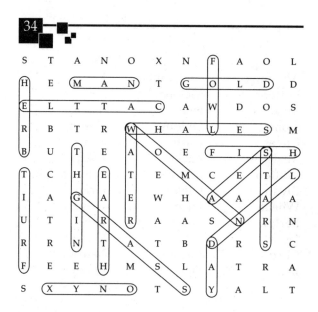

33

Bonus: ROYAL PRIESTHOOD

36

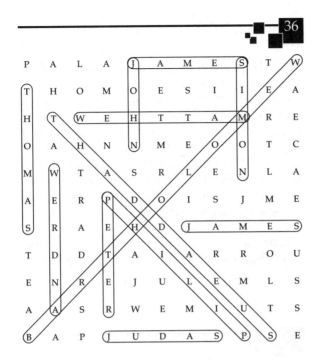

37

That He would grant you, according to the riches of His glory, to be stregthened with might through His Spirit in the inner man, that Christ may dwell in your hearts through faith; that you, being rooted and grounded in love, may be able to comprehend with all the saints what is the width and length and depth and height—to know the love of Christ which passes knowledge; that you may be filled with all the fullness of God. (Ephesians 3:16-19, NKJ)

Starting at the end of the clue, write the letters in the blank spaces beginning at the top left.

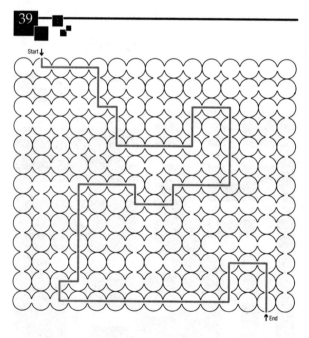

40

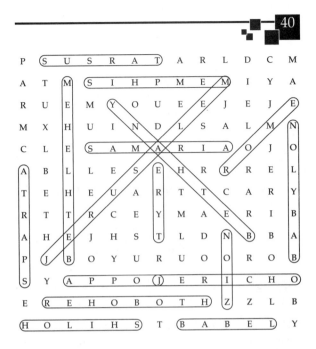

41

$$7 \times 2 \times 2 \times 17 + 150 - 40 + 10 + 3 + 4 - 3 = 600$$

42

43

Commit thy works unto the Lord, and thy
thoughts shall be established. (Proverbs 16:3)

PUZZLE ANSWERS

44

Isaiah	Jeremiah	John
Obadiah	Nahum	Ezra
Paul	Habakkuk	Zechariah
Mark	Luke	Joshua
Hosea	Ezekiel	Amos
Micah	Solomon	Moses
Malachi	James	Peter
Jude	Samuel	David
Haggai	Daniel	Matthew
Zephaniah	Jonah	

All of these people are AUTHORS
of books in the Bible.

45

And God blessed them, and God said unto
them, Be fruitful and multply, and replenish the
earth, and subdue it: and have dominion over
the fish of the sea, and over the fowl of the air,
and over every living thing that moveth upon
the earth. (Genesis 1:28)

46

Unscrambled letters: THE LORD, HE IS GOD!

47

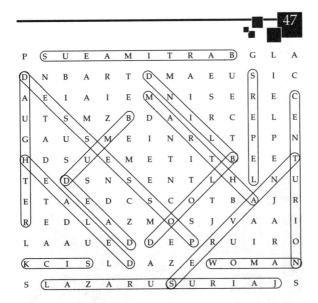

48

49

$$2 \times 40 \times 10 \div 2 + 250 - 600 + 20 = 70$$

PUZZLE ANSWERS

50

Elijah	Hosea	Nahum
Micaiah	Isaiah	Zephaniah
Jonah	Micah	Habakkuk
Elisha	Uriah	Obadiah
Amos	Jeremiah	

Response to a prophet: Hearken

51

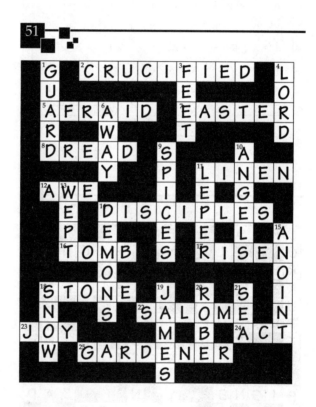

52

FREE GIFT	MERCY
SORROW	RESTORATION
REDEMPTION	SHED BLOOD OF JESUS
CONFESSION	JUSTIFICATION
RIGHTEOUSNESS	PARDON
PROPITIATION	CLEANSING
TURNING TO GOD	BAPTISM
BELIEVING	REPENTANCE
WE FORGIVE OTHERS	REMISSION OF SINS

53

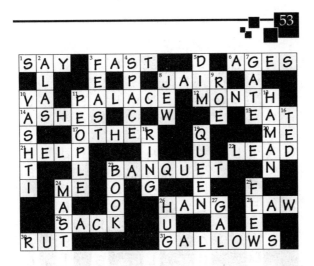

54

START

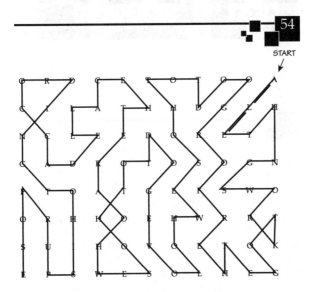

ALL THINGS WORK TOGETHER FOR GOOD TO
THOSE WHO LOVE GOD. TO THOSE WHO ARE
THE CALLED ACCORDING TO HIS PURPOSE.

PUZZLE ANSWERS

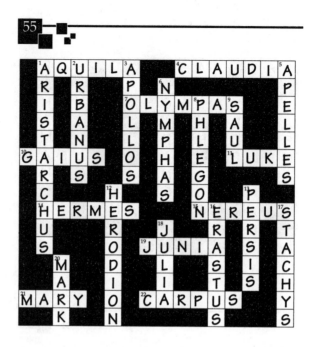

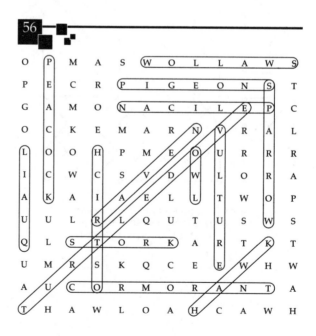

57

PAUL	ADULTERESS
MARY MAGDALENE	BARTIMAEUS
LEPER	CENTURION
SIMON PETER	DEMONIAC
JOHN	WOMAN AT WELL

BE MADE WHOLE

58

Thou shalt fear the Lord thy God, and serve him, and shalt swear by his name. (Deuteronomy 6:13)

59

60

Suffer little children, and forbid them not, to come unto me: for of such is the kingdom of heaven. (Matthew 19:14)

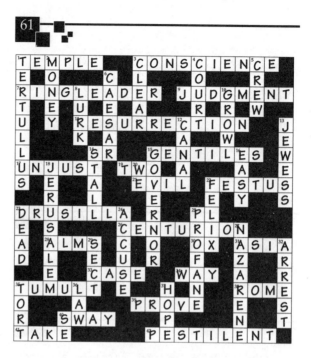

61

62

Tragedy

ill **H**ealth

t**E**ars

torme**NT**

d**E**ath

sorro**W**

mis**J**udgment

en**E**mies

wor**R**y

h**U**nger

Sin

p**A**in

fai**L**ure

pov**E**rty

punish**M**ent

63

JERUSALEM
GARMENTS
PALM
BRANCHES
COLT
JESUS
PASSOVER
FEAST

BLESSED
MOUNT OF OLIVES
REJOICE
PRAISE
PEACE
GLORY
STONES

HOSANNA

64

$$13 - 8 \times 4 + 41 + 2 \div 9 = 7$$

65

Starting at the upper left, read every other
letter on every other line to reveal the message:
BE STRONG IN THE LORD, AND IN THE
POWER OF HIS MIGHT. (Ephesians 6:10)

Reading from the bottom right corner, you'll
find this message interlocked with the command from Paul:
PRINCIPALITIES and POWERS and RULERS
OF THE DARKNESS OF THIS WORLD and
SPIRITUAL WICKEDNESS IN HIGH PLACES
and THE WILES FO THE DEVIL (Ephesians
6:11-12)

PUZZLE ANSWERS

And God said to Moses, "I am who I am."
And He said, "Thus you shall say to the
children of Israel, 'I AM has sent me to you.'"
(Exodus 3:14, NKJ)

Unscrambled letters:
HOSANNA IN THE HIGHEST

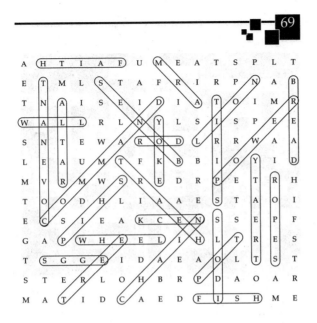

Abraham
Amminadab
Abijah
Ahaz
Abiud
Azor
Achim
Eliakim
Eliud

Eleazar
Jehoshaphat
Jotham
Josiah
Jeconiah
Jacob
Salmon
Solomon
Shealtiel

They are included in the
genealogy of Jesus Christ.

Puzzle Answers

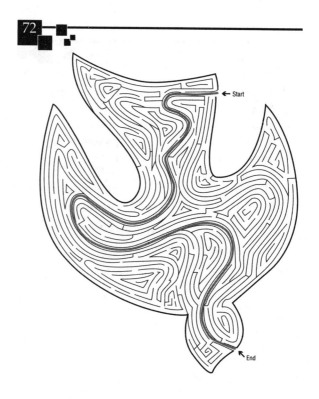

71

73

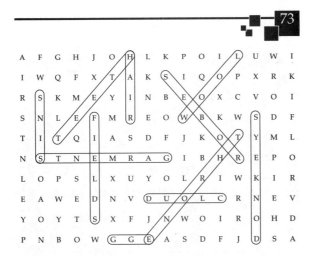

74

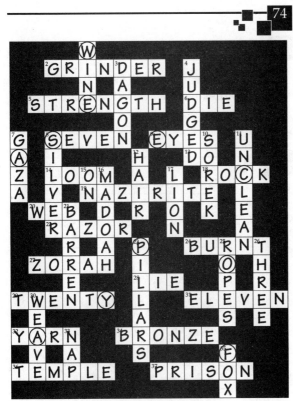

Unscrambled letters:
WAY OF ESCAPE

PUZZLE ANSWERS

75

76

Heaven and earth will pass away, but My words will by no means pass away. (Mark 13:31, NKJ)

77

```
W  D  E  R  J  E  R  U  S  A  L  E  M  C  B
T  O  P  J  N  I  M  O  L  C  P  A  L  E  H
S  E  S  I  L  O  P  O  C  I  N  T  I  L  C
R  S  A  T  I  O  H  E  R  N  U  P  L  O  O
P  U  T  E  O  L  I  I  C  O  N  I  U  M  I
I  C  E  M  W  O  L  A  E  L  O  H  W  E  T
H  A  P  O  L  E  I  M  S  A  E  T  R  Z  N
A  R  T  R  I  W  P  E  A  S  N  N  E  A  A
L  Y  S  T  R  A  P  M  E  S  R  I  O  D  I
U  S  W  I  C  N  I  L  O  E  B  R  E  D  S
S  U  N  C  P  L  A  A  R  H  V  O  E  A  G
W  A  E  R  E  B  O  T  H  T  K  C  O  I  N
W  E  R  T  S  E  A  H  D  L  O  R  I  N  G
L  S  U  S  E  H  P  E  R  A  T  H  C  Y  T
I  S  C  O  R  T  E  N  S  O  P  E  N  M  I  X
P  N  I  Y  C  Z  G  S  R  H  E  G  I  U  M
```

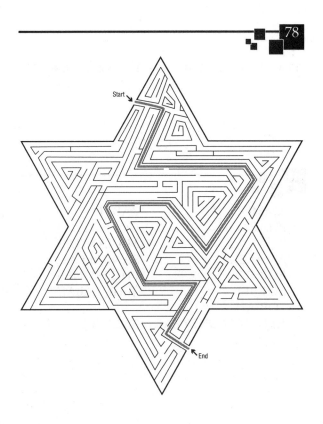

Start

End

PUZZLE ANSWERS

80

$12 + 12 - 7 - 3 + 100 - 66 + 3 = 16$ and $1 + 6 = 7$

81

AMMONITES	ZABAD
PHARAOH	GOLIATH
OG	MIDIANITES
AMALEK	SANBALLAT
EGLON	PHILISTINES
JEZEBEL	JEHOZABAD
TOBIAH	
NEBUCHADNEZZAR	ENEMIES

82

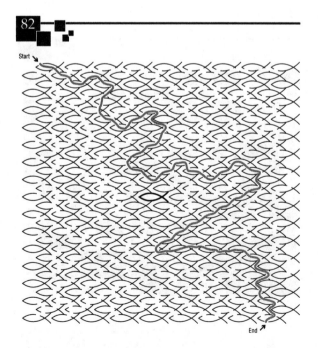

83

84

Jesus said to him, "I am the way, the truth, and the life. No one comes to the Father except through Me." (John 14:6, NKJ)

Puzzle Answers

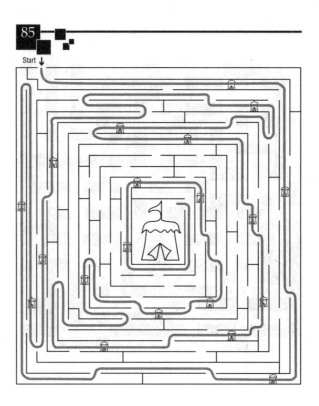

1. FIELD is the WORLD
2. GOOD SEEDS are the SONS OF THE KINDGOM
3. TARES are the SONS OF THE WICKED ONE
4. ENEMY is the DEVIL
5. HARVEST is the END OF THE AGE
6. REAPERS are the ANGELS

He who has ears to hear, let him hear!
(Matthew 13:43)

Puzzle Answers

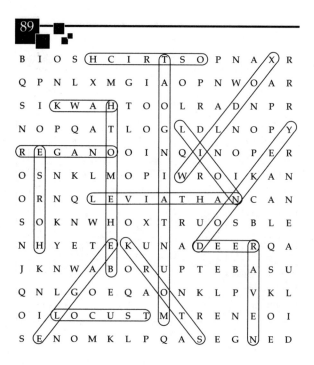

89

B I O S H C I R T S O P N A X R
Q P N L X M G I A O P N W O A R
S I K W A H T O O L R A D N P R
N O P Q A T L O G L D L N O P Y
R E G A N O O I N Q I N O P E R
O S N K L M O P I W R O I K A N
O R N Q L E V I A T H A N C A N
S O K N W H O X T R U O S B L E
N H Y E T E K U N A D E E R Q A
J K N W A B O R U P T E B A S U
Q N L G O E Q A O N K L P V K L
O I L O C U S T M T R E N E O I
S E N O M K L P Q A S E G N E D

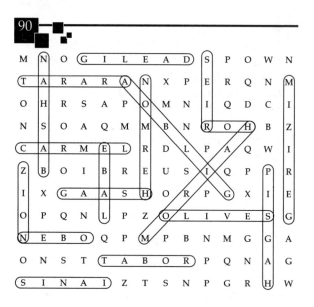

90

M N O G I L E A D S P O W N
T A R A R A N X P E R Q N M
O H R S A P O M N I Q D C I
N S O A Q M M B N R O H B Z
C A R M E L R D L P A Q W I
Z B O I B R E U S I Q P P R
I X G A A S H O R P G X I E
O P Q N L P Z O L I V E S G
N E B O Q P M P B N M G G A
O N S T A B O R P Q N A G
S I N A I Z T S N P G R H W

Blessed are them meek, for they shall inherit the earth. (Matthew 5:5)

PUZZLE ANSWERS

93

Crossword grid (answers):

| S O F T A N S W E R | S C O F F E R |

Filled-in words include:
SOFTANSWER, SCOFFER, WISDOM, RUBIES, COLD, UP, SOLOMON, BETTER, LOOK, HEART, PROUD, TRUST, CAMELS, ASTONE, LIGHT, EAT, SERPENT, TONGUE, PRAISE, LORD, EAGLE, ALL, NONE

94

BAN**Q**UET
PURIM
ZER**E**SH
HEGAI
HAMA**N**
AHASU**E**RUS
GALLOW**S**
VASH**T**I
SHUS**H**AN
F**E**ASTS
MO**R**DECAI

95

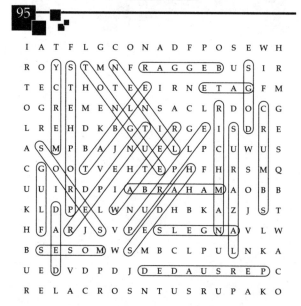

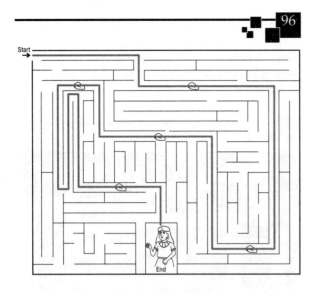

Start

End

Start

End

PUZZLE ANSWERS

Blessed are those who hunger and thirst for righteousness, for they shall be filled. (Matthew 5:6)

I will make you a great nation; I will bless you and make your name great; and you shall be a blessing. I will bless those who bless you, and I will curse him who curses you; and in you all the families of the earth shall be blessed. (Genesis 12:2–3)

101

1. **CHR**IST
2. ST**U**MBLE
3. S**N**ATCHED AWAY
4. WICKE**D** ONE
5. CA**R**ES
6. HE**A**RT
7. **D**EPTH
8. **F**RUIT
9. CH**O**KE
10. TRIBU**L**ATION
11. WOR**D** OF GOD

FREEDOM
FORGIVENESS
CONVICTION
RESTORATION
CONFESSION
CREATION
BIRTHING
CLEANSING
FAITH
RENEWAL
REPENTANCE
SUBMISSION
JOY
UNION

PUZZLE ANSWERS

104

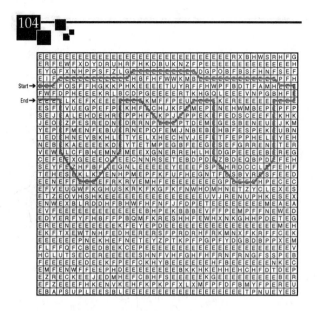

105

$$5{,}000 \div 10 \times 3 \div 12 + 38 - 6 + 4 - 1 \div 4 - 7 + 2 \times 2 = 70$$

106

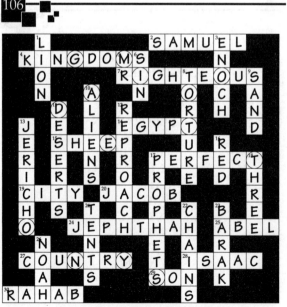

Unscrambled letters: A GOOD TESTIMONY

107

Blessed are the merciful, for they shall obtain mercy. (Matthew 5:7)

108

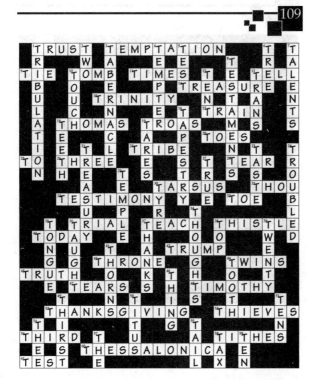

109

PUZZLE ANSWERS

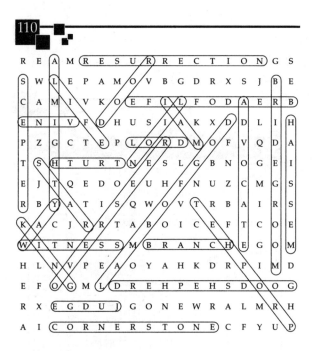

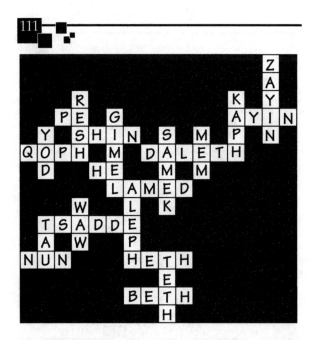

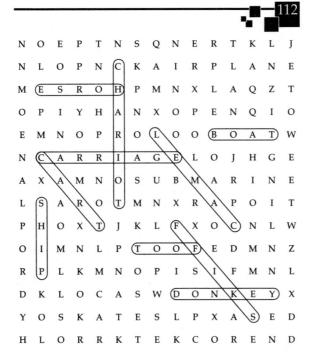

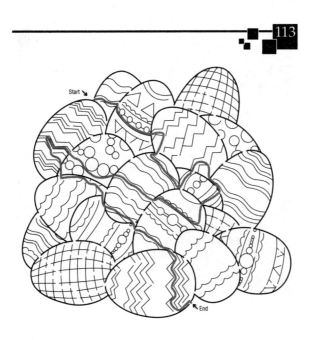

113

Puzzle Answers

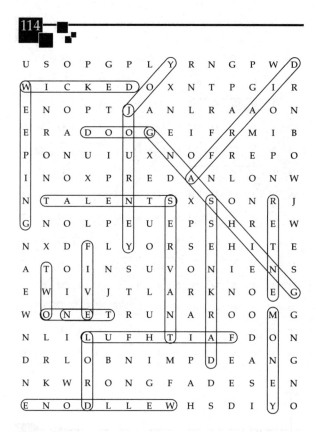

EGYPTIAN SLAVERY
MOSES APPOINTED LEADER
PLAGUES AND DEATH OF FIRSTBORN
FREEDOM
ACROSS THE RED SEA ON DRY GROUND
PHARAOH DEFEATED
WATER AND MANNA PROVIDED
MOUNT SINAI
REBELLION IN WILDERNESS OF PARAN
40 YEARS IN THE WILDERNESS
CROSSING THE JORDAN RIVER
CONQUERING CANAANITE KINGS
THE PROMISED LAND

LET MY PEOPLE GO

E	N	A	E	E	Y	M
E	D	H	D	D	W	N
R	T	T	A	N	O	I
F	H	U	N	I	R	E
U	E	R	D	S	D	D
O	T	T	Y	E	Y	I
Y	R	E	O	L	O	B
E	U	H	U	P	U	A
K	T	T	S	I	A	U
A	H	W	H	C	R	O
M	S	O	A	S	E	Y
L	H	N	L	I	M	F
L	A	K	L	D	Y	I

If you abide in My word, you are My
disciples indeed. And you shall know the
truth, and the truth shall make you free.
(John 8:31–32)

118

119

I must work the works of Him who sent me while it is day; the night is coming when no one can work. (John 9:4)

(Begin with the second letter and take every other letter to solve the puzzle. The number reference comes at the end of the string.)

WATER
EL**I**M
A**L**TAR
CLOU**D**
TRE**E**
MA**R**AH
MAN**N**A
AMAL**E**KITES
SINAI
SIN
PRAYED
OME**R**
BR**O**NZE
AD**V**ANCE
MER**I**BAH
BA**S**HAN
QUA**I**L
H**O**REB
PARA**N**

Puzzle Answers

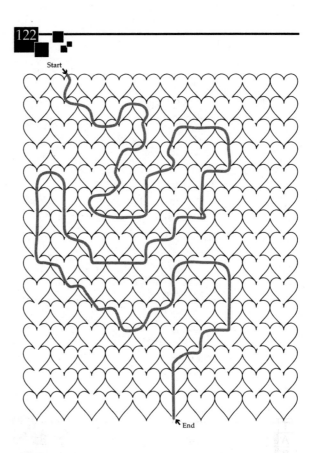

Start

End

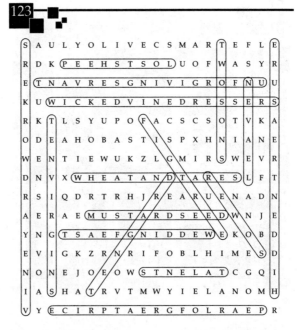

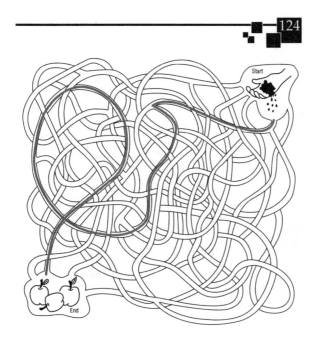

123

PUZZLE ANSWERS

126

1. Cummin	8. Grape	15. Oak
2. Rose	9. Olive	16. Henna
3. Lily	10. Palm	17. Bean
4. Gourd	11. Broom	18. Wheat
5. Mint	12. Aloe	19. Willow
6. Fig	13. Cedar	20. Almond
7. Anise	14. Apple	21. Garlic

127

Blessed are the pure in heart, for they shall see God. (Matthew 5:8)

128

$$40 - 5 + 1{,}260 \div 3.5 - 70 \div 6 + 17 - 25 - 42 = 0$$

129

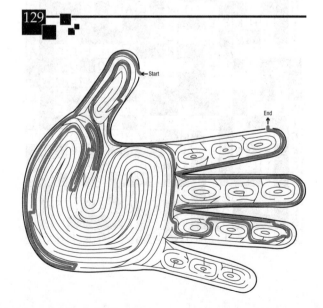

130

Bonus: Everywhere

131

Most assuredly, I say to you, he who believes in
Me, the works that I do he will do also; and
greater works than these he will do, because I go
to My Father. (John 14:12)

PUZZLE ANSWERS

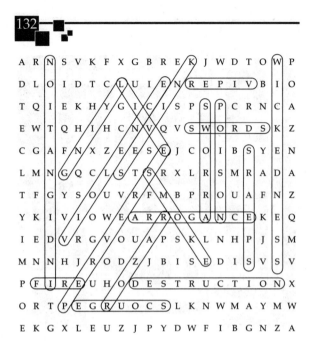

Unscrambled letters: The King is coming!

134

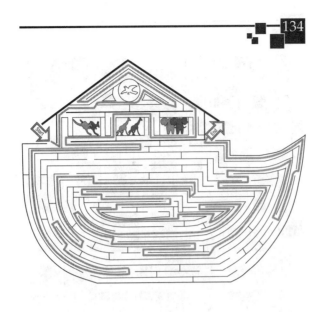

135

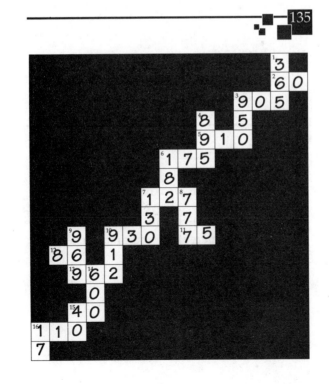

PUZZLE ANSWERS

For we do not have a High Priest who cannot sympathize with our weaknesses, but was in all points tempted as we are, yet without sin. Let us therefore come boldy to the throne of grace, that we may obtain mercy and find grace to help in time of need. (Hebrews 4:15–16)

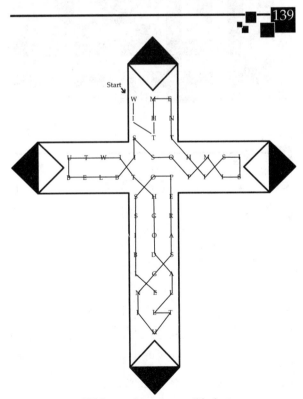

With men this is impossible, but
with God all things are possible.
(Matthew 19:26)

Puzzle Answers

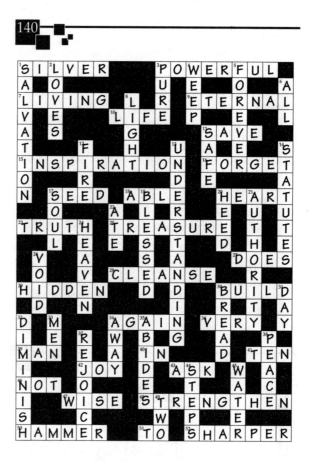

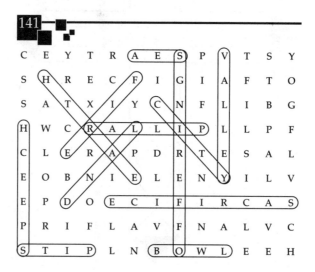

142

Blessed are the peacemakers, for they shall be called sons of God. (Matthew 5:9)

143

144

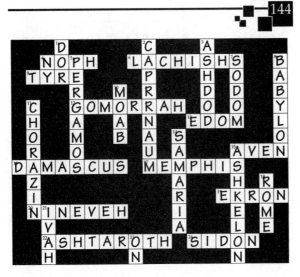

PUZZLE ANSWERS

145

Start

End

146

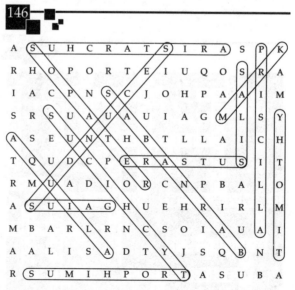

147

My food is to do the will of Him who sent Me,
and to finish His work. (John 4:34)

148

149

PUZZLE ANSWERS

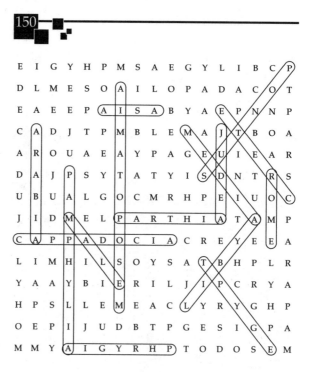

150

```
E  I  G  Y  H  P  M  S  A  E  G  Y  L  I  B  C  P
D  L  M  E  S  O  A  I  L  O  P  A  D  A  C  O  T
E  A  E  E  P  A  I  S  A  B  Y  A  E  P  N  N  P
C  A  D  J  T  P  M  B  L  E  M  A  J  T  B  O  A
A  R  O  U  A  E  A  Y  P  A  G  E  U  I  E  A  R
D  A  J  P  S  Y  T  A  T  Y  I  S  D  N  T  R  S
U  B  U  A  L  G  O  C  M  R  H  P  E  I  U  O  C
J  I  D  M  E  L  P  A  R  T  H  I  A  T  A  M  P
C  A  P  P  A  D  O  C  I  A  C  R  E  Y  E  E  A
L  I  M  H  I  L  S  O  Y  S  A  T  B  H  P  L  R
Y  A  A  Y  B  I  E  R  I  L  J  I  P  C  R  Y  A
H  P  S  L  L  E  M  E  A  C  L  Y  R  Y  G  H  P
O  E  P  I  J  U  D  B  T  P  G  E  S  I  G  P  A
M  M  Y  A  I  G  Y  R  H  P  T  O  D  O  S  E  M
```

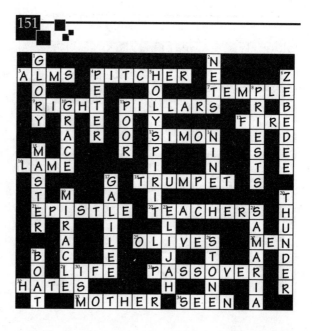

151

	¹G							²N			⁶Z
³A L M S		⁴P I T C H E R			E			
	O	E			O			⁷T E M P L E			E
⁹R I G H T	R	¹¹P I L L A R S			R			B
	R	R A		O R			¹²F I R E		E	D
	Y	A C		O R	¹³S I M O N		I		E	E
		¹⁵M	E R		P			N		S	E
¹⁶L A M E				I			T		S	E
S			¹⁷G	¹⁸T R U M P E T		S	
²¹E P I S T L E	²²T E A C H E R S	²³S	²⁰T
R	R A		L			A	H
			²⁵O L I V E S	²⁶M E N	U
²⁸B		L		J	T	A	N
O	³⁰L I F E		³¹P A S S O V E R	R	D
³²H A T E S		H		N	I	E
T	³³M O T H E R	³⁴S E E N	A	R

152

In order to read the words MENE MENE TEKEL UPHARSIN, turn the page on its side! The twenty-one letters of this phrase are in order reading from left to right.

153

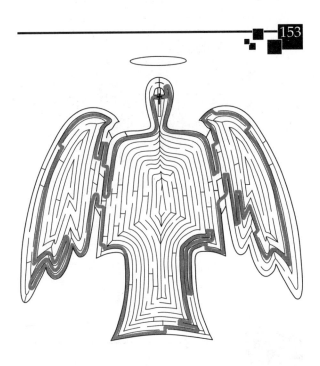

154

MENE: God has numbered your kindgom, and finished it
TEKEL: You have been weighed in the balances, and found wanting
PERES: Your kingdom has been divided, and given to the Medes and Persians

155

Blessed are those who are persecuted for righteousness' sake, for theirs is the kingdom of heaven. (Matthew 5:10)

PUZZLE ANSWERS

156

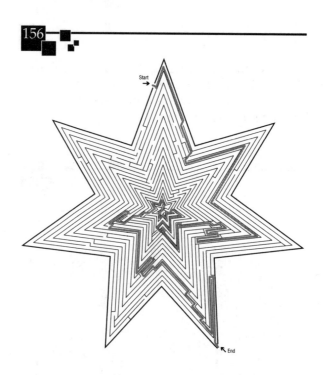

Start →

← End

157

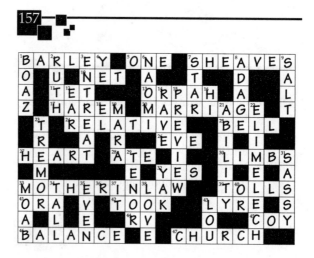

158

ABRAHAM   JOSEPH
ESAU   ISAIAH
JACOB   MOSES
SAMUEL

JOSEP**H**
   ESAU
  AB**R**AHAM
SAMU**E**L
  ISA**I**AH
    J**A**COB
     MOSES

Each of these key Bible figures said, "HERE I
AM" to the Lord or to the Lord's representative
of blessing.

159

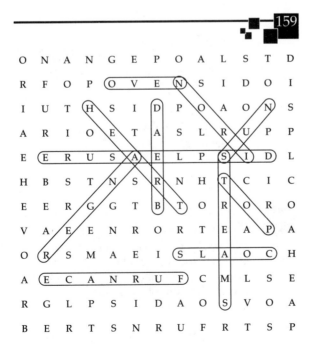

PUZZLE ANSWERS

160

GOOD SHEPHERD

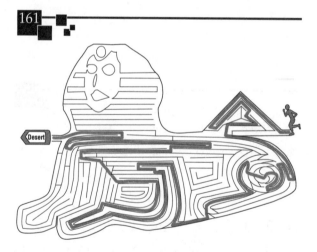

161

162

I know your works, that you are neither cold nor
hot. I could wish you were cold or hot. So then,
because your are lukewarm, and neither cold nor
not, I will vomit you out of My mouth.
(Revelation 3:15–16)

Each clue letter is two letters behind the actual
letter in the verse.

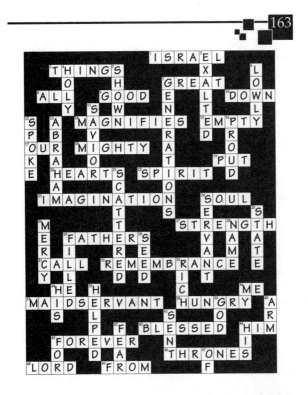

Start

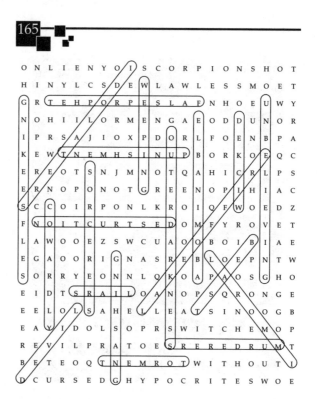

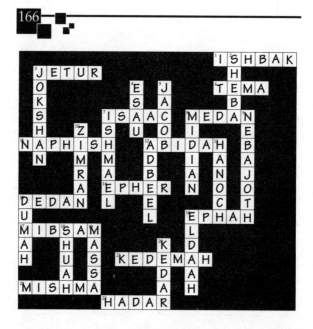

End

Start

PUZZLE ANSWERS

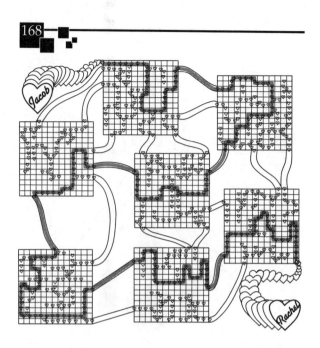

If My people who are called by My name will humble themselves, and pray and seek My face, and turn from their wicked ways, then I will hear from heaven, and will forgive their sin and heal their land. (2 Chronicles 7:14)

PUZZLE ANSWERS

172

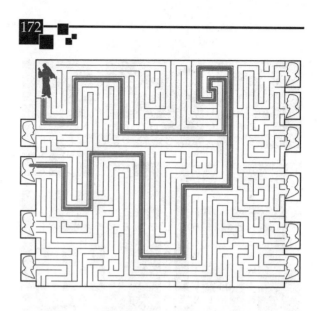

173

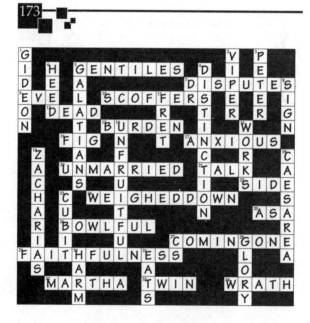

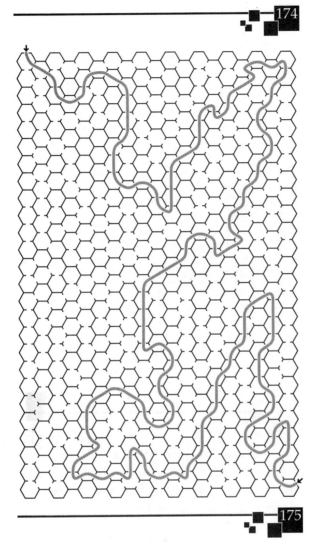

RU**T**H
JEHOS**H**ABEATH
JA**E**L
E**L**IZABETH
T**A**MAR
NAO**M**I
RE**B**EKAH
SARAH
A**B**IGAIL
DEBO**R**AH
Z**I**PPORAH
JOCHEBE**D**
AS**E**NATH

THE LAMB'S BRIDE

PUZZLE ANSWERS

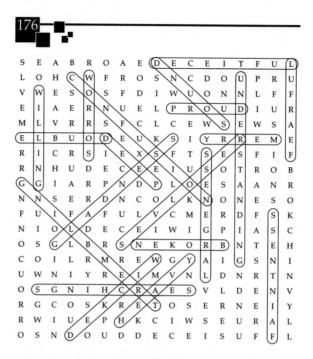

He shall be like a tree planted by the rivers of water, that brings forth its fruit in its season, whose leaf also shall not wither; and whatever he does shall prosper. (Psalm 1:3)

PUZZLE ANSWERS

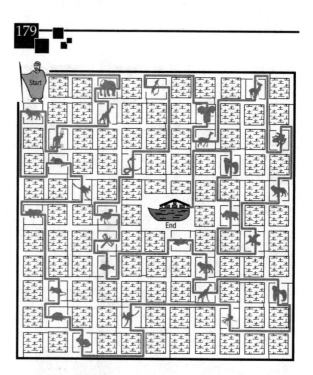

179

180

Watch, stand fast in the faith, be brave, be strong. Let all that you do be done with love. (1 Corinthians 16:13–14)

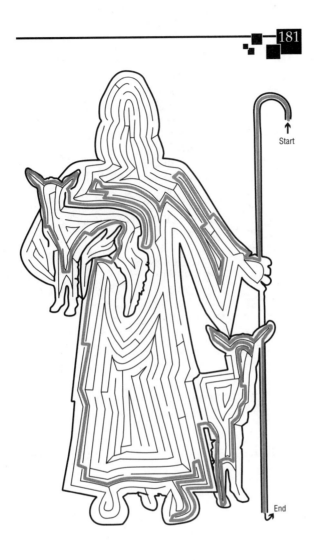

181

Start

End

HEA**R**TS
F**E**AST
JOY
S**O**NG
GOOD TH**I**NG
DAN**C**E
FI**E**LD
AGAIN **I** WILL SAY, REJOICE!
HA**N**D
GEN**T**ILES
HEAVENS
NAM**E**
LIPS
GO**O**DNESS
DESE**R**T
WOR**D**
SAL**V**ATION
EXCEEDING**L**Y
WINGS
VENGE**A**NCE
YOUTH
TRU**S**T

REJOICE IN THE LORD ALWAYS
(Philippians 4:4)

PUZZLE ANSWERS

184

STRENGTH
HAIL
THUND**E**RBOLT
TI**M**E
FOUND**A**TIONS
JOY
S**E**A
MORNING **S**TARS
DEA**T**H
TERRITOR**Y**
SN**O**W
FOOD
WA**T**ER
BREAD**T**H
IC**E**
D**A**WN
LOOSE
WISDO**M**
W**I**ND
LI**G**HT
LIG**H**TNINGS
UNDERS**T**ANDING
WA**Y**
SPRING**S**
FR**O**ST
DEW

**THE MAJESTY OF THE
ALMIGHTY GOD**

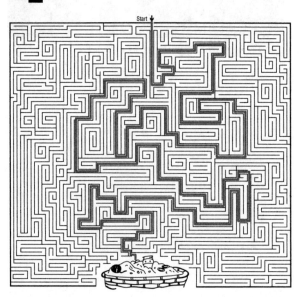

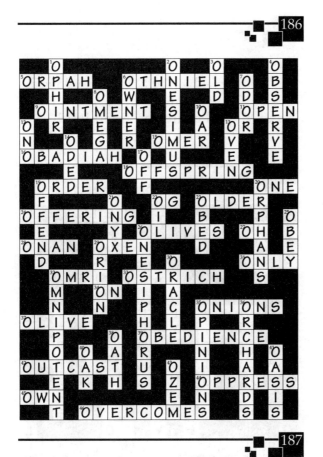

185

The crossword grid (#186) contains the following answers:

ORPAH, OTHNIEL, OINTMENT, OPEN, OMER, OBADIAH, OFFSPRING, ORDER, ONE, OG, OLDER, OFFERING, OLIVES, ONAN, OXEN, ONLY, OMRI, OSTRICH, ONIONS, OLIVE, OBEDIENCE, OATH, OUTCAST, OPPRESS, OWN, OVERCOMES

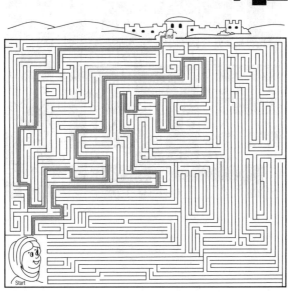

Start

End

188

5,000 − 4,000 ÷ 5 × 3 − (70 × 7) or 490
− 70 × 11 − 40 ÷ 100 × 10 − 1 + 38 + 3
− 12 − 30 − 18 − 8 ÷ 12 = 1
I and My Father are one. (John 10:30)

189

My food is to do the will of Him who sent Me, and to finish His work. (John 4:34)

PUZZLE ANSWERS

192

BO**D**Y
SH**O**WBREAD
EA**T**
FAT**H**ER
AB**I**DES
FLE**S**H
DR**I**NK
LIVI**N**G
ETE**R**NAL LIFE
UPP**E**R ROOM
EXA**M**INE
NEW COV**E**NANT
COMM**U**NION
BLOOD
FO**R**EVER
UNLE**A**VENED
HU**N**GER
PRO**C**LAIM
GAV**E** THANKS
PASS**O**VER
LI**F**E
REM**I**SSION
BR**E**AD

DO THIS IN REMEMBRANCE OF ME
(Luke 22:19)

194

Heaven and earth will pass away, but
My words will by no means pass away.
But of that day and hour no one knows,
not even the angels in heaven, nor the
Son, but only the Father.
(Mark 13:31–32)

195

196

About opposite "the fourth watch of the night"
And before "night"
And even before "evening"
After "dawn"
And after "early in the morning"
Before "the tenth hour"
And after "the third hour" of His crucifixion
Ended at the "ninth hour" when Jesus cried from the cross.
Began at "the sixth hour" when Jesus sat by the well at Sychar

The time period is the "sixth to ninth hours" (about 12 noon to 3 P.M.).

"Now when the sixth hour had come, there was darkness over the whole land until the ninth hour" [as Jesus hung on the cross]. (Mark 15:33)

197

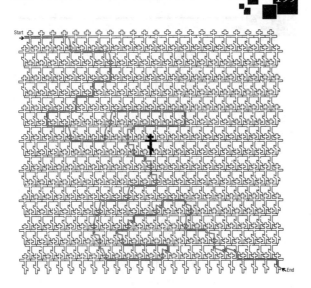

PUZZLE ANSWERS

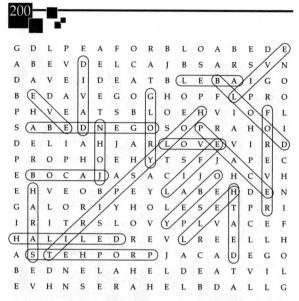

200

```
G  D  L  P  E  A  F  O  R  B  L  O  A  B  E  D  E
A  B  E  V  D  E  L  C  A  J  B  S  A  R  S  V  N
D  A  V  E  I  D  E  A  T  B  L  E  B  A  I  G  O
B  E  D  A  V  E  G  O  G  H  O  P  F  L  P  R  O
P  H  V  E  A  T  S  B  L  O  E  H  V  I  O  F  L
S  A  B  E  D  N  E  G  O  S  O  P  R  A  H  O  I
D  E  L  I  A  H  J  A  R  L  O  V  E  V  I  R  D
P  R  O  P  H  O  E  H  Y  T  S  F  J  A  P  E  C
E  B  O  C  A  J  A  S  A  C  I  J  O  H  C  V  H
E  H  V  E  O  B  P  E  Y  L  A  B  E  H  D  E  N
G  A  L  O  R  I  Y  H  O  L  E  S  E  T  P  R  I
I  R  I  T  R  S  L  O  V  Y  P  L  V  A  C  E  F
H  A  L  I  L  E  D  R  E  V  L  R  E  E  L  L  H
A  S  T  E  H  P  O  R  P  J  A  C  A  D  E  G  O
B  E  D  N  E  L  A  H  E  L  D  E  A  T  V  I  L
E  V  H  N  S  E  R  A  H  E  L  B  D  A  L  L  G
```

OBEY EVE JOHN PROPHETS LIFE SARAH
ABEL DAVID LOVE HOLY SPIRIT GLORY
ABED-NEGO DELILAH JACOB HELL
DEATH PEACE FOREVER BLOOD EVIL

201

REST
EDIFIED
MOTHER'S
ENEMIES
MATTER
BRETHREN
ENTER
RESTING
TRIBULATION
HOLY
ENJOY
SEVENTH
ASLEEP
BECAUSE
BOUNTIFULLY
ADVERSITY
TROUBLE
HALLOWED
DOVE
ARK
YOKE

REMEMBER THE SABBATH DAY

202

ISAAC　　　　　AZARIAH
JEHU　　　　　PETHUEL
NOAH　　　　　ELEAZAR
SOLOMON　　　JACOB
JEHOSHAPHAT　JESSE
AMRAM

Unscrambled letters:
INHERITANCE

203

PUZZLE ANSWERS

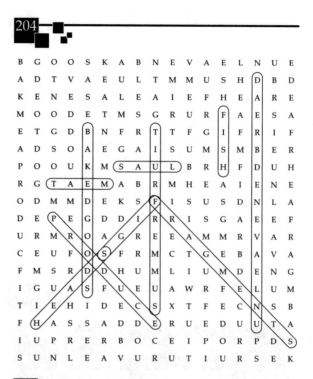

204

```
B G O O S K A B N E V A E L N U E
A D T V A E U L T M M U S H D B D
K E N E S A L E A I E F H E A R E
M O O D E T M S G R U R F A E S A
E T G D B N F R T T F G I F R I F
A D S O A E G A I S U M S M B E R
P O O U K M S A U L B R H F D U H
R G T A E M A B R M H E A I E N E
O D M M D E K S F I S U S D N L A
D E P E G D D I R R I S G A E E F
U R M R O A G R E E A M M R V A R
C E U F O S F R M C T G E B A V A
F M S R D D H U M L I U M D E N G
I G U A S F U E U A W R F E L U M
T I E H I D E C S X T F E C N S B
F H A S S A D D E R U E D U U T A
I U P R E R B O C E I P O R P D S
S U N L E A V U R U T I U R S E K
```

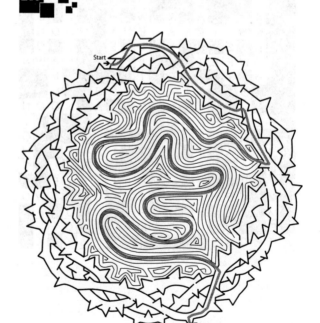

205

206

Bonus: REPENTANCE

207

Do not fear, little flock, for it is your
Father's good pleasure to give you the
kingdom. (Luke 12:32)

208

Puzzle Answers

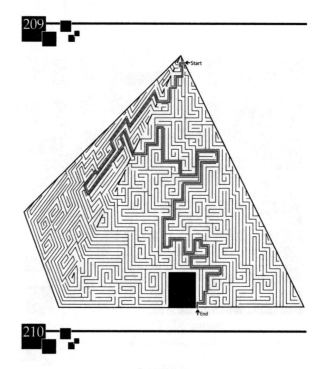

209

Start

End

210

CATTLE
HEAD
STOREHOUSES
ESTABLISH
PLENTY
ABOVE
INCREASE
TREASURE
FRUIT
COUNTRY
GO
PRODUCE
FLOCKS
WORK
BOWL
HERDS
LAND
HIGH
ENEMIES
RAIN
COME
LEND

THE BLESSING OF OBEDIENCE

211

212

$$2 \times 11 \times 6 \times 130 \times 70 \div 2 + [10 \times 5 \times 5 \times 5 \times 2 = 2{,}500] + [(12 + 12 + 12 + 12) \times 7 = 336] + [50 \times 2 = 100] + 14 = 603{,}550$$

213

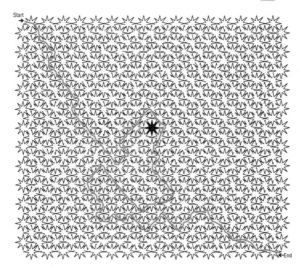

ANGELS

MULTIPLE CHOICE 1

1. When he cloaked Himself as an angel, God appeared to whom by the spring on the way to Shur?
   A. Hagar
   B. Abraham
   C. a leprechaun
   D. Sarah

2. Who appeared to Moses in the burning bush, according to Exodus 3:2?
   A. God
   B. Yahweh
   C. the Angel of the Lord
   D. The Lord of Hosts

3. How did the Angel of the Lord address Gideon?
   A. Gideon, the little wimp!
   B. Gideon, man of God
   C. Gideon, mighty warrior
   D. mighty man of valor

4. Why did the Angel of the Lord call out, "Abraham, Abraham!"
   A. so that he would turn and flee from danger
   B. so that he would not sacrifice his son Isaac
   C. because he was about to trip and fall into the animal's feeding trough, and he wanted to warn him
   D. so that he would repent from his sin and turn to God

5. What animal did an angel appear to?
   A. Balaam's donkey
   B. Cleopatra's cat
   C. Jonah's whale
   D. Samson's lion

6. The Angel of the Lord declared God's covenant of protection with Israel void at Bochim because of Israel's sin in:
   A.   not obeying God
   B.   not sacrificing all the loot they recovered on their raids
   C.   the Watergate scandal
   D.   creating idols to worship instead of God

7. Where did the Angel of the Lord sit when he appeared to Gideon?
   A.   on Gideon's cloak, in the cool of the day
   B.   on a nettle
   C.   under the terebinth tree which belonged to Gideon's father
   D.   on the roof of Gideon's home

8. What did the Angel of the Lord say to Manoah's wife?
   A.   she would give birth to Samuel
   B.   she would give birth to Isaiah
   C.   she would give birth to a submarine sandwich
   D.   she would give birth to Samson

MATCHING 1

1. Created Being

A. "Are they not all ministering spirits sent forth to minister for those who will inherit salvation?"

2. God's Servant

B. "Suddenly, a hand touched me, which made me tremble on my knees and on the palms of my hands."

3. Invisible

C. "nor can they die anymore, for they are equal to the angels and are sons of God, being sons of the resurrection."

4. Limited Spatially

D. "Praise Him, all His angels...For He commanded and they were created."

5. Organized in Ranks

E. "For by him all things were created that are in heaven and that are on the earth, visible and invisible, whether thrones or dominions or principalities or powers."

6. Named

F. "Bless the Lord, you His angels, who excel in strength, who do His word, heeding the voice of His word."

7. Unmarried

G. "For in the resurrection they neither marry nor are given in marriage, but are like angels of God in heaven."

8. Spirits

H. "Now in the sixth month the angel Gabriel was sent by God to a city of Galilee named Nazareth."

9. Undying

I. "his face was like the appearance of lightning, his eyes like torches of fire, his arms and feet like burnished bronze in color, and the sound of his words like the voice of a multitude."

MATCHING 2

1. **Hagar**

2. **Lot's Wife**

3. **Wife for Isaac**

4. **Samson's Mother**

5. **Mary's betrothed**

6. **Women at the empty tomb**

7. **Elizabeth's husband**

8. **Mary**

9. **Shepherds who came to see Mary and Jesus**

A. Gabriel announced the birth of John the Baptist to him.

B. The Angel of the Lord announced an end to her barrenness and described the special nature of her son's ministry.

C. Angels led her and her family by the hand, away from their burning home.

D. Angels announced the birth of Jesus to them near Bethlehem.

E. The Angel of the Lord gave helpful instructions, announced her future descendants, and offered comfort.

F. Gabriel told her that she empty tomb would be the mother of the Messiah, even though she had never been with a man.

G. An angel calmed his fears of band his wife's infidelity and announced her role in history to him.

H. An angel appeared to tell them that Jesus was alive.

I. An angel guided Abraham's came to see servant to the right woman.

SHORT ANSWER 1

1. What stood above the train of God's robe in Isaiah 6? _____

2. What did the seraphim look like? _____

_____

3. What did the seraphim say to one another? _____

_____

4. Who said "Holy, holy, holy, Lord God Almighty, Who was and is and is to come"

   in Revelation? _____

_____

5. What is the name of the angel who saves George Bailey's life?

_____

UNSCRAMBLE 1 *(the names for Satan)*

1. Dabadon   _____

2. Nolyopla   _____

3. Ezebelubb   _____

4. Liebla   _____

5. Lived   _____

6. Rangod   _____

7. Neyem   _____

8. Ficuler   _____

9. Tanas   _____

10. Petermt   _____

TRUE OR FALSE 1

1. Angels sleep.

_____

2. Angels are called "sons of God."

_____

3. Satan is called the god of this age.

_____

4. The angels will bring peace among men on earth when Christ returns.

_____

5. God, Himself, will separate the wicked from among the just at the end of the age.

_____

6. The angels will gather the elect from the four winds, from the farthest part of earth to the farthest part of heaven.

_____

7. An angel will bind Satan with a chain for one thousand years.

_____

8. Satan is called the angel of the bottomless pit.

_____

9. Angel hair pasta is made from actual angel hair.

_____

10. The elder, not the angel, held the golden censer at the altar.

_____

MULTIPLE CHOICE 2

1. Angels appeared to Abraham in the form of:
   A. three men
   B. white birds
   C. W-4s
   D. a multitude of women

2. The angel who appeared as a "certain man" to Daniel wore what?
   A. a turban
   B. sandals of sapphire
   C. linen
   D. a gold belt
   E. pins

3. The angel-men who wore shining garments appeared to whom at the tomb?
   A. Peter and Thomas
   B. the women who had followed Jesus from Galilee
   C. John and Peter
   D. Peter, Paul, and Mary

4. How do the angels minister in Psalm 104?
   A. with flames of fire
   B. with a spirit of justice
   C. with the Evangelism Explosion method
   D. with a rod of discipline

5. In Psalm 68, God describes his angels as twenty- thousand what?
   A. voices
   B. stars
   C. teeny-boppers
   D. chariots

6. When did an angel rescue Paul?
   A. when he had too much credit card debt
   B. when he was in a storm on the sea
   C. when he walked on water
   D. when a crowd began to stone him

7. Angels do which of the following: (more than one answer)
   A. announce events
   B. quilt
   C. attend church
   D. carry messages
   E. interpret visions
   F. appear in dreams
   G. investigate and punish sin
   H. watch over saints
   I. marry

8. Which of the following people were guided by angels?
   A. Hagar
   B. Rebekah
   C. Joseph
   D. Cornelius
   E. All of the above

ANSWERS

MULTIPLE CHOICE 1

1. A
2. C
3. D
4. B
5. A
6. A
7. C
8. D

MATCHING 1

1. D
2. F
3. E
4. B
5. I
6. H
7. G
8. A
9. J

MATCHING 2

1. E
2. C
3. I
4. B
5. G

6. H
7. A
8. F
9. D

SHORT ANSWER 1

1. Seraphim
2. Each one had six wings: two covered its face, two covered its feet, and with two it flew
3. "Holy, holy, holy is the Lord of hosts; The whole earth is full of His glory!"
4. The four living creatures, each having six wings, were full of eyes around and within.
5. Harold

UNSCRAMBLE 1

1. Abaddon
2. Apollyon
3. Beelzebub
4. Belial
5. Devil
6. Dragon
7. Enemy
8. Lucifer
9. Satan
10. Tempter

TRUE OR FALSE 1

1. False
2. True
3. True
4. False
5. False
6. True
7. True
8. True
9. False
10. False

MULTIPLE CHOICE 2

1. A
2. C, D
3. B
4. A
5. D
6. A, C, D, E, G, H
7. A, D, E, F, H
8. E

BIBLE TRANSLATIONS

MULTIPLE CHOICE 1

1. The word "Bible" literally means:
   A. the books
   B. the words of God
   C. many words, small print
   D. holy words

2. Which group of people do NOT use the New Testament?
   A. Christians
   B. Muslims
   C. Jews
   D. Saints

3. In the 18th and 19th centuries, and following, the divine inspiration of Scripture was:
   A. rejected
   B. questioned
   C. undoubtedly accepted
   D. on vacation in the Caribbean

4. Pope Leo XIII called the sacred writers:
   A. infallible geniuses
   B. boy wonders
   C. progenitors of God's will
   D. instruments of the Holy Spirit

5. Which word, meaning "a measuring rod, or a law," is the term used to describe the body of Scripture?
   A. canon
   B. rifle
   C. Torah
   D. Septuagint

6. Martin Luther suggested that which book be removed from the canon?
   A. Leviticus
   B. Gone With the Wind
   C. The Gospel of Matthew
   D. The Epistle of James

7. Which is NOT one of the three parts of the Hebrew Scriptures:
   A. Law
   B. Poetry
   C. Prophets
   D. Writings

8. Which of Josephus' rules for the Old Testament canon is incorrect:
   A. the fixed number of books
   B. that they are sacred
   C. their divine origin
   D. that they were written between the time of Moses and Artaxerxes I

TRUE OR FALSE 1

1. Catholics and Protestants agree on which books should be included in the Bible.

   ———

2. The section of the Hebrew Old Testament called "Law" is also known as "The Pentatuch."

   ———

3. "The Prophets" is the section of the Bible that Protestants know as the books of Isaiah through Malachi.

   ———

4. In 200 B. C. major religious leaders gathered together and closed the Old Testament canon.

   ———

5. The B-I-B-L-E, that's the book for me!

   ———

6. The apocrypha is the religious books not included in the canon of Scripture.

   ———

7. Most of the Old Testament was written in Hebrew, but parts were written in Aramaic and parts in Greek.

   ———

8. All of the New Testament was composed in Greek.

   ———

9. The first Old Testament book to be printed was Genesis in Bologna, A.D. 1477.

   ———

10. The Dead Sea Scrolls were discovered in caves near the ancient community of Qumran.

   ———

SHORT ANSWER 1

1. Who produced a very famous critical text of Scripture in A.D. 1882?

_____

2. What method did Westcott and Hort use in producing their text?

_____

3. What contribution did J. J. Wettstein make to the printing of the New Testament?

_____

4. The translation of the Hebrew Scriptures into Greek in the 3rd century B.C. is known as what?

_____

5. The legend surrounding the Septuagint says that this number of translators were sent from Jerusalem to Alexandria.

_____

6. St. Jerome's translation of the Scriptures into Latin was called what?

_____

7. The Vulgate was printed in A.D. 1455 by whom?

_____

8. The first Catholic Bible to be printed in the United States of America was printed in A. D. 1790 in what city?

_____

PUT THE FOLLOWING IN ORDER 1 *(from earliest to latest)*

1. Tyndale Bible _____

2. New International Version _____

3. King James Version _____

4. Revised Version _____

5. Geneva Bible _____

6. New King James Version _____

7. American Standard Version _____

MULTIPLE CHOICE 2

1. Erasmus was a member of what church?
   A. Lutheran
   B. First Baptist of Paducah
   C. Catholic
   D. Greek Orthodox

2. Groups of manuscripts that are similar are called:
   A. text-types
   B. common groups
   C. look-alikes
   D. manuscript groupings

3. Which of the text-types is the largest group?
   A. Alexandrian
   B. Byzantine
   C. Roman
   D. Coptic

4. Which text-types, older than Byzantine, came from Egypt?
   A. Alexandrian
   B. Memphian
   C. Nileian
   D. Coptic

5. Which text-type is called the Majority Text?
   A. Alexandrian
   B. Roman
   C. the one that lots of people like to use
   D. Byzantine

6. Which text-type were available to Erasmus?
   A. Byzantine
   B. Roman
   C. Coptic
   D. boldfaced Times Roman

7. Critical Texts usually include:
   A. criticism from scholars
   B. bad attitudes
   C. essays and maps
   D. alternate wordings from other manuscripts

8. Higher Criticism is when a scholar argues a text's:
   A. height
   B. author and date
   C. location
   D. validity

MATCHING 1

Bible Version

1. **King James Version**

2. **Revised Authorized Version**

3. **Revised Standard Version**

4. **New English Bible**

5. **Revised Version**

6. **New American Bible**

7. **Jerusalem Bible**

8. **American Standard Version**

9. **New International Version**

10. **New Revised**

Version It Is Based on or Translators

A. Catholic Bible Association of America

B. American Standard Version

C. Revised Standard Version

D. Bishop's Bible Bible

E. King James Version

F. New King James Version

G. New York Bible Society

H. La Bible de Jérusalem and Vulgate

I. Revised Version tional Version

J. original languages only Standard Version

UNSCRAMBLE 1 *(the Bible translations)*

1. Wne Tinarlonetian Sevrnio   _____

2. Wen Rasujemle Libeb   _____

3. Hutridoaze Risoven   _____

4. Nigvil Bleib   _____

5. Dogo Wesn Liebb   _____

6. Nestiwretsm Sonevri   _____

    fo het Lohy Pitresucr   _____

7. Viresde Danstrad Sivoner   _____

8. Siprocue Temonsm Libeb   _____

9. Lavugte Libbe   _____

10. Dacoevrel's Elbib   _____

ANSWERS

MULTIPLE CHOICE 1

1. A
2. C
3. B
4. D
5. A
6. D
7. B
8. D

TRUE OR FALSE 1

1. False
2. True
3. False (also includes Joshua through Kings)
4. False (There was never any meeting to close the Old Testament canon.)
5. Up to you!
6. True
7. True
8. True
9. False (Psalms)
10. True

SHORT ANSWER 1

1. Westcott and Hort
2. verse-by-verse comparison
3. capital letters
4. the Septuagint
5. 72, thus the "Septuagint"
6. the Vulgate
7. Johann Gutenberg
8. Philadelphia

PUT THE FOLLOWING IN ORDER 1

1. Tyndale Bible (1525)
2. Geneva Bible (1557)
3. King James Version (1611)
4. Revised Version (1881)
5. American Standard Version (1901)
6. New International Version (1973)
7. New King James Version (1982)

MULTIPLE CHOICE 2

1. C
2. A
3. B
4. D
5. D
6. A
7. D
8. B

MATCHING 1

1. D
2. F
3. B
4. J
5. E
6. A
7. H
8. I
9. G
10. C

UNSCRAMBLE 1

1. New International Version
2. New Jerusalem Bible
3. Authorized Version
4. Living Bible
5. Good News Bible
6. Westminster Version of the Holy Scriptures
7. Revised Standard Version Bible Translations
8. Precious Moments Bible
9. Vulgate Bible
10. Coverdale's Bible

ENGLISH TRANSLATIONS

English readers have had access to many versions of the Bible in the past four centuries. This list gives the date, title, and translator of over two hundred English versions of Scripture. It is based upon more extensive lists by John H. Skilton and A. S. Herbert. Where the translator's name is unknown, or where a group of translators contributed to a particular work, the version is identified by the publisher's name (shown in parentheses):

DATE	VERSION	TRANSLATOR/PUBLISHER
1526	(The New Testament: untitled)	William Tyndale
1530	The Psalter of David in Englishe	George Joye
1530	(The Pentatuch: untitled)	William Tyndale
1531?	The Prophete Jonas	William Tyndale
1534	Jeremy the Prophete, translated into Englisshe	George Joye
1534	The New Testament	George Joye
1535	Biblia: The Byble	George Coverdale
1536	The Newe Testament yet once agayne corrected	William Tyndale
1537?	(The New Testament)	Miles Coverdale
1537	The Byble	(Richard Grafton and Edward Whitchurch)
1539	The Most Sacred Bible (Taverner's Bible)	Richard Taverner

1539	The Byble in Englyshe (The Great Bible)	(Richard Grafton and Edward Whitchurch)
1539	The newe Testament of oure sauyour Jesu Christ	Miles Coverdale
1539	The Nevv Testament in Englysshe	Richard Taverner
1539	The Byble in Englyshe	(Richard Grafton and Edward Whitchurch)
1540	The Byble in Englyshe	Miles Coverdale
1548?	Certayne Psalmes chose out of the Psalter	Thomas Starnhold
1549	The first tome or volume of the Paraphrase of Erasmus vpon The newe Testament	(Edward Whitchurch)
1557	The Nevve Testament of ovr Lord Jesus Christ	William Whitingham
1560	The Bible and Holy Scriptvres conteyned in the Olde and Newe Testament (The Geneva Bible)	William Wittingham
1562	The Whole Booke of Psalmes	Thomas Starnhold and I. Hopkins
1568	The holie Bible (The Bishops' Bible)	Matthew Parker
1582	The Nevv Testament of Iesvs Christ (Rheims New Testament)	Gregory Martin
1611	The Holy Bible (The King James Version)	(Robert Barker)
1612	The Book of Psalmes	Henry Ainsworth
1657	The Dutch Annotations upon the whole Bible	Theodore Haak
1700	The Psalmes of David	C. Caryll
1726	A new version of all the Books of the New Testament	(J. Batly and S. Chandler)
1727	The books of Job, Psalms, proverbs, Eccle-seastes, and the Song of Solomon	(J. Walthoe)
1731	The New Testament...Translated out of the Latin Vlugate about 1378 by John Wiclif... about 1378	John Lewis
1741	A new version of St. Matthew's Gospel	Daniel Scott
1745	Mr. Whiston's Primitive New Testament	William Whiston
1761	Divers parts of the holy Scriptures	Mr. Mortimer
1764	All the books of the Old and New Testament	Anthony Purver

1764	The New Testament	Richard Wynne
1765	The Psalms of David	Christopher Smart
1765	The New Testament	Philip Doddridge
1768	A Liberal Translation of the New Testament	Edward Harwood
1770	The New Testament or New Covenant	John Worsley
1771	The Book of Job	Thomas Scott
1773	The Pentateuch of Moses and the Historical Books of the Old Testament	Julius Bate
1779	Isaiah	Robert Lowth
1779	Essay towards a literal English version of the New Testament, in the Epistle of the Apostle Paul directed to the Ephesians	John Callander
1782	The Gospel of St. Matthew	Gilbert Wakefield
1784	Jeremiah and Lamentations	Benjamin Blayney
1787	The First (-Fifth) Book of Moses	David Levi
1787	The Apostle Paul's First and Second Epistles to the Thessalonians	James MacKnight
1789	A new English Translation of the Pentateuch	Isaac Delgado
1789	The Four gospels	George Campbell
1790	The Book of Psalms	Stephen Street
1791	The New Testament	Gilbert Wakefield
1795	The New Testament	Thomas Haweis
1796	Jonah	George Benjoin
1796	An Attempt toward revising our English translation of the Greek Scriptures	William Newcome
1797	The Holy Bible	Alexander Geddes
1799	A Revised Translation and Interpretation of the Sacred Scriptures	David Macrae
1805	The Book of Job	Joseph Stock
1807	The Gothic Gospel of Saint Samuel	Henshall Matthew
1808	The Holy Bible	Charles Thomson
1810	The Book of Job	Elizabeth Smith
1811	Canticles: or Song of Solomon	John Fry
1812	The Book of Job	John Mason Good
1812	The New Testament	W. Williams

1816	The English Version of the Polyglott Bible	(Samuel Bagster)
1819	Lyra Davidis (Psalms)	John Fry
1822	The Epistles of Paul the Apostle	Thomas Belsham
1825	The Book of Job	George Hunt
1825	The Psalms	J. Parkhurst
1827	An Amended Version of the Book of Job	George R. Noyes
1827	Liber Ecclesiasticus, the Book of the Church	Luke Howard
1828	The Gospel of God's Anointed	Alexander Greaves
1831	The Book of Psalms	George R. Noyes
1833	A literal translation from the Hebrew of the twelve Minor Prophets	A. Pick
1833	A New and Corrected Version of the New Testament	Rodolphus Dickinson
1834	The Gospel according to Matthew	William J. Aislabie
1835	The Book of the Law from the Holy Bible (The Pentateuch)	Joseph Ablett
1837	A New Translation of the Hebrew Prophets	George R. Noyes
1837	The Gospel of John	William J. Aislabie
1843	The Gospel according to Saint Matthew, and part of the first chapter of the Gospel according to Saint Mark	Sir John Cheke
1843	Horae aramaicae: comprising concise notices of the Aramean dialects in general and of the versions of the Holy Scripture extant in them: with a translation of Matthew	J. W. Etheridge
1846	The book of Psalms	John Jebb
1846	A New Translation of the Proverbs, Ecclesiastes and the Canticles	George R. Noyes
1846	The Four Gospels from the Peschito	J. W. Etheridge
1848	The New Testament	Jonathan Morgan
1848	St. Paul's Epistle to the Romans	Herman Heinfetter
1849	The Apostolic Acts and Epistles	J. W. Etheridge
1850	The Bible Revised	Francis Barham
1851	The New Testament	James Murdock
1851	The Epistle of Paul to the Romans	Joseph Turnbull

1851	The Epistles of Paul the apostle to the Hebrews	Herman Heinfetter
1854	The Epistles of Paul the Apostle	Joseph Turnbull
1855	The Book of Genesis	Henry E. J. Howard
1855	A Translation of the Gospels	Andrews Norton
1857	The Books of Exodus and Leviticus	Henry E. J. Howard
1858	The New Testament	Leicester A. Sawyer
1859	A Revised Translation of the New Testament	W. G. Cookesley
1860	The Psalms	Lord Congleton
1861	Jewish School and Family Bible	A. Benisch
1861?	The New Testament...As Revised and Corrected by the Spirits	Leonard Thorn
1862	The New Testament	H. Highton
1863	The Holy Bible	Robert Young
1863	The Psalms	W. Kay
1863	The Book of Daniel	John Bellamy
1864	The Book of Job	J. M. Rodwell
1864	The Emphatic Diaglott	Benjamin Wilson
1867	The Minor Prophets	John Bellamy
1869	The Book of Job in metre	William Meikle
1869	The Book of Psalms	Charles Carter
1870	The New Testament	John Bowes
1871	The Book of Job	Francis Barham
1871	The Book of Psalms	Francis Barham and Edward Hare
1871	St. John's Epistles	Francis Barham
1871?	The Gospels, Acts, Epistles, and Book of Revelation	John Darby
1876	The Holy Bible	Julia E. Smith
1877	The New Testament	John Richter
1877	Revised English Bible	(Eyre and Spottiswoode)
1881	The New Testament: English Revised Version	(Kambridgel University Press)
1882?	St. Paul's Epistle to the Romans	Ferrar Fenton
1884	The Psalter...and certain Canticles	Richard Rolle
1884	The Book of Psalms	T. K. Cheyne
1884	St. Paul's Epistles in Modern English	Ferrar Fenton

1885	The Old Testament Scriptures	Helen Spurrell
1885	The Holy Bible: Revised Version	(Oxford University Press)
1894	A Translation of the Four Gospels from the Syriac of the Sinaitic Palimpsest	Agnes S. Lewis
1897	The New Dispensation: The New Testament	Robert Weekes
1898	The Book of Job	Ferrar Fenton
1898	The Twentieth Century New Testament	(W. and J. Mackay and Co.)
1898	The Four Gospels	Seymour Spencer
1899	The Old and New Testament	(J. Clarke and Co.)
1900	St. Paul's Epistle to the Romans	W. G. Rutherford
1901	The Holy Bible: American Standard Version	(Thomas Nelson and Sons)
1901	The Five Books of Moses	Ferrar Fenton
1901	The Historical New Testament	James Moffatt
1902?	The Bible in Modern English	Ferrar Fenton
1903	The Book of Psalms	Kaufman Kohler
1903	The New Testament in Modern Speech	Richard Weymouth
1903	The Revelation	Henry Forster
1904	The New Testament	Adolphus S. Worrell
1906	St. John's Gospel, Epistles, and Revelation	Henry Forster
1908	Thessalonians and Corinthians	W. G. Rutherford
1912	The Book of Ruth	R. H. J. Steuart
1913	The New Testament	James Moffatt
1914	The Poem of Job	Edward King
1916	The Wisdom of Ben-Sira (Ecclesiasticus)	W.O.E. Oesterley
1917	The Holy Scriptures according to the Masoretic text	(The Jewish Publication Society of America)
1918	The New Testament (The Shorter Bible)	Charles Foster Kent
1920?	Amos	Theodore H. Robinson
1921	The Old Testament (The Shorter Bible)	Charles Foster Kent
1921	Mark's Account of Jesus	T.W. Pym
1923	The New Testament. An American Translation	Edgar J. Goodspeed
1923	The Riverside New Testament	William G. Ballantine
1924	The Old Testament	James Moffatt

1924	Centenary Translation of the New Testament	Helen B. Montgomery
1925	Hebrews	F. H. Wales
1927	The Old Testament	J. M. Powis Smith, T.J. Meek, Alexander R. Gordon, Leroy Waterman
1927	St. Matthew's Gospel	(T. and T. Clark)
1928	The Psalms Complete	William W. Martin
1928	The Christian's Bible: New Testament	George LeFevre
1933	The Four Gospels according to the Eastern Version	George M. Lamsa
1933	The Four Gospels	Charles C. Torrey
1936	The Song of Songs	W. O. E. Oesterley
1937	The Psalms and the Canticles of the Divine Office	George O'Neill
1937	The New Testament	Johannes Greber
1937	The New Testament	Charles B. Williams
1937	St. Paul from the Trenches	Gerald Cornish
1938	Job	George O'Neill
1938	The New Testament	Edgar M. Clementson
1939	Ecclesiasticus	A. D. Power
1944	The New Testament	Ronald A. Knox
1945	The Berkeley Version of the New Testament	Gerrit Verkuyl
1946	The Psalms . . . Also the Canticles of the Roman Breviary	(Benziger Bros.)
1946	The New Testament (Revised Standard Version)	(Thomas Nelson and Sons)
1947	The Psalms Ronald	A. Knox
1947	The New Testament	George Swann
1947	Letters to Young Churches: Epistles of the New Testament	J. B. Phillips
1949	The Old Testament	Ronald A. Knox
1950	The New Testament of Our Messiah and Saviour Yahshua	A. B. Traina
1950	New World Translation: New Testament	(Watchtower Bible and Tract Society)
1952	The Four Gospels	E.V. Rieu

1952	The Holy Bible: Revised Standard Version	(Thomas Nelson and Sons)
1954	The New Testament	James A. Kliest and Joseph Lilly
1954	The Amplified Bible: Gospel of John	The Lockman Foundation
1955	The Authentic New Testament	Hugh J. Schonfield
1956	The Inspired Letters in Clearest English	Frank C. Laubach
1957	The Holy Bible from Ancient Eastern Manuscripts	George M. Lamsa
1958	The New Testament in Modern English	J. B. Phillips
1958	The Amplified Bible: New Testament	The Lockman Foundation
1959	The Holy Bible: The Berkeley Version in Modern English	(Zondervan Publishing Co.)
1960	The Holy Bible (New American Standard)	(Thomas Nelson and Sons)
1960	The New World Translation: Old Testament	(Watchtower Bible and Tract Society, Inc.)
1961	The New English Bible: New Testament	(Oxford University Press and Cambridge University Press)
1962	The Children's Version of the Holy Bible	J. P. Green
1962	Modern King James Version of the Holy Bible	(McGraw-Hill)
1962	Living Letters: The Paraphrased Epistles	Kenneth Taylor
1962	The Amplified Bible: Old Testament Part II	The Lockman Foundation
1962	The New Jewish Version	Jewish Publication Society
1963	The New Testament in the Language of Today	William Beck
1963	The New American Standard Bible: New Testament	The Lockman Foundation
1964	The Amplified Bible: Old Testament Part I	The Lockman Foundation
1966	Good News for Modern Man: The New Testament	(American Bible Society)
1966	The Living Scriptures: A New Translation in the King James Tradition	(American Bible Society)
1966	The Jerusalem Bible	
1968	The Cotton Patch Version of Paul's Epistles	Clarence Jordan
1968	The New Testament of Our Master and Saviour	(Missionary Dispensary Bible Research)
1969	The New Testament: A New Translation	William Barclay

1969	Modern Language New Testament	(Zondervan Publishing Co.)
1969	The Cotton Patch Version of Luke and Acts	Clarence Jordan
1970	New American Bible	(St. Anthony Guild Press)
1970	New English Bible	(Oxford University Press and Cambridge University Press)
1970	The Cotton Patch Version of Matthew and John	Clarence Jordan
1971	Letters from Paul	Boyce Black-Welder
1971	New American Standard Bible	The Lockman Foundation
1971	King James II Version of the Bible	(Associated Publishers and Authors)
1971	The Living Bible	(Tyndale House)
1972	The New Testament in Modern English, Revised Edition	J.B. Phillips
1973	The New International Version: New Testament	(Zondervan Bible Publishers)
1973	The Translator's New Testament	(The British and Foreign Bible Society)
1973	The Cotton Patch Version of Hebrews and the General Epistles	Clarence Jordan
1973	The Poetic Bible	Veo Gray
1976	Good News Bible	(American Bible Society)
1977	The Holy Bible in the Language of Today	William Beck
1978	The New International Version	(Zondervan Bible Publishers)
1979	The New King James Version: New Testament	(Thomas Nelson Publishers)
1982	The Holy Bible, New King James Version	(Thomas Nelson Publishers)
1986	The New Jerusalem Bible	
1989	New Revised Standard Bible	(Thomas Nelson Publishers and others)
1989	Revised English Bible	(Oxford University Press and Cambridge University Press)
1991	Contemporary English Version New Testament	(American Bible Society and Thomas Nelson Publishers)
1995	Contemporary English Version	(American Bible Society and Thomas Nelson Publishers)
1996	New Living Bible	(Tyndale Publishers)

FAMOUS (AND NOT-SO FAMOUS) FIGURES

MULTIPLE CHOICE 1

1. Who hovered over the surface of the waters during Creation?
   A. arch-angels
   B. cherubim and seraphim
   C. the Spirit of God
   D. Adam and Eve

2. Adam's name means:
   A. man
   B. earth
   C. first person
   D. mankind's sorrow

3. Eve's name means:
   A. mother of all people
   B. life-giver
   C. lover of fruit
   D. woman

4. In which order were Adam, Eve, and the serpent cursed?
   A. Adam, Eve, Serpent
   B. Eve, Adam, Serpent
   C. Serpent, Eve, Adam
   D. Kappa Alpha Order

MATCHING 1

1. Sarah	*A.* King Ahasuerus
2. Zipporah	*B.* Samuel
3. Gilbert	*C.* Moses
4. Rachel	*D.* Jacob
5. Potiphar's Wife	*E.* David
6. Esther	*F.* Abraham
7. Rebekah	*G.* Sullivan
8. Michal	*H.* Joseph
9. Hagar	*I.* Isaac
10. Hannah	*J.* Ishmael

SHORT ANSWER 1

1. Of whom was it said, "This one shall give us rest from our work and from the toil of our hands arising from the ground which the Lord has cursed"?

_____

_____

2. Who said the following to whom? "Please let there be no strife between you and me, nor between my herdsmen and your herdsmen, for we are brothers."

_____

_____

3. List the ten miraculous deeds that the Lord performed through Moses and Aaron before Pharaoh.

_____

_____

4. Name Job's three friends.

_____

_____

_____

5. Define the following names of God.

   A. Abba

_____

_____

B. Shaddai

_____

_____

C. 'Elohim

_____

_____

D. 'Adonai

_____

_____

E. Yahweh

_____

_____

TRUE OR FALSE 1

1. Miriam became leprous when she questioned God's speaking through Moses alone.

   ____

2. Sarah and Abraham had the same father.

   ____

3. Isaac loved Jacob and Rebekah loved Esau.

   ____

4. The phrase "Holiness to the Lord" appeared on a priest's turban.

   ____

5. Chedorlaomer was an ancient Sumerian love poem.

   ____

6. The sun obeyed Joshua's command to stand still.

   ____

7. Samson's wife was a Moabite.

   ____

8. Saul was made King by his people in Israel.

   ____

9. Cyrus, the Persian King, declared that the captive Israelites should leave his land and build a temple for their Lord.

   ____

10. The Philistines sold the people of Judah and Jerusalem to the Greeks.

    ____

MULTIPLE CHOICE 2

1. Jesus' birth to a virgin was predicted by which Old Testament Prophet?
   A. Daniel
   B. Isaiah
   C. Jeremiah
   D. Nebuchadnezzar

2. Jesus' birth in Bethlehem was predicted by which Old Testament prophet?
   A. Micah
   B. Isaiah
   C. Saul
   D. Ezekiel

3. What did Tamar, Rahab, Ruth, and Mary have in common?
   A. They all are mentioned in the book of Exodus.
   B. They are all in the genealogy of Jesus.
   C. They all sang songs to God's glory.
   D. They were all Jewish.

4. What did Herod the tetrarch give to his wife's daughter for her birthday?
   A. silk from the Orient
   B. a fortress beside the Dead Sea
   C. the head of John the Baptist
   D. the city of Tiberias

5. Which Jewish sect did not believe in the resurrection of the dead?
   A. the Pharisees
   B. the Sadducees
   C. the Zealots
   D. the Platonists

FILL IN THE BLANKS 1

1. This queen's servant was converted by Philip on the road from Jerusalem to

Gaza: _____.

2. On Paul's first missionary journey he traveled to _____.

3. The book of Philemon is written about a _____.

MATCHING 2

1. Ethiopian Eunuch

2. Jesus (after the resurrection)

3. Saul

4. Jesus and Simon a Cyrenian

A. the Road to Damascus

B. the Road to Golgotha

C. the Road to Emmaus

D. the Road from Jerusalem to Gaza

TRUE OR FALSE 2

1. Titus went to work with the Corinthians.

_____

2. Paul tells the Galatians how he confronted Andrew face to face in Antioch.

_____

3. Paul speaks of the Whole Armor of God in Ephesians.

_____

4. Paul was married.

_____

5. Onesimus was a runaway slave of the household of Philemon.

_____

6. Hebrews was written by Paul.

_____

7. Joseph worried about how Mary's pregnancy would look to other people.

_____

8. John wrote, in Revelation, that the church of Ephesus lost their love for Jesus.

_____

9. Jezebel appears in the book of Revelation and encourages believers at Smyrna to worship false gods.

_____

SHORT ANSWER 2

1. The apostle formerly known as Saul

   _____

2. The seas struck during this trumpet's blast

   _____

3. The title of this book means "Law"

   _____

4. She laughed when told she would have a child

   _____

5. The last line of this 48-chapter book: "The Lord is there."

   _____

6. This angel had a flaming sword that "turned every direction" while he guarded the tree of life

   _____

7. This woman was saved from Jericho by placing a scarlet rope outside her window

   _____

8. This Old Testament figure asked to be a vegetarian

   _____

9. This man blew trumpets and smashed pitchers to destroy an army

   _____

10. The governor of Judah (in Haggai 2:21)

    _____

11. What Mordecai and others put on their heads when they are desperate before God

_____

12. Revelation's Seventh Seal

_____

13. Adam, Eve, and this were cursed in the Fall

_____

14. Pharaoh's relative that discovered Moses in a basket

_____

15. The tax collecters were criticized for this

_____

16. One name for Jesus

_____

17. Abraham would have as many children as this

_____

18. Sacrificed in place of Isaac

_____

19. What Lazarus called Mary or Martha

_____

20. The first five books of the Bible

_____

21. This king of Salem and famous High Priest blessed Abraham

_____

ANSWERS

MULTIPLE CHOICE 1

1. C
2. A
3. B
4. C

MATCHING 1

1. F
2. C
3. G
4. D
5. H
6. A
7. I
8. E
9. J
10. B

SHORT ANSWER 1

1. Noah
2. Water in the Nile turned to blood
   Frogs invade the land
   Lice
   Egyptian cattle die
   Plague of boils
   Plague of hail
   Plague of locusts
   Darkness over Egypt
   Death of First Born
4. Eliphaz, Bildad, Zophar
5. Abba—Daddy
   Shaddai—Almighty All-Powerful God
   'Elohim—God;
   The Creator 'Adonai—Lord;
   The Master Yahweh—LORD; the most intimate name for God; the Israelites wrote it without the vowels: YHWH

TRUE OR FALSE 1

1. True
2. True
3. False
4. True
5. False
6. True
7. False
8. False
9. True
10. True

MULTIPLE CHOICE 2

1. B
2. A
3. B
4. C
5. B

FILL IN THE BLANKS 1

1. Candace, Queen of Ethopia
2. Galatia and Cyprus
3. runaway slave

MATCHING 2

1. D
2. C
3. A
4. B

TRUE OR FALSE 2

1. True
2. False
3. True
4. True
5. Traditionally believed to be False. However, a close study of Philippians 4 raises doubts. In Phil 4:3 Paul addresses his "true companion," which is, in the Greek, the word used for spouse—it literally means "yoke fellow."
6. True
7. False. The author of Hebrews is unknown.
8. True
9. True

SHORT ANSWER 2

1. Apostle Paul
2. The Second
3. Leviticus
4. Sarah
5. Ezekiel
6. Cherubim
7. Rahab
8. Daniel
9. Gideon
10. Zerubbabel
11. Ashes
12. Trumpets
13. Snake
14. Daughter
15. Usury
16. The Teacher
17. Sands
18. Ram
19. Sister
20. Pentatuch
21. Melchizedek

MIRACLES

SHORT ANSWER 1

1. What is the first miracle?

_____

_____

2. How did Enoch die?

_____

_____

3. Where did God enact the miracle of confusing language?

_____

_____

4. What did God do to Pharaoh's house when Sarah stayed there under the guise of Abraham's sister?

_____

_____

5. What miracle occurred when God changed Sarai's name to Sarah?

_____

_____

6. What did the angels do to the men who approached Lot's home?

_____

_____

7. How did God destroy Sodom?

_____

_____

8. How did Lot's wife die?

_____

_____

MULTIPLE CHOICE 1

1. What was Moses doing when God appeared to him in the burning bush?
   A. drawing water from his father-in-law's well
   B. tending his father-in-law's sheep
   C. tending his own sheep
   D. taking a nap

2. Why was Moses' rod turned into a serpent?
   A. to impress Pharaoh
   B. for extra protection from Pharaoh
   C. so that the Egyptians would believe God had appeared to Moses
   D. to shock the people into obedience

3. What happened when Moses put his hand in his bosom?
   A. it turned leprous
   B. it fell off
   C. he passed out
   D. it bled but no skin was broken

4. Which miracles did Moses and God talk about at the burning bush?
   A. his rod turning into a serpent
   B. parting the Red Sea
   C. his hand becoming leprous
   D. water from the Nile turning to blood

5. When Moses and Aaron turned the water to blood how much water was affected?
   A. just the water in the Nile
   B. the water in the Nile, as well as ponds and tributaries
   C. the water in the Nile, ponds, tributaries, buckets and pitchers
   D. only the water at Pharaoh's feet

6. Pharaoh's magicians imitated which of the Lord's miraculous plagues on Egypt?
   A. frogs
   B. lice
   C. darkness
   D. bubonic

7. What did Aaron strike that became lice?
    A. a nerve
    B. stone
    C. wood
    D. dust

8. Pharaoh's magicians gave credit to whom for the plague of lice?
    A. Baal
    B. God
    C. Ra
    D. Anat

9. Which of the following miracles occurred on the way to Sinai?
    A. healing the bitter waters
    B. multiplication of the loaves and fishes
    C. quail provided by God
    D. victory over Amalek

10. Which of the following were miracles of Elijah?
    A. multiplies oil
    B. multiplies food
    C. restores rains
    D. purifies poison

11. Which of the following were miracles of Elisha?
    A. heals a spring
    B. purifies poison
    C. brings a drought
    D. destroys alter of Baal

12. Which of the following miracles happened in Daniel?
    A. Writing on the wall
    B. idol of Dagon falls on its face
    C. King Nebuchadnezzar's madness
    D. Israel delivered from captivity

UNSCRAMBLE 1 (the objects of miracles)

1. Erd Ase _____

2. Nideogs Elefec _____

3. Ticy fo Reijoch _____

4. Loi _____

5. Dojarn Evirr _____

6. Nilos Ned _____

7. Niew _____

8. Mostr _____

SHORT ANSWER 2

1. What happened to Aaron's rod that signified his family should be the priestly family?

_____

_____

2. What did God send among the Israelites when they complained about their food and water?

_____

_____

3. What did Balaam's donkey say to him when he saw the angel?

_____

_____

4. How did Balaam react when the donkey spoke to him?

_____

_____

5. How did God separate the waters of the Jordan River?

_____

_____

6. What did the Israelites do differently on their seventh trip around Jericho?

_____

_____

7. Who commanded the sun to stand still, and it did?

_____

_____

8. God chased and killed the Amorites with what force of nature?

_____

_____

MULTIPLE CHOICE 2

1. Jesus turned water into wine at:
　A. a wedding in Nazareth, his hometown
　B. a wedding in Cana of Galilee
　C. Jehosaphat's home
　D. a wedding in Damascus

2. Jesus healed the nobleman's son in:
　A. Cana of Galilee
　B. Timbuktu
　C. Damascus
　D. Bethsaida

3. Jesus cast out an unclean spirit while preaching in a synagogue after it said to him:
　A. I am a legion, and I will destroy your work in the world.
　B. I am a legion, and I know who you are—Son of Man.
　C. I will return
　D. I know who You are—the Holy One of God!

4. Jesus healed Peter's mother of:
　A. a demon
　B. a tumor
　C. a high fever
　D. the stress Peter caused her

5. Whose boat was Jesus in when he miraculously caught a great number of fish?
　A. Simon Peter's
　B. John's
　C. Tiberius's

6. The man who was let in through the roof to see Jesus was:
   A. dead
   B. paralyzed
   C. sick with a high fever
   D. deaf

7. When Jesus healed the man at the pool of Bethesda, he told:
   A. the Pharisees, who sought to know where he lived
   B. the children
   C. the Roman government, who sought to silence him
   D. the Jews, who sought to kill him

8. The centurion believed that Jesus only had to do what for his servant to be healed?
   A. say the word
   B. touch him
   C. burn incense
   D. send one of his disciples

TRUE OR FALSE 1

1. Jesus raised the son of the widow of Nain from the dead.

_____

2. Jesus calmed the storm the same day that he told the parable of the sower.

_____

3. The hemorrhaging woman was healed after she told Jesus she believed that he was the Christ.

_____

4. The man whose daughter was healed was the ruler of the centurions.

_____

5. Jesus healed two blind men who followed him and said, "Son of David, have mercy on us!"

_____

6. Jesus fed the five thousand barley loaves and fish.

_____

7. Jesus and the twelve disciples starred in the musical about their lives called Godspell.

_____

8. After Jesus walked on the water, he got in the boat with the disciples and immediately the boat was at the place where they were going.

_____

9. Jesus told the mother of the demon-possessed girl that it is not good to throw the children's food to the dogs

_____

10. To heal the deaf and dumb man, Jesus put His fingers in his ears, spat, touched his tongue, sighed and said, "Be opened," and he was healed.

_____

MATCHING 1

1. deaf and dumb man healed

2. man born blind healed

3. woman bound by Satan healed

4. man with dropsy healed

5. Lazarus raised from the dead

6. ten lepers healed

7. second catch of fish

8. graves opened at Calvary

9. Jesus' graveclothes were undisturbed

10. two disciples see the resurrected Jesus

A. Matthew

B. Mark

C. Luke

D. John

ANSWERS

SHORT ANSWER 1

1. Creation
2. He didn't.
3. Tower of Babel
4. plagued them
5. fertility
6. struck them with blindness
7. with brimstone and fire
8. She turned into salt.

MULTIPLE CHOICE 1

1. B
2. C
3. A
4. A, C, D
5. C
6. A
7. D
8. B
9. A, C, D
10. B, C
11. A, B
12. A, C

UNSCRAMBLE 1

1. Red Sea
2. Gideon's Fleece
3. City of Jericho
4. Oil
5. Jordan River
6. Lions' Den
7. Wine
8. Storm

SHORT ANSWER 2

1. this rod put forth buds and blossoms
2. fiery serpents
3. What have I done to you, that you have struck me these three times?
4. answered his question
5. the elders put their feet in and the water piled in a heap
6. shouted
7. Joshua
8. hailstorm

MULTIPLE CHOICE 2

1. B
2. A
3. D
4. C
5. A
6. B
7. D
8. A

TRUE OR FALSE 1

1. True
2. True
3. False
4. False
5. True
6. True
7. False
8. True
9. True
10. True

MATCHING 1

1. B
2. D
3. C
4. C
5. D
6. C
7. D
8. A
9. D
10. C

THE MIRACLES OF JESUS CHRIST

1. Cleansing a Leper Matthew 8:2; Mark 1:40; Luke 5:12
2. Healing a Centurion's Servant of Paralysis Matthew 8:5; Luke 7:1
3. Healing Peter's Mother-in-Law Matthew 8:14; Mark 1:30; Luke 4:38
4. Healing the Sick at Evening Matthew 8:16; Mark 1:32; Luke 4:40
5. Stilling the Storm Mathew 8:23; Mark 4:35; Luke 8:22
6. Demons Entering a Herd of Swine Mathew 8:28; Mark 5:1; Luke 8:26
7. Healing a Paralytic Mathew 9:2; Mark 2:3; Luke 5:18
8. Raising the Ruler's Daughter Mathew 9:18, 23; Mark 5:22, 35; Luke 8:40,49
9. Healing the Hemorrhaging Woman Mathew 9:20; Mark 5:25; Luke 8:43
10. Healing Two Blind Men Mathew 9:27
11. Curing a Demon-possessed, Mute Man Mathew 9:32
12. Healing a Man's Withered Hand Mathew 12:9; Mark 3:1; Luke 6:6
13. Curing a Demon-possessed, Blind and Mute Man Mathew 12:22; Luke 11:14
14. Feeding the Five Thousand Matthew 14:13; Mark 6:30; Luke 9:10; John 6:1
15. Walking on the Sea Matthew 14:25; Mark 6:48; John 6:19
16. Healing the Gentile Woman's Daughter Matthew 15:21; Mark 7:24
17. Feeding the Four Thousand Matthew 15:32; Mark 8:1
18. Healing the Epileptic Boy Matthew 17:14; Mark 9:17; Luke 9:38
19. Temple Tax in the Fish's Mouth Matthew 17:24
20. Healing Two Blind Men Matthew 20:30; Mark 10:46; Luke 18:35
21. Withering the Fig Tree Matthew 21:18; Mark 11:12
22. Casting Out an Unclean Spirit Mark 1:23; Luke 14:33
23. Healing a Deaf Mute Mark 7:31
24. Healing a Blind Paralytic at Bethsaida Mark 8:22
25. Escape from the Hostile Multitude Luke 4:30
26. Draught of Fish Luke 5:1
27. Raising of a Widow's Son at Nain Luke 7:11
28. Healing the Infirm, Bent Woman Luke 13:11
29. Healing a Man with Dropsy Luke 14:1
30. Cleansing the Ten Lepers Luke 17:11
31. Restoring a Servant's Ear Luke 22:51
32. Turning Water into Wine John 2:1
33. Healing the Nobleman's Son of Fever John 4:46
34. Healing an Infirm Man at Bethesda John 5:1
35. Healing the Man Born Blind John 9:1
36. Raising of Lazarus John 11:43
37. Second Drought of Fish John 21:1

OTHER GODS OF OTHER NATIONS

MULTIPLE CHOICE 1

1. Anat (or Anath) was a(n):
    A. Amorite warrior goddess
    B. Hittite love goddess
    C. Philistine goddess of wheat
    D. God of the harvest

2. Anat is a virgin and also:
    A. slave
    B. queen
    C. wet nurse
    D. deer

3. The first mention of Anat is around:
    A. 2000 A.D. —the new millenium!
    B. 1780 B.C.
    C. 1581 B.C.
    D. 572 B.C.

4. Asherah was the Canaanite mother of all the gods and represented:
    A. life giving and the primeval sea
    B. familial relationships
    C. perfect parenting
    D. music and peace

5. Asherah was the principal goddess of:
   A. the landlocked cities Ephesus and Alexandria
   B. Damascus Other Gods of Other Nations
   C. the lost city of Atlantis
   D. the coastal cities Tyre and Sidon

6. Canaanites considered Asherah to be a consort of:
   A. Anat
   B. the Israelite's God, El
   C. Hector
   D. Ninlil

7. Asherah's sons are:
   A. Tree, Tornado, Snow
   B. Life, Death, and Humanity
   C. Waves, Death, and Rabbim (the Many)
   D. Water, Fire, and Sky

8. The Phonecians created images of Asherah as a:
   A. pole
   B. dog
   C. elephant
   D. cat

TRUE OR FALSE 1

1. Astarte was the sister of Baal.

_____

2. Astarte was the goddess of war, love, storms, the storehouse, and the evening star.

_____

3. Solomon built a "high place" for Astarte.

_____

4. Athar replaced Baal as high god of the Canaanites.

_____

5. Baal was the father of Dagon.

_____

6. The Greek god Zeus is derived from Baal.

_____

7. Dagon, god of the Philistines, fell on his face before the ark of the covenant.

_____

8. The Philistine god Dagon and the Sumerian goddess Ninlil went to prom together.

_____

9. The Canaanites thought of Elohim as a bull, thus the golden calf.

_____

10. Horon was a major Canaanite god, the god of the underworld.

_____

SHORT ANSWER 1

1. Which Egyptian diety was only viewed as an animal and never as a human with an animal head?

_____

2. Amen, the patron diety of the city of Thebes, is represented by what animals?

_____

3. Who was worshipped as the jackal god, inventor of embalming, and the son of Isis and Osiris?

_____

4. The Egyptians had a goddess who protected cats; what was her name?

_____

5. Anuket was the dispenser of cool water and was represented in what form?

_____

6. Who was depicted as a sun disk with rays, the only true diety during Amenhotep IV's reign?

_____

7. The four sons of Horus protected parts of the body of whom?

_____

8. What is the name of Amen's famous temple, the largest structure ever built by ancient humans?

_____

MATCHING 1

Goddess	Goddess of	Image
1. Edijo	A. love, beauty	i. frog joy
2. Heqt	B. newborns, destiny	ii. human
3. Isis	C. fertility	iii. serpent
4. Thermuthis	D. fertility, women bin labor	iv. lion-headed
5. Meskhenet	E. the Delta	v. serpent- headed
6. Hathor	F. justice	vi. serpent
7. Thoueris	G. war, sickness	vii. human
8. Maat	H. resurrection, fertility	viii. cow-headed human
9. Sekhmet	I. fate, fertility, harvest	ix. hippopotamus
10. Heket	J. life, healing	x. vulture, human

TRUE OR FALSE 2

1. Heqet is a goddess with the head of a frog and is worshipped as one of the eight gods at Hermopolis.

_____

2. Horus is the divine prototype of the Pharaoh.

_____

3. Imhotep was a historical figure who became deified.

_____

4. Isis was the mother of Osiris.

____

5. Isis was incapable of performing magic.

____

6. The god Khepri is sybolized as a scarab beetle.

____

7. Maat was the daughter of Isis and Osiris.

____

8. Osiris ruled the world of men after Ra abandoned it to rule the sky.

____

9. Osiris is the god of the dead, resurrection into eternal life, ruler, protector, and judge of the deceased.

____

10. Ra, a hawk or hawk-headed man, was god of the sun in dynastic Egypt.

____

UNSCRAMBLE 1 *(names)*

1. Nema   _____

2. Patorharsec   _____

3. Hempiot   _____

4. Tama   _____

5. Sisrio   _____

6. Tisa   _____

7. Busina   _____

8. Joed   _____

9. Queeth   _____

10. Siis   _____

MULTIPLE CHOICE 3

1. Apsu, begetter of the skies and earth, could not:
    A. live within her creations
    B. quell the noise of his children
    C. have children
    D. make his wife happy

2. After her death, Tiamat's eyes became:
    A. jewels
    B. Crete and Cyprus
    C. gates to heaven
    D. sources for the Tigris and Euphrates rivers

3. Lahmu and Lahamu wear:
   A. a triple sash
   B. polish
   C. a golden necklace
   D. rings of ruby

4. Anshar, father of Anu and son of Tiamat and Apsu—his name means:
   A. water and rain
   B. cow
   C. whole sky
   D. earth and vegetation

5. Anu's role was:
   A. father and king of the gods
   B. to play with the animals
   C. protector of Tiamat
   D. guard of the underworld

6. Aruru, the mother goddess, is responsible for:
   A. death
   B. the creation of man
   C. the ethics of her children gods
   D. art among the mortals

7. Mammetum made:
   A. art
   B. death
   C. fate
   D. the sky

8. Nammu is one of the:
   A. gods of hate
   B. pure goddesses
   C. muses
   D. gods of destruction

SHORT ANSWER 2

1. Ellil, leader of the pantheon, relinquished his throne to whom?

_____

2. What is Ellil's sacred symbol?

_____

3. Ea, Anshar's son, is the master of what crafts?

_____

4. Mummu, attendant to Ea and Apsu's vizier, is responsible for what?

_____

5. What did Qingu give his army?

_____

6. Sin, or Nannar, has a beard made of what?

_____

7. Ishtar is the goddess of what?

_____

8. What human did Ishtar ask to be her husband— offering him gifts and status?

_____

MATCHING 2

1. Siduri

A. lawgiver, guarded by scorpion people

2. Nusku

B. Ellil's doorkeeper

3. Bel

C. god of fire

4. Kakka

D. the great wild cow

5. Zaltu

E. strife

6. Dumkina

F. barmaid

7. Ninsun

G. cleverest of gods

8. Marduk

H. Anshar and Anu's vizier

9. Shamash

I. central figure of Babylonian pantheon

10. Kalkal

J. mother of Bel and Marduk

TRUE OR FALSE 2

1. Nammu is the goddess of the watery abyss and Enki's sister.

_____

2. Ningal begs Enlil to spare her city, Ur, from the flood.

_____

3. Ereshkigal is the king of the underworld.

_____

4. Nidaba was the goddess of wine.

_____

5. Dumuzi was a shepherd when he was human.

_____

6. Gilgamesh was probably the historical king of Erech.

_____

7. Gilgamesh became a god.

_____

8. Enkidu was Gilgamesh's brother.

_____

9. Ningishzida was the god of dawn.

_____

10. Neti was the chief gatekeeper.

_____

ANSWERS

MULTIPLE CHOICE 1

1. A
2. C
3. B
4. A
5. D
6. B
7. C
8. A

TRUE OR FALSE 1

1. True
2. True
3. True
4. False (failed to replace him and was made god of the underworld)
5. False (his son)
6. True
7. True
8. False
9. True
10. False (a minor god)

SHORT ANSWER 1

1. Apis, the bull
2. goose and ram
3. Anubis
4. Bast
5. gazelle with a feathered crown on her human head
6. Aten
7. Osiris
8. Karnak

MATCHING 1

1. E, iii
2. H, v
3. J, ii
4. I, vi
5. B, x
6. A, viii
7. D, ix
8. F, vii
9. G, iv
10. C, i

TRUE OR FALSE 2

1. True
2. True
3. True
4. False (wife and sister)
5. False (She was a master magician.)
6. True
7. False (Ra)
8. True
9. True
10. True

UNSCRAMBLE 1

1. Amen
2. Harpocrates
3. Imhotep
4. Maat
5. Osiris
6. Sati
7. Anubis
8. Edjo
9. Heqetu
10. Isis

MULTIPLE CHOICE 2

1. B
2. D
3. A
4. C
5. A
6. B
7. C
8. B

SHORT ANSWER 2

1. Anu
2. seven small circles representing the Pleiades
3. writing, building, farming, and magic
4. Tiamat's peace and quiet
5. fire-quenching breath and paralyzing venom
6. lapis lazuli
7. love, procreation, and war
8. Gilgamesh

MATCHING 2

1. F
2. C
3. G
4. H
5. E
6. J
7. D
8. I
9. A
10. B

TRUE OR FALSE 3

1. False (mother)
2. True
3. False (queen)
4. False (writing)
5. True
6. True
7. True
8. False (servant)
9. True
10. True

PROMISES AND COVENANTS

TRUE OR FALSE 1

1. God's complete promise to Abraham was to make his descendents numerous and his nation great.

_____

2. The Abrahamic covenant is the first promise in the Bible.

_____

3. God promised to bless those who blessed Abraham.

_____

4. God promised Noah that He would never again destroy the world.

_____

5. God made His covenant with Moses on Mt. Sinai.

_____

6. In the Davidic covenant, God told David that He would be a Father to him

_____

7. God promised that David's kingdom and house would endure before Him forever.

_____

8. Nathan delivered God's promise to David.

_____

9. God made his covenant directly with "Abraham."

_____

10. The Mosaic covenant was intended to replace the Abrahamic covenant.

_____

MULTIPLE CHOICE 1

1. The Hebrew word for covenant is:
   - A. Qumran
   - B. Caleb
   - C. Berit
   - D. Amen

2. The three functions of the Mosaic covenant were to:
   - A. reveal God
   - B. Establish unity in exile
   - C. reveal sin
   - D. define God's expectations for man

3. Which covenants are found in Genesis?
   - A. Davidic
   - B. Adamic
   - C. Abrahamic
   - D. New

4. In the Abrahamic covenant, God first commands Abraham to:
   - A. sacrifice his son, Isaac
   - B. get out of his country and away from his family and father's house
   - C. build an altar
   - D. build a towe

5. Abraham thought he had fulfilled God's covenant when:
   - A. he built an altar
   - B. he left his home
   - C. he gave Sarah to Saul
   - D. Ishmael was born

6. What did God do when Abraham asked how he knew the covenant would come to pass:
   - A. passed a smoking oven and burning torch between a sacrifice
   - B. commanded him to be silent
   - C. gave him Hagar
   - D. fulfilled the covenant

7. When did God change Abraham's name from Abram?
   A. when He first appeared to him
   B. after he left his home at age 75
   C. when he was 99 years old
   D. after Isaac was born

8. Who laughed when God promised Abraham and Sarah a child?
   A. Abraham
   B. Sarah
   C. Isaac
   D. Ishmael

MATCHING 1

1. Adam

2. Eve

3. Serpent

A. eat dust all the days of your life

B. sorrow will multiply

C. enmity between you and the woman

D. in toil you shall eat

E. in sweat you shall eat

F. your desire shall be for a mate

G. you will return to dust

H. your clothes will be made from animal skins

I. you will be sent out of the garden

SHORT ANSWER 1

1. Who brought news of God's covenant with David to David?

_____

2. What time of day did the word of the Lord come to Nathan?

_____

3. What had David desired to do before he learned of the covenant?

_____

4. What did God tell David He would do for the people of Israel?

_____

5. Why was David not to build a Temple?

_____

6. What would be established forever?

_____

7. God promised to do what to Solomon, as well as establish his throne?

_____

8. What was David's response to God's covenant?

_____

MULTIPLE CHOICE 2

1. God promised Jacob that He would:
   A. make Reuben king
   B. not leave until He fulfilled His Word
   C. make him the ruler of many people
   D. give him a place of honor among his people

2. Joseph's promise of power over his brothers came to him in a(n):
   A. dream about gold
   B. instant message
   C. dream about wheat
   D. vision of famine

3. God promised Moses what, which was the opposite of his fears:
   A. power
   B. wealth
   C. many children
   D. success

4. God promised to give Solomon which of his requests:
   A. wisdom
   B. riches
   C. honor
   D. a kingdom that stretched to Greece

5. Naaman believed the prophet's promise of healing from what disease:
   A. blindness
   B. paralysis
   C. lame feet
   D. leprosy

6. Because Jehu did what was right in God's sight, God promised him:
   A. that his sons would sit on the throne for four generations
   B. that he would rule a nation
   C. a giant temple
   D. wealth and prosperity

7. Isaiah assured Hezekiah that his enemy would turn and go to his own land because:

   A. he will be afraid of the size of Hezekiah's army
   B. his land will be attacked
   C. he will hear a rumor about his home
   D. their firstborn would die

8. God promised Josiah that he would not see

   A. the death of his sons
   B. the calamity He would bring on this place
   C. the end of the reign of David
   D. the rise of Neco

ANSWERS

TRUE OR FALSE 1

1. False
2. False
3. True
4. False
5. True
6. False
7. True
8. True
9. False
10. False

MULTIPLE CHOICE 1

1. C
2. A, C, D
3. B, C
4. B
5. D
6. A
7. C
8. A, B

MATCHING 1

1. D, E, G, H ,I
2. B, F, H, I
3. A, C

SHORT ANSWER 1

1. Nathan
2. night
3. build a Temple
4. appoint a place for them
5. God didn't desire one at the time—Solomon should build it.
6. David's house and throne
7. discipline him
8. he praised Him and dedicated Israel to Him

MULTIPLE CHOICE 2

1. B
2. C
3. D
4. A
5. D
6. A
7. C
8. B

SAY A LITTLE PRAYER FOR ME

SHORT ANSWER 1

1. Paul prayed for what after being threatened by Jewish leaders in Acts?

_____

_____

2. How did the Lord first describe Saul of Tarsus to Ananias?

_____

_____

3. Paul commanded Simon the Sorcerer to pray for forgiveness from what?

_____

_____

4. Paul prayed and healed whom on the island of Malta?

_____

_____

5. The apostles named two men—Barsabbas and Matthias— and then prayed about what?

_____

_____

6. Paul prayed over Tabitha for what?

_____

_____

7. The apostles chose seven men to care for widows, and then prayed over them with what result?

_____

_____

8. What were Paul and Silas doing when their chains fell off in prison?

_____

_____

MATCHING 1

1. Abraham

2. David

3. Beniah

4. Gideon

5. Asa

6. Hezekiah

7. Dion Warwick

8. Amos

9. Hannah

10. Elijah

A. "Lord, it is nothing for you to help... donot let this man prevail against You!"

B. "May [the Lord] be with Solomon, and make his throne greater than the throne of my lord King David."

C. "If you will... give your maidservant a male child... no razor shall come upon his head."

D. "The moment I wake up, before I put on my makeup, I say a little prayer for you."

E. "Lord God of Abraham, Isaac, and Israel, let it be known this day that You are God in Israel and I am your servant."

F. "Oh, that Ishmael might live before You!"

G. "If You will save Israel by my hand as You have said— look . . ."

H. "O Lord, I pray, turn the counsel of Ahithophel into foolishness."

I. "Remember now, O Lord, I pray, how I have walked before You in truth and with a loyal heart, and have done what was good in your sight."

J. "O Lord God, cease, I pray! Oh, that Jacob may stand, for he is small!"

MULTIPLE CHOICE 1

1. When Elisha prayed for the Lord to open the servant's eyes, his servant saw:
   A. hills full of horses and chariots of fire
   B. towers crumbling
   C. steam rising off the oceans
   D. Elisha

2. When he prayed before the Lord, Hezekiah spread out:
   A. a fleece
   B. a grain offering
   C. a map
   D. a letter from King Sennacherib

3. Whose request, "O that you would bless me and enlarge my territory," did God grant?
   A. David's
   B. Jabez's
   C. Adam's
   D. Ahab's

4. When Jacob prayed because of his fear of Esau, he did what to his people for protection?
   A. divided them into two groups, so one could run away
   B. gave them skins and told them to hide among the flocks
   C. sent them back to Laban
   D. camped in the valley, so that they would see an army coming over the hills

5. What was Jacob's attitude when he prayed for his sons?
   A. proud
   B. angry
   C. bereaved
   D. lonely

6. Where did Jehoshaphat pray for Judah?
   A. in Jerusalem, in the King's court
   B. in front of the new courtyard at the new Temple
   C. in the privacy of his tent
   D. he didn't

7. How did the people of Bethel ask the Lord about fasting?
   A. they offered sacrifices themselves
   B. they asked their leaders
   C. they didn't
   D. they sent two leaders (and their men) to ask the priests and prophets

8. What did Joshua pray after Israel defeated the Amorites?
   A. that the Amonites wouldn't be too mad
   B. thanksgiving to God for his protection
   C. for the sun to stand still
   D. that the Amorites would be punished for their sins

TRUE OR FALSE 1

1. The Hebrew word "Amen" means "I now conclude."

_____

2. The Egyptian plan for prayer was to manipulate the gods.

_____

3. Lot prayed that his wife would become like "the salt of the earth."

_____

4. When the Israelites worshipped the Golden Calf, Moses prayed, "Oh God, free me from service to these pagan people!"

_____

5. Moses called on God to not respect the offering of a priest in a competition at the altar.

_____

6. Naomi prayed that her daughters-in-law would remarry.

_____

7. Elijah asked to be known as God's servant when he challenged the prophets of Baal.

_____

8. After the pagan sailors threw Jonah overboard, they gloated in victory and cursed God.

_____

9. Jesus prayed in the Garden of Gethsemane that God's will be done.

_____

10. Isaiah, after being cleansed with coal, said to God, "Here am I, send me."

_____

MULTIPLE CHOICE 2

1. The rosary is a Roman Catholic prayer consisting of fifteen sets of ten:
   A. Bible quotes
   B. Hail Marys
   C. rosarys
   D. Mother Marys

2. What book contains morning and evening prayers, as well as thirty-nine articles of faith:
   A. The English Book of Prayer
   B. The Westminster Confession of Faith
   C. Revised Common Lectionary
   D. Book of Common Prayer

3. In Roman Catholic theology, prayers for the dead are for those people who are in:
   A. Purgatory
   B. Hell
   C. Heaven
   D. Limbo

4. Tibetan Buddhists use what when reciting mantras:
   A. prayer chains
   B. prayer wheel
   C. verses from the Quran
   D. prayer books

5. Which of the following statements is found in the Lord's prayer:
   A. not my will but Thine be done
   B. give us this day our daily bread
   C. do unto us as we have done unto others
   D. I'm in the Lord's army

6. What famous site in Jerusalem is the location of many Jewish prayers:
   A. the temple of Jerusalem
   B. the market place
   C. the Wailing Wall
   D. the Church of the Sacred

TRUE OR FALSE 2

1. Paul says that women should never pray aloud at church.

_____

2. All early believers prayed in tongues.

_____

3. Paul says we should pray "always."

_____

4. Christians should pray for their rulers so that life will be quiet and peaceable in godliness and reverence.

_____

5. The Holy Spirit is not involved with human prayers.

_____

ANSWERS

SHORT ANSWER 1

1. boldness
2. he is praying
3. the thought in his heart
4. Publius' father
5. which one of the two should replace Judas
6. that she would be raised from the dead
7. the Word of God spread
8. praying and singing hymns

MATCHING 1

1. F
2. H
3. B
4. G
5. A
6. I
7. D
8. J
9. C
10. E

MULTIPLE CHOICE 1

1. A
2. D
3. B
4. A
5. C
6. B
7. D
8. C

TRUE OR FALSE 1

1. False
2. True
3. False
4. False
5. True
6. True
7. True
8. False
9. True
10. True

MATCHING 2

1. J
2. G
3. F
4. A
5. C
6. I
7. D
8. H
9. E
10. B

MULTIPLE CHOICE 2

1. B
2. D
3. A
4. B
5. B
6. C

TRUE OR FALSE 2

1. False
2. False
3. True
4. True
5. False

PRAYERS OF THE BIBLE

Abijah's army (for victory)............................. 2 Chronicles 13:14

Abraham (for a son) ....Genesis 15:1–6

Abraham (for Ishmael)..Genesis 17:18–21

Abraham (for Sodom ....Genesis 18:20–32

Abraham (for Abimelech) ....Genesis 20:17

Abraham's servant (for guidance) ....Genesis 24:12–52

Asa (for victory)............................... 2 Chronicles 14:11

Cain (for mercy)..Genesis 4:13–15

Centurion (for his servant) ....Matthew 8:5–13

Christians (for Peter)..Acts 12:5–12

Christians (for kings in authority) ....1 Timothy 2:1, 2

Corinthians (for Paul)....................................2 Corinthians 1:9–11

Cornelius (for enlightenment) ....Acts 10:1–33

Criminal (for salvation) .... Luke 23:42, 43

Daniel (for the Jews)..Daniel 9:3–19

Daniel (for knowledge)..Daniel 2:17–23

David (for blessing)........................... 2 Samuel 7:18–29

David (for help) .... 1 Samuel 23:10–13

David (for guidance)............................ 2 Samuel 2:1

David (for grace) .... Psalm 25:16

David (for justice) .... Psalm 9:17–20

Disciples (for boldness) ....Acts 4:24–31

Elijah (for drought and rain)........................ James 5:17, 18

Elijah (for the raising to life of the widow's son).................Kings 17:20–23

Elijah (for triumph over Baal).............................. 1 Kings 18:36–38

Elijah (for death) .... 1 Kings 19:4

Elisha (for blindness and sight) .... 2 Kings 6:17–23

Ezekiel (for undefilement)........................... Ezekiel 4:12–15

Ezra (for the sins of the people) ....Ezra 9:6–15

Gideon (for proof of his call)........................... Judges 6:36–40

Habakkuk (for deliverance)........................... Habakkuk 3:1–19

Habakkuk (for justice) .... Habakkuk 1:1–4